# Motor Vehicle Studies for NVQ

# V. A. W. Hillier   I.Eng, MIRTE, FIMI

WITHDRAWN

STANLEY THORNES

Stanley Thornes (Publishers) Ltd

D0315994

© V. A. W. Hillier, 1995

The right of V. A. W. Hillier to be identified as author of this work has been asserted by him in accordance with the Copyright, Designs and Patents Act 1988.

All rights reserved. No part of this publication may be reproduced or transmitted in any form or by any means, electronic or mechanical, including photocopy, recording, or any information storage and retrieval system, without permission in writing from the publisher or under licence from the Copyright Licensing Agency Limited. Further details of such licences (for reprographic reproduction) may be obtained from the Copyright Licensing Agency Limited, of 90 Tottenham Court Road, London W1P 9HE.

First published in 1995 by:
Stanley Thornes (Publishers) Ltd
Ellenborough House
Wellington Street
CHELTENHAM GL50 1YW
U.K.

| BROMLEY COLLEGE OF FURTHER & HIGHER EDUCATION | |
|---|---|
| ACCN. | 83.752 |
| CLASSN. | 629.2 |
| CAT. | LOCN. |

97  98  99  00  01  /  10  9  8  7  6  5  4  3  2

A catalogue record for this book is available from the British Library.

ISBN 0 7487 2011 1

Cover photographs reproduced by kind permission of Rover Group (top); Vauxhall (middle); and Ford Motor Co Ltd (bottom)

Typeset by Paston Press Ltd, Loddon, Norfolk
Printed and bound in Great Britain by
Redwood Books, Trowbridge, Wiltshire

# Contents

# Preface

Industrial training has been extensively modified with the introduction of National Vocational Qualifications (NVQs) and Scottish Vocational Qualifications (SVQs). These competence-based schemes were promoted by the Government through the National Council for Vocational Qualifications (NCVQ) and the Scottish Vocational Education Council (SCOTVEC).

Each industrial sector has a Lead Body charged by the Government to develop suitable occupational standards for the industry that it represents. In the case of the retail motor industry and related sectors the Lead Body is the Motor Industry Training Standards Council (MITSC).

The NVQ scheme is based on 'training outcomes' which are expressed in terms of 'units of competence'. These units specify what a candidate should be able to do in their working environment rather than what they know as tested by a written examination. Various levels of attainment (Levels I, II, III etc.) and specific work functions have been identified by MITSC. After a candidate has proved to a qualified assessor that the level of competence has been reached in a given activity, a certificate endorsed by NCVQ is awarded.

National administration of the schemes for each industrial sector is undertaken by a number of authorised bodies such as the City and Guilds of London Institute. Working in conjunction with various lead bodies, these establishments have amplified the occupational standards to provide assessment programmes, organised verification systems and introduced the necessary documentation to administer the NVQ scheme.

Each unit in the occupational standard specifies the 'underpinning knowledge' that must be understood before the person can become competent in the given work function; this knowledge includes the associated business activities and technology aspects that are considered to be essential elements of each practical activity. The topics included in the underpinning knowledge shows that in addition to being able to do the job, trainees must also know what they are doing, why they are doing it and be aware of their company's business commitments.

The purpose of this book is to cover selected 'elements of competence' contained in the MITSC document, *Occupational Standards for Maintaining Vehicle Mechanical and Electronic Systems*. The book includes business activities as well as providing the appropriate back-up needed to understand the motor vehicle systems included in my other books:

- *Fundamentals of Motor Vehicle Technology*
- *Fundamentals of Automotive Electronics*.

Using these books, together with instruction given by qualified personnel in the practical and technical fields, will enable the reader to gain the underpinning knowledge required for the programme. In some cases the subject in the book has been treated in a manner that will require readers to research topics in their workplace in order to meet the published performance criteria. Coverage of these topics has been confined to an explanation of the subject fundamentals; this will provide foundational material to allow personal research to be directed along the appropriate path. Documentary evidence of this personal investigation is required when the unit is to be assessed. By using this method, as an alternative to quoting some passage in a book, the candidate and the company will both benefit.

Sincere thanks are expressed to the staff of the Motor Industry Training Standards Council and the City and Guilds of London Institute for the advice given during the preparation of this book.

*V. A. W. Hillier*
*February 1995*

# *Acknowledgements*

During the preparation of this book, considerable assistance was given to me by many friends in various companies and organisations. In particular I wish to thank the following for photographs, technical literature and scheme details, and, where specified in the book, permission to use copyright material.

City and Guilds of London Institute

Crypton
Ford Motor Co Ltd
Motor Industry Training Standards Council
Retail Motor Industry Federation
Rover Group Ltd
Sykes-Pickavant Ltd
V.A.G. (United Kingdom) Ltd
Vauxhall Motors Ltd

# Study matrix for NVQ units and elements

On the following pages you will find a grid linking the chapters in this book with NVQ units and elements. The full titles of the NVQ units are given in the table below.

| C & G No. | MITSC Unit No. | Title |
|---|---|---|
| 001 | A1–G | Contract with customers to provide for their vehicle needs |
| 002 | A8–L2 | Identify faulty components/units which affect system performance – LV (level 2) |
| 003 | A9–L2 | Remove and replace vehicle components/units – LV (level 2) |
| 004 | A11–L | Prepare new, used or repaired vehicles for customer's use – LV |
| 005 | A12–G | Maintain effective working relationships |
| 006 | A13–G | Maintain the health, safety and security of the working environment |
| 007 | A7–L | Routinely service the vehicle to maintain optimum performance – LV |
| 008 | A7–H | Routinely service the vehicle to maintain optimum performance – HV |
| 009 | A8–L3 | Identify faults which affect system performance – LV (level 3) |
| 010 | A8–H3 | Identify faults which affect system performance – HV (level 3) |
| 011 | A9–L3 | Rectify faults in vehicle systems – LV (level 3) |
| 012 | A9–H3 | Rectify faults in vehicle systems – HV (level 3) |
| 013 | A10–LH | Augment vehicle systems to meet customer requirements – LV & HV |
| 014 | A11–H | Prepare new, used or repaired vehicles for customer's use – HV |
| 015 | A6–G | Reinstate the cleanliness of the vehicle |

*Unit code.* G = general unit; L = light vehicle; H = heavy vehicle

**National Vocational Qualifications in Vehicle Mechanical and Electronic Systems**

| C & G Unit No. | | 001 | | 002 | | 003 | | | | 004 | | 005 | | 006 | | | 007 | | 008 | |
|---|---|---|---|---|---|---|---|---|---|---|---|---|---|---|---|---|---|---|---|---|
| MITSC Unit No. | | A1–G | | A8–L2 | | A9–L2 | | | | A11–L | | A12–G | | A13–G | | | A7–L | | A7–H | |
| MITSC Element No. | | 1.1 | 1.2 | 8.1 | 8.2 | 9.1 | 9.2 | 9.3 | 9.4 | 11.1 | 11.2 | 12.1 | 12.2 | 13.1 | 13.2 | 13.3 | 7.1 | 7.2 | 7.1 | 7.2 |
| **A  SAFETY** | | | | | | | | | | | | | | | | | | | | |
| Safety in the workplace | 1.1 | | | • | • | • | • | • | • | • | • | | | • | • | • | • | • | • | • |
| | 1.2 | | | • | • | • | • | • | • | • | • | | | • | • | • | • | • | • | • |
| | 1.3 | | | • | • | • | • | • | • | • | • | | | • | • | • | • | • | • | • |
| | 1.4 | | | • | • | • | • | • | • | • | • | | | • | • | • | • | • | • | • |
| | 1.5 | | | • | • | • | • | • | • | • | • | | | • | • | • | • | • | • | • |
| | 1.6 | | | • | • | • | • | • | • | • | • | | | • | • | • | • | • | • | • |
| | 1.7 | | | • | • | • | • | • | • | • | • | | | • | • | • | • | • | • | • |
| Vehicle and road safety | 2.1 | • | | | | | | | • | • | | | | | | | • | | • | |
| | 2.2 | • | | | | | | | • | • | | | | | | | • | | • | |
| **B  MATERIALS AND PROCESSES** | | | | | | | | | | | | | | | | | | | | |
| Materials | 3.1 | | | • | • | • | • | • | | | | | | | | | | | | |
| | 3.2 | | | • | • | • | • | • | | | | | | | | | | | | |
| | 3.3 | | | | • | • | • | • | | | | | | | | | | | | |
| | 3.4 | | | | • | • | • | • | | | | | | | | | | | | |
| | 3.5 | | | | | | • | • | | | | | | | | | | | | |
| | 3.6 | | | | • | • | • | • | | | | | | | | | | | | |
| | 3.7 | | | | | • | • | • | | | | | | | | | | | | |
| Tools and equipment | 4.1 | | | | | • | • | • | | | | | | | | | | • | | • |
| | 4.2 | | | | | • | • | • | | | | | | | | | | • | | • |
| | 4.3 | | | | | • | • | • | | | | | | | | | | • | | • |
| Measurement | 5.1 | | | • | • | • | • | • | | | | | | | | | | • | | • |
| | 5.2 | | | | | | • | • | | | | | | | | | | | | |
| | 5.3 | | | | | | • | • | | | | | | | | | | | | |
| Metal jointing and fastening | 6.1 | | | | | • | • | • | | | | | | | | | | | | |
| | 6.2 | | | | | • | • | • | | | | | | | | | | | | |
| | 6.3 | | | | | • | • | • | | | | | | | | | | | | |
| | 6.4 | | | | | | | • | | | | | | | | | | | | |
| | 6.5 | | | | | | | • | | | | | | | | | | | | |
| **C  DRAWING INTERPRETATION** | | | | | | | | | | | | | | | | | | | | |
| Drawing principles | 7.1 | | | • | • | • | • | • | • | | • | | | | | | • | • | • | • |
| | 7.2 | | | • | • | • | • | • | • | | • | | | | | | • | • | • | • |
| | 7.3 | | | | | • | • | • | • | | • | | | | | | • | • | • | • |
| | 7.4 | | | • | • | • | • | • | • | | • | | | | | | • | • | • | • |
| **D  RELATED PRINCIPLES** | | | | | | | | | | | | | | | | | | | | |
| Mechanics and machines | 8.1 | | | • | • | • | • | • | | | | | | | | | | | | |
| | 8.2 | | | • | • | • | • | • | | | | | | | | | | | | |
| | 8.3 | | | • | • | • | • | • | | | | | | | | | | | | |
| | 8.4 | | | | | • | • | • | • | | | | | | | | | | | |
| | 8.5 | | | | | • | • | • | • | | | | | | | | | | | |
| | 8.6 | | | | | • | • | • | • | | | | | | | | | | | |

**Header structure**

C & G Unit No. / MITSC Unit No. / MITSC Element No.:

| C & G Unit No. | MITSC Unit No. | MITSC Element No. |
|---|---|---|
| 009 | A8–L3 | 8.1, 8.2 |
| 010 | A8–H3 | 8.1, 8.2 |
| 011 | A9–L3 | 9.1, 9.2, 9.3, 9.4, 9.5 |
| 012 | A9–H3 | 9.1, 9.2, 9.3, 9.4, 9.5 |
| 013 | A10–LH | 10.1, 10.2 |
| 014 | A11–H | 11.1, 11.2 |
| 015 | A6–G | 6.1, 6.2 |

| | | 009 8.1 | 009 8.2 | 010 8.1 | 010 8.2 | 011 9.1 | 011 9.2 | 011 9.3 | 011 9.4 | 011 9.5 | 012 9.1 | 012 9.2 | 012 9.3 | 012 9.4 | 012 9.5 | 013 10.1 | 013 10.2 | 014 11.1 | 014 11.2 | 015 6.1 | 015 6.2 |
|---|---|---|---|---|---|---|---|---|---|---|---|---|---|---|---|---|---|---|---|---|---|
| **A SAFETY** | | | | | | | | | | | | | | | | | | | | | |
| Safety in the workplace | 1.1 | • | • | • | • | • | • | • | • | • | • | • | • | • | • | • | • | • | • | • | • |
| | 1.2 | • | • | • | • | • | • | • | • | • | • | • | • | • | • | • | • | • | • | • | • |
| | 1.3 | • | • | • | • | • | • | • | • | • | • | • | • | • | • | • | • | • | • | • | • |
| | 1.4 | • | • | • | • | • | • | • | • | • | • | • | • | • | • | • | • | • | • | • | • |
| | 1.5 | • | • | • | • | • | • | • | • | • | • | • | • | • | • | • | • | • | • | • | • |
| | 1.6 | • | • | • | • | • | • | • | • | • | • | • | • | • | • | • | • | • | • | • | • |
| | 1.7 | • | • | • | • | • | • | • | • | • | • | • | • | • | • | • | • | • | • | • | • |
| Vehicle and road safety | 2.1 | | | | | | | | | • | | | | | | • | • | • | • | | |
| | 2.2 | | | | | | | | | • | | | | | | • | • | • | • | | |
| **B MATERIALS AND PROCESSES** | | | | | | | | | | | | | | | | | | | | | |
| Materials | 3.1 | • | • | • | • | • | • | • | • | | • | • | • | • | | • | | | | | |
| | 3.2 | | • | | • | • | • | • | • | | • | • | • | • | | • | | | | | |
| | 3.3 | | • | | • | • | • | • | • | | • | • | • | • | | | | | | | |
| | 3.4 | | • | | • | • | • | • | • | | • | • | • | • | • | | | | | | |
| | 3.5 | | • | | • | • | • | • | • | | • | • | • | • | | | | | | | |
| | 3.6 | | • | | • | • | • | • | • | | • | • | • | • | | | | | | | |
| | 3.7 | | • | | • | • | • | • | • | | • | • | • | • | | | | | | | • |
| Tools and equipment | 4.1 | | | | | • | • | • | • | • | • | • | • | • | • | | | • | | • | • |
| | 4.2 | | | | | • | • | • | • | • | • | • | • | • | • | | | • | | • | • |
| | 4.3 | | | | | • | • | • | • | • | • | • | • | • | • | | | • | | • | • |
| Measurement | 5.1 | | • | | • | | • | • | • | | • | • | • | | | | | | | | |
| | 5.2 | | • | | • | | • | • | • | | • | • | • | | | | | | | | |
| | 5.3 | | • | | • | | • | • | • | | • | • | • | | | | | | | | |
| Metal jointing and fastening | 6.1 | | • | | • | | | • | • | | • | • | | | | | | | | | |
| | 6.2 | | • | | • | | | • | • | | • | • | | | | | | | | | |
| | 6.3 | | • | | • | | | • | • | | • | • | | | | | | | | | |
| | 6.4 | | • | | • | | • | • | | | • | • | | | | | | | | | |
| | 6.5 | | • | | • | | • | • | | | • | • | | | | | | | | | |
| **C DRAWING INTERPRETATION** | | | | | | | | | | | | | | | | | | | | | |
| Drawing principles | 7.1 | • | • | • | • | • | • | • | • | • | • | • | • | • | • | | • | • | • | | |
| | 7.2 | • | • | • | • | • | • | • | • | • | • | • | • | • | • | | • | • | • | | |
| | 7.3 | • | • | • | • | • | • | • | • | • | • | • | • | • | • | | • | • | • | | |
| | 7.4 | • | • | • | • | • | • | • | • | • | • | • | • | • | • | | • | • | • | | |
| **D RELATED PRINCIPLES** | | | | | | | | | | | | | | | | | | | | | |
| Mechanics and machines | 8.1 | | • | | • | • | • | • | • | | • | • | • | • | | | | | | | |
| | 8.2 | | • | | • | • | • | • | • | | • | • | • | • | | | | | | | |
| | 8.3 | | • | | • | • | • | • | • | | • | • | • | • | | | | | | | |
| | 8.4 | | • | | • | • | • | • | • | | • | • | • | • | | | | | | | |
| | 8.5 | | • | | • | • | • | • | • | | • | • | • | • | | | | | | | |
| | 8.6 | | • | | • | • | • | • | • | | • | • | • | • | | | | | | | |

continued

| C & G Unit No. | | 001 | | 002 | | 003 | | | | 004 | | 005 | | 006 | | | 007 | | 008 | |
|---|---|---|---|---|---|---|---|---|---|---|---|---|---|---|---|---|---|---|---|---|
| MITSC Unit No. | | A1–G | | A8–L2 | | A9–L2 | | | | A11–L | | A12–G | | A13–G | | | A7–L | | A7–H | |
| MITSC Element No. | | 1.1 | 1.2 | 8.1 | 8.2 | 9.1 | 9.2 | 9.3 | 9.4 | 11.1 | 11.2 | 12.1 | 12.2 | 13.1 | 13.2 | 13.3 | 7.1 | 7.2 | 7.1 | 7.2 |
| **D RELATED PRINCIPLES – continued** | | | | | | | | | | | | | | | | | | | | |
| Mechanics and machines | 8.7 | | | | • | • | • | • | | | | | | | | | | | | |
| | 8.8 | | | | • | • | • | • | | | | | | | | | | | | |
| | 8.9 | | | | • | • | • | • | | | | | | | | | | | | |
| | 8.10 | | | • | • | • | • | • | | | | | | | | | | | | |
| | 8.11 | | | | • | • | • | • | | | | | | | | | | | | |
| Heat | 9.1 | • | | • | • | • | • | • | | | | | | | | | | | | |
| | 9.2 | • | | • | • | • | • | • | | | | | | | | | | | | |
| | 9.3 | | | • | • | • | • | • | | | | | | | | | | | | |
| | 9.4 | | | | • | • | • | • | | | | | | | | | | | | |
| | 9.5 | | | | • | • | • | • | | | | | | | | | | | | |
| | 9.6 | | | | • | • | • | • | | | | | | | | | | | | |
| | 9.7 | | | | • | • | • | • | | | | | | | | | | | | |
| Combustion and engine performance | 10.1 | | | | • | • | • | • | | | | | | | | | | | | |
| | 10.2 | • | | • | • | • | • | • | | | | | | | | | • | | • | |
| | 10.3 | | | • | • | • | • | • | | | | | | | | | | | | |
| | 10.4 | | | | | • | • | • | | | | | | | | | • | | • | |
| Electricity | 11.1 | • | | • | • | • | • | • | | | | | | | | | • | | • | |
| | 11.2 | | | • | • | • | • | • | | | | | | | | | | | | |
| | 11.3 | | | • | • | • | • | • | | | | | | | | | • | | • | |
| | 11.4 | • | | • | • | • | • | • | | | | | | | | | • | | • | |
| | 11.5 | | | | • | • | • | • | | | | | | | | | | | | |
| | 11.6 | | | | • | • | • | • | | | | | | | | | | | | |
| **E BUSINESS ACTIVITIES** | | | | | | | | | | | | | | | | | | | | |
| The customer | 12.1 | | | | | | | | | | | • | | | | | | | | |
| | 12.2 | | | | | | | | | | | • | | | | | | | | |
| | 12.3 | | • | | | | | | • | | | | | | | | • | | • | |
| | 12.4 | | | | | | | | | | | • | | | | | | | | |
| | 12.5 | | | | | | | | | | | | • | | | | | | | |
| | 12.6 | • | | | | | | | | | | • | | | | | | | | |
| | 12.7 | | | | | | | | | | | • | | | | | | | | |
| | 12.8 | • | | | | | | | | | | • | | | | | | | | |
| Company systems | 13.1 | • | | | | | | | | | • | | | | | | | | | |
| | 13.2 | • | • | | | | | | | • | • | | | | | | • | | • | |
| | 13.3 | | • | | | | | | | | | | | | | | | | | |
| | 13.4 | | • | | • | | | | | • | • | | | | | | • | • | • | • |
| Personnel | 14.1 | | | | | | | | | | | | • | | | | | | | |
| | 14.2 | | | | | | | | | | | | • | | | | | | | |
| | 14.3 | | • | | | | | | | | | | • | | | | | | | |

| C & G Unit No. | | 009 | | 010 | | 011 | | | | | 012 | | | | | 013 | | 014 | | 015 | |
| MITSC Unit No. | | A8–L3 | | A8–H3 | | A9–L3 | | | | | A9–H3 | | | | | A10–LH | | A11–H | | A6–G | |
| MITSC Element No. | | 8.1 | 8.2 | 8.1 | 8.2 | 9.1 | 9.2 | 9.3 | 9.4 | 9.5 | 9.1 | 9.2 | 9.3 | 9.4 | 9.5 | 10.1 | 10.2 | 11.1 | 11.2 | 6.1 | 6.2 |
|---|---|---|---|---|---|---|---|---|---|---|---|---|---|---|---|---|---|---|---|---|---|
| **D  RELATED PRINCIPLES – continued** | | | | | | | | | | | | | | | | | | | | | |
| Mechanics and machines | 8.7 | | • | | • | • | • | • | • | • | • | • | • | • | | | | | | | |
| | 8.8 | | • | | • | • | • | • | • | • | • | • | • | • | | | | | | | |
| | 8.9 | | • | | • | • | • | • | • | • | • | • | • | • | | | | | | | |
| | 8.10 | | • | | • | • | • | • | • | • | • | • | • | • | | | | | | | |
| | 8.11 | | • | | • | • | • | • | • | • | • | • | • | • | | | | | | | |
| Heat | 9.1 | | • | | • | • | • | • | • | • | • | • | • | • | | | | | | | |
| | 9.2 | | • | | • | • | • | • | • | • | • | • | • | • | | | | | | | |
| | 9.3 | | • | | • | • | • | • | • | • | • | • | • | • | | | | | | | |
| | 9.4 | | • | | • | • | • | • | • | • | • | • | • | • | | | | | | | |
| | 9.5 | | • | | • | • | • | • | • | • | • | • | • | • | | | | | | | |
| | 9.6 | | • | | • | • | • | • | • | • | • | • | • | • | | | | | | | |
| | 9.7 | | • | | • | • | • | • | • | • | • | • | • | • | | | | | | | |
| Combustion and engine performance | 10.1 | • | • | • | • | • | • | • | | | • | • | • | | | | | | | | |
| | 10.2 | • | • | • | • | • | • | • | | • | • | • | • | | • | | • | | | | |
| | 10.3 | • | • | • | • | • | • | • | | | • | • | • | | | | | | | | |
| | 10.4 | • | | • | | • | • | • | | • | • | • | • | | • | • | | | | | |
| Electricity | 11.1 | • | • | • | • | • | • | • | • | • | • | • | • | • | • | • | • | • | | | |
| | 11.2 | • | • | • | • | • | • | • | • | • | • | • | • | • | • | • | • | • | | | |
| | 11.3 | • | • | • | • | • | • | • | • | • | • | • | • | • | • | • | • | • | | | |
| | 11.4 | • | • | • | • | • | • | • | • | • | • | • | • | • | • | • | • | • | | | |
| | 11.5 | • | • | • | • | • | • | • | • | • | • | • | • | • | • | • | • | • | | | |
| | 11.6 | • | • | • | • | • | • | • | • | • | • | • | • | • | • | • | • | • | | | |
| **E  BUSINESS ACTIVITIES** | | | | | | | | | | | | | | | | | | | | | |
| The customer | 12.1 | | | | | | | | | | | | | | | | | | | | |
| | 12.2 | | | | | | | | | | | | | | | | | | | | |
| | 12.3 | | | | | | | | | • | | | | | • | | | • | | | |
| | 12.4 | | | | | | | | | | | | | | | | | • | | | |
| | 12.5 | | | | | | | | | | | | | | | | | | | | |
| | 12.6 | | | | | | | | | | | | | | | | | | | | |
| | 12.7 | | | | | | | | | | | | | | | | | | | | |
| | 12.8 | | | | | | | | | | | | | | | | | | | | |
| Company systems | 13.1 | | | | | | | | | | | | | | | | | | | | |
| | 13.2 | | | | | | | | | | | | | | | | | | | | |
| | 13.3 | | | | | | | | | | | | | | | • | | | | | |
| | 13.4 | | | | | | | | | | | | | | | | | • | • | | |
| Personnel | 14.1 | | | | | | | | | | | | | | | | | | | | |
| | 14.2 | | | | | | | | | | | | | | | | | • | • | | |
| | 14.3 | | | | | | | | | | | | | | | | | | | | |

# Part A

# *Safety*

# *1*      *Safety in the workplace*

## What is covered in this chapter

→ accidents
→ safety laws
→ accident prevention
→ employee's responsibilities
→ electrical hazards
→ fire prevention
→ fire fighting

Unless all people in a motor vehicle workshop put safety first, it can be a very dangerous place. With little mental effort you will realise that many fuels, gases and chemicals you handle are highly flammable and very explosive when exposed to certain conditions. During the early part of your training you will be taught to recognise these and other hazards so that you can take the necessary precautions to protect yourself, your colleagues and your working environment.

## 1.1   Accidents

Safety laws insist that both employer and employee must observe a number of statutory safety regulations. These have been introduced over the years to protect everyone, including the public, in the vicinity of the workshop. In the past these regulations only applied to the employer, but nowadays the Law also requires **YOU**, an employee, to exercise care and use a safe working practice to protect the health and safety of all persons in, and around, the working area.

The safety code should not only be associated with the workshop; you should also apply it to other practical activities that take place in your home, on the road or whilst you are engaged in leisure activities.

Some dangerous situations are obvious, but initially you may not appreciate that there are others. Whereas in the past many unfortunate persons learnt the hard way by their mistakes, today the main hazards are highlighted in a good safety training programme. This does not mean that every dangerous situation can be identified; if you feel that a certain work activity is dangerous, then it is your duty to report it to your superior so that he/she can advise you of the precautions to take.

In the workshop all staff should be safety conscious and vigilant. Where there is a likelihood that a fellow worker is unaware of a possible hazard, it is your duty to give an appropriate warning to protect yourself and other people in the vicinity.

---

### SAFE PRACTICE

**Accidents can be caused by:**

- fits of temper
- lack of concentration
- carelessness
- improper behaviour and dress
- fatigue
- alcohol and drug taking
- negligence

---

Safety laws often use the words *hazard* and *risk*:

- a hazard is something with potential to cause harm;
- a risk is the likelihood of that potential being realised.

Your attention is drawn to the many accidents that have been caused by poor training, lack of experience, poor supervision and human weakness. Insufficient safety care exercised at these times can have serious and sometimes tragic results.

You know that an accident has many drawbacks; these include:

- injury or death to oneself or other persons;
- loss of income;
- loss of production;
- high cost of medical care to oneself or the country.

## 1.2 Safety laws

### EC Directives

The safety laws in force today should conform to the *European Community Directives on Health and Safety*. The EC Directives comprise a series of regulations which include:

- *Management of Health and Safety at Work Regulations*
- *Provision and Use of Work Equipment Regulations*
- *Personal Protective Equipment at Work (PPE) Regulations*
- *Environmental Protection Act*
- *Control of Substances Hazardous to Health Regulations 1988*

In the UK much of the content of the EC Directives is already contained in current regulations. It is the employer's responsibility to display, and make known to all staff, the various Acts of Parliament that are applicable to the premises in which work is being carried out, especially when the nature of the work is specialised and hazardous. In this book only an outline is given of the various safety laws, so in view of this, you must make yourself aware, and understand, the regulations that apply to your own workplace.

### UK Safety Laws

These laws require an **employer** to accept responsibility towards the maintenance of safety in terms of providing:

- a safe place of work, e.g. to provide a safe access and exit;
- safe plant and equipment, e.g. machinery should have safety guards, screens and fences, working notices should be displayed;

- a safe system of work, safe working methods and provision of protective clothing where applicable;
- a safe working environment with maintenance of a reasonable working temperature and effective fume/dust control with provision for adequate washing, sanitation and first aid facilities;
- safe methods of handling, storing and transporting goods; correct siting, storing and identification of dangerous materials, e.g. compressed gases; mechanical handling aids must be available for moving heavy goods;
- an emergency procedure;
- health surveillance where appropriate;
- a system for the reporting of accidents; the keeping of an accident register;
- information, instruction, training and supervision of employees; each employee must be made aware that they are accountable for their own accidents, and are responsible for hazard and accident reporting;
- a safety policy, subject to regular review jointly by employer and employee representatives
- a system to ensure that no person may work with any substance, or operate any equipment or machine, unless trained and authorised to do so.

### Personal Protective Equipment at Work (PPE) Regulations

This directive requires an employer to supply suitable protective equipment where a hazard has been identified. This equipment includes special clothing (other than ordinary working clothes), eye, foot and head protection, safety harnesses, life jackets and high visibility clothing. In addition to the supply, an employer must also maintain, clean and replace equipment, provide for its storage, ensure it is correctly used and give the appropriate training, information and instruction to employees.

## REMEMBER

### Important UK workshop regulations

- *Health and Safety at Work Act*
- *Factories Act*
- *Local by-laws*
- *Control of Substances Hazardous to Health Regulations 1988 (COSHH)*
- *Electricity at Work Regulations*

**Environmental Protection Regulations**

Workshop applications of these regulations relate to the use of solvents used in coatings and for cleaning equipment. Employees must be aware that:

- solvent-based materials should be reduced to a minimum;
- gaseous emissions from solvent-based materials or paint should be kept to a minimum;
- disposal of high solids waste material should be in accordance with the regulations.

## 1.3 Accident prevention

As a wise person you will take precautions to lower the risk of an accident. After training you will adopt a safety policy that recognises the dangers associated with your trade and takes preventative measures where necessary to either eliminate or reduce the risk of injury. To do this you may have to eliminate the hazard by doing something less dangerous and/or by using extra protection to guard against the hazard.

As a newcomer to the motor industry you must appreciate that in a repair workshop dangerous situations can arise both from the vehicle and from the working environment (including the highway). The training you have been given will persuade you and your colleagues to adopt a positive personal attitude to safety so that all of you can protect yourselves, the public and the environment. To do this you need to be aware of the dangers that can occur, what protection is available and how you can prevent accidents.

## 1.4 Employee's responsibilities

**Personal protection**

By law it is your responsibility as an employee to adopt safety procedures to prevent injury or discomfort to your own (or colleagues') skin, eyes, hands, limbs and lungs. Good personal hygiene is necessary and special care is needed to protect your hands by applying a *barrier cream* before your skin comes into contact with any oil or solvent-based product. Handling these substances, especially diesel fuel, without taking this precaution can lead to a skin condition called *dermatitis*; this causes inflammation and irritation of the skin and in serious cases results in a forced change of the person's occupation. You should wear suitable gloves when handling any dangerous substance or objects likely to cause injury.

A clean non-slip floor, good lighting and an ample working space are essential factors for a safe working environment

*Ford Motor Co Ltd*

For health reasons brake dust must be prevented from polluting the air in the workshop. The use of a special dust extractor ensures a safe working environment.

*Retail Motor Industry Federation*

Many workshop processes generate *fumes* and *abrasive dust* so, in addition to the dust removal systems used in the workshop, you must use goggles, face protectors and respirators (all made to the appropriate BS specification) where this hazard is present.

You must take precautions to prevent *long hair* and *loose clothing* getting caught in moving machinery. Also you must wear protective clothing suitable for the work being done. This clothing when soiled must be cleaned to reduce the risk of fire and skin irritation.

### Motor vehicle hazards

Many vehicle systems create their own hazards so when you study the technical features of a component, it is vital that you also consider the safety aspects associated with any practical activity involving that component. This study will ensure that you know the hazard and understand the precautions that must be taken.

It is difficult to say which hazard on a motor vehicle is the most serious, because many can result in loss of life. There is little consolation knowing that a fatal accident was caused by an uncommon hazard – the person killed is unlikely to appreciate this rarity! An example of this situation arises in areas where petrol vapour is present; you see cases where mechanics are working in vehicle compartments (or garage forecourts) that are severely contaminated with petrol fumes. Some people seem to

Protective clothing should be safe to wear and smart in appearance. Precautions should be taken to ensure that clothing belts, ties and long hair cannot become entangled with rotating shafts, belts and pulleys.

*Ford Motor Co Ltd*

have no worries when they produce sparks and naked flames in these areas; they think that because they have done it before an accident will not happen to them. Periodically you read about these people when a major explosion is reported. The only safe policy is: **DON'T CHANCE IT, you only have one life**.

For all serious accidents, a qualified first aider should be called in, and hospital treatment sought, as soon as possible. Since there may be occasions when you are the only person present, it is advisable that you can render first aid to cover the main injuries encountered in the workshop.

### Accident reporting

By law an employer has to keep an accident register and under the terms of the *Reporting of Injuries, Diseases, and Dangerous Occurrences Regulations 1985* an employer must report all serious accidents to the Health and Safety Executive within a stated time limit. Major injuries must be reported to the enforcing authority by telephone immediately and this must be followed up with a written report within 7 days. Minor injuries also must be reported within 7 days.

A report to the enforcing authority is needed when an employee:

- is admitted to hospital for more than 24 hours
- has sustained a minor injury that incapacitated him/her for normal work for a period of more than 3 days.

---

## SAFE PRACTICE

**Special safety precautions are necessary when:**

- working with flammable liquids, gases and harmful substances
- working on vehicle electrical systems, diesel and petrol fuel systems, cooling systems, tyres and wheels, tilt cabs and tipping bodies
- running and manoeuvring vehicles especially in confined spaces
- working on an unsafe or defective vehicle
- hoisting, lifting and jacking-up a vehicle
- using garage machinery and equipment for drilling, grinding, providing compressed air and welding
- using hand and power tools
- dispensing petrol and acids
- storing, stacking, binning, issuing and handling spare parts, especially heavy components

---

To allow the employer to conform with these regulations, it is essential that all employees inform their superiors of all injuries they receive in the workplace at the time they occur.

### Component cleaning

Sometimes you will need to clean vehicle components, garage equipment and your working area. This involves the use of equipment that often contains dangerous cleaning materials for doing particular jobs. At these times you must only use the equipment and materials that are authorised for your workplace and you must not undertake any cleaning task that is outside your authority.

All employees must be aware of the safety precautions that must be observed before cleaning is undertaken on certain equipment. These precautions involve, as appropriate, the isolation of the machinery from the power source, the display of suitable hazard warning notices, the wearing of protective clothing and the attendance of an extra person for safety support. When the cleaning task has been completed, the disposal of the materials should be in accordance with procedures authorised by the company.

## 1.5 Electrical hazards

It is well known that an electric shock, especially that given by the 230 V mains supply, can kill. For this reason any tool or equipment that uses a high voltage must be handled with care. The *Electricity at Work Regulations* demands special standards and codes of practice to reduce the dangers. It is necessary that all high voltage electrical equipment used in the workshop, as well as the working procedures, comply with these regulations. One essential requirement is that all equipment using mains electricity is *correctly earthed*; this reduces the risk of the operator receiving a fatal electric shock. In the past, high-voltage inspection lamps (lead lamps) have caused a number of accidents due to faulty cables, poor insulation or defective plugs. This danger is eliminated by using low voltage (24 V) lamps.

The ignition system used on modern cars can produce a voltage in excess of 40 kV at the sparking plug, so you must be careful when testing this system. Although fatalities from this high voltage, low amperage system are rare, it is dangerous to take a chance in case you are a person who is one of the 'rare breed'.

A poster is displayed in your workshop to show how resuscitation is carried out; you should study and make sure you understand this notice – **ask if in doubt**,

## REMEMBER

**In cases of electric shock:**

- remove the casualty from the source of the shock as soon as possible
- if power cannot be switched off immediately, the casualty should be carefully moved making sure that you do not receive a shock; dry clothing or some other insulating material should be utilised for this purpose
- if the casualty appears to have stopped breathing, resuscitation must be applied immediately
- call an ambulance

because it can be fatal for your workmate if, at the time of an emergency, you delay action until you have read the notice. In all serious cases of electric shock, the casualty should be taken to hospital and in minor cases a doctor should be consulted if any ill-effects occur.

## 1.6 Fire prevention

Even in a well-managed motor vehicle repair workshop there is a high risk of fire. The presence of highly volatile fuels and solvents, dry combustible materials, explosive conditions, electrical sparks and naked flames all contribute to provide the natural conditions for a fire.

Unless the staff are very careful, or lucky, it is likely that a fire will occur at some time during your working life. This may be started by some negligent human being, defective workshop equipment or failure of some part of the vehicle. Accepting the fact that fires begin in many ways, it is necessary to identify the high-risk situations and then take appropriate precautions to prevent, or minimise, their occurrence. Fire prevention calls for attention to be given to cleanliness of the working area and removal of all combustible materials from high fire-risk zones, because dirty conditions lead to a rapid spread of the fire. Normally it should be possible to contain and extinguish small fires, but if the fire spreads it soon becomes a major incident for the fire brigade.

Fires often occur after an explosion, so special care must be taken when working with processes that use explosive gases.

## 1.7 Fire fighting

In your workshop the fire-fighting equipment must be suitable for the flammable materials that are used in the building; the equipment should include:

- fire blanket
- water hose
- fire extinguishers: water, $CO_2$, foam, dry powder, vaporising liquids.

In the past, water from a bucket was used on solid fuel fires; buckets of sand were used to smother small liquid fuel fires. Today the convenience of a portable fire extinguisher has made the fire bucket obsolete.

A fire blanket, made of fire-resistant material, positioned close to the area where liquid fires might occur will provide a quick method of smothering a small fire.

A fire needs three elements to advance; heat, fuel and air, so when one of these elements is separated from the other two, the fire is extinguished; this is the function of a fire extinguisher. The extinguisher that should be used is dictated by the type of fire; these are:

- solid fuel fires
- flammable liquids
- electrical.

**Types of extinguisher and their uses**

Extinguishers should be sited around the workshop and the model that is provided at each point should be suitable for the type of fire that is likely to occur in that area. You should know the position of each extinguisher and be aware of the limitations and precautions associated with each type: e.g. you must not use water and foam types on electrical fires. Regulations require employers to provide training in fire-fighting for their workforce. Also they should arrange regular fire drills to ensure that escape routes are known by all.

Fires are more difficult to suppress when a delay occurs while you read the operating instructions on the

## REMEMBER

If you are alone when a fire occurs, you should:

- call the Fire Brigade, and then
- attempt to contain the fire

If other persons are in the vicinity, you should:

- shout FIRE!
- call for assistance from authorised persons

who will then

- call the Fire Brigade and
- sound the alarm

| Extinguisher type | Colour code | Uses |
|---|---|---|
| Water – pressurised | RED | wood, paper, textiles, etc. UNSAFE ON ELECTRICAL |
| Water – soda acid | RED | wood, paper, textiles, etc. UNSAFE ON ELECTRICAL |
| Foam | CREAM | flammable liquids UNSAFE ON ELECTRICAL |
| $CO_2$ gas pressure | BLACK | any fire including flammable liquids |
| Dry powder | BLUE | any fire including flammable liquids |
| Vaporising liquid | GREEN | any fire including flammable liquids |

**Table 1.7.1** Types of fire extinguisher and their uses

fire extinguisher. Be acquainted with the various types and their use, as shown in Table 1.7.1.

### Fire alarms

All workshops involved in vehicle repair must have an adequate fire warning system that can be heard above the general noise of the workshop. Alarm points should be situated around the workshop, especially in high risk areas.

You should know the location of each alarm point, the method of activation, and the type of warning used to signal a fire. Furthermore you must know the suggested evacuation route from the different areas.

*Action in the event of a fire*    A small fire which can be extinguished with the available equipment will not justify the call-out of the Fire Brigade. Small confinable fires are those which are unlikely to spread to other flammable materials in the area and are:

- clearly visible such that the seat of the fire can be accessed;
- not creating toxic fumes and dense smoke.

If you are doubtful about any of these, you should raise the alarm.

## PROGRESS CHECK 1

1.  The observation of safety laws is the responsibility of the:
(a)  company
(b)  employee
(c)  management
(d)  employer and employee.

2.  When employees identify potential hazards they:
(a)  should present them at their yearly meetings
(b)  must report them to their superiors immediately
(c)  make a written report to the Safety Inspector
(d)  do not have to take action because it is not their responsibility.

3.  As applied to safety, the meaning of the term 'hazard' is:
(a)  any condition that leads to a fire
(b)  the likelihood of a dangerous situation
(c)  something with potential to cause harm
(d)  a situation causing injury or death.

4.  The UK Safety Laws requires the employer to accept sole responsibility for:
(a)  a safe place of work
(b)  all actions of the employees
(c)  cleaning of all working clothes
(d)  the enforcement of employees to use the safety equipment provided.

5.  When an employee is seriously injured at work, it is the duty of the employer to:
(a)  report the accident to the Health and Safety Executive
(b)  state, in writing, the period of sick leave granted by the company
(c)  check the medical history of the person injured
(d)  check that the employee has reported the accident to the Health and Safety Executive.

6.  When a person has received what appears to be a fatal electric shock, you should remove the person from the source and then:
(a)  call an ambulance
(b)  give resuscitation treatment
(c)  encourage them to walk about
(d)  allow them to recover in fresh air.

7.  A small quantity of liquid fuel that has ignited should be extinguished with a:
(a)  water hose
(b)  fire blanket
(c)  bucket of water
(d)  soda-acid extinguisher.

8.  A small fire has occurred in the vicinity of a high voltage electrical supply. The recommended type of fire extinguisher to use is:
(a)  foam
(b)  soda-acid
(c)  water pressurised
(d)  $CO_2$ gas pressure.

9.  Fire extinguishers are colour coded. Which one of the following pairs is correctly coded?

|      | RED          | GREEN            |
|------|--------------|------------------|
| (a)  | foam         | $CO_2$           |
| (b)  | $CO_2$       | dry powder       |
| (c)  | dry powder   | water            |
| (d)  | water        | vaporising liquid |

10. You are working in a workshop with other people and a fire occurs on your job. Your first action should be:
(a)  shout FIRE!
(b)  call for assistance
(c)  call the fire brigade
(d)  escape from the building.

# 2 *Vehicle and road safety*

## What is covered in this chapter:

→ statutory requirements for vehicles
→ road safety

UK Law stipulates that all motor vehicles used on the public highway must conform to certain safety regulations. Before undertaking any work on a vehicle you must be aware of these regulations; this is necessary because some repairs you may be asked to undertake may make it illegal for the vehicle to be used. A more serious situation will arise if, as the result of a fatal accident, an investigation finds that your repair, rectification or modification work was the cause.

This chapter gives you an outline of the main regulations affecting the construction, repair and operation of motor vehicles. This awareness is intended to make you hesitate before doing certain jobs; it is hoped that it will prompt you to consult the relevant Act as appropriate.

## 2.1 Statutory requirements for vehicles

Statutory regulations in most countries ensure that vehicles using the public highways meet stringent safety standards. Prior to the production of a new model that is to be sold in the UK, a prototype has to be submitted to a Department of Transport establishment to obtain *type approval*. The award of this approval shows that the vehicle has been fully examined, tested under laboratory conditions, and subjected to crash simulations to ensure that the construction and operation of the vehicle meet the safety and environmental standards. Countries, such as the USA, have their own regulations, so vehicles that are to be imported into, or exported out of, the United Kingdom must be modified as appropriate. During recent years the European Union, formally called the European Community (EC), has harmonised many of these safety regulations by publishing Directives; these contain 'recommendations' which all member governments are required to incorporate into their own legislation. In the UK the rulings in the directives have been embodied in the *Road Vehicles (Construction & Use) Regulations*; this is the main statute that governs the design of all parts of a motor vehicle that affect either its safety or the environment in which it operates.

### Road Vehicles (Construction & Use) Regulations 1986

The general legislative requirements for road vehicles insist that the condition of a vehicle, any trailer that it is drawing, its load and the number of passengers and the way in which they are carried are such that they do not involve danger of injury to the owner or others and that the detailed regulations require the different parts of the vehicle to be kept in good condition and working order. This long legal paragraph covers most things; it prescribes the general design, governs the way the vehicle is operated and it underlines the need for efficient maintenance. The regulations cover the brakes, steering, lights, windscreens and windows, exhaust, tyres, seat belts and fittings, speedometer, number plates and horn.

Like many other Acts, the 'construction and use regulations' are periodically amended, so it is necessary to keep up-to-date with any changes that are likely to affect your work. This updating is communicated to your company either from the Department of Transport, or via the industrial press; this includes publications which specialise in motor trade law.

### Environmental regulations

Protection of the environment against pollution caused by road users has prompted many governments to introduce legislation that is intended to 'clean up the motor vehicle'. These laws cover vehicle design features and are aimed at reducing the emission of dangerous gases from the engine compartment, exhaust system and fuel tank. A major change in engine design was necessary when regulations limiting the lead content in a fuel came into force. Environmental considerations are important political issues, so it is expected that more new laws on pollution and energy saving will be introduced in the next few years.

### Vehicle changes

Occasions may arise when you are asked to undertake some modification to the vehicle; e.g. fitting of extra lights, changing the tyres or altering the structure in some way. Before starting any job of this nature, you should check to see that the vehicle will still conform to the statutory requirements after the work has been completed. This means that reception staff responsible for booking work, and workshop staff who undertake it, must be aware of current regulations that relate to a particular job.

### MOT tests

In the UK all vehicles older than 3 years have to be tested each year by a Test Station, approved by the Department of Transport, to assess the mechanical condition of the vehicle in relation to safety. This test was introduced many years ago by a government body called the Ministry of Transport (MOT) and since that time it has been called the MOT test. Provided the vehicle condition is satisfactory an *MOT Certificate* is issued; this certificate must be presented when the vehicle is taxed and if demanded by a Police Officer.

Over the years the inspection has been strengthened by including tests on more systems. The standard required is laid down in the *MOT Tester's Manual*; this states the items that must be tested and the limits allowed. To become an authorised tester, the person must attend a short course run by the Department of Transport.

Large goods vehicles (LGV) and public service vehicles (PSV) have to be tested annually at special test stations administered by the government.

## 2.2  Road safety

### Roadtests

Often it is necessary to roadtest a vehicle to either diagnose a particular fault, or assess the performance after it has been repaired. In a large company this work is performed by either a qualified service adviser or an experienced tester. A smaller firm authorises one or more mechanics to undertake this work and the company's insurance gives cover for these persons to drive and test customer's vehicles.

---

## REMEMBER

### MOT test covers:

- tyres
- brakes
- lights
- steering
- horn
- doors
- mirrors
- emissions
- speedometer
- fuel systems
- seat security
- load security
- body condition
- exhaust system
- registration plate
- seat belts and fittings
- driver's view of the road

---

## REMEMBER

### Highway code

During a roadtest attention must be given to advice given in the Highway Code as it applies to:

- vehicle condition
- loads
- tiredness or illness
- vision
- alcohol
- learner drivers
- seat belts
- children
- car telephones and microphones
- signals
- speed limits
- stopping distances
- driving in fog
- pedestrians/pedestrian crossings
- emergency vehicles
- police stopping procedures
- lane discipline/overtaking/road junctions/parking and waiting
- breakdowns and accidents
- motorways

If you are unauthorised to carry out a road test, then you must brief the tester of the work that you have done. During the test the driver will check to see that the stated fault has been corrected and that no additional faults have been created by your work.

To assess the performance of a vehicle it is sometimes necessary to use a driving technique that is different to normal; e.g. it may be necessary to vary the speed such as when testing the acceleration or checking the brakes. At all times safety is paramount and consideration must be given to other road users. On occasions when the vehicle owner is required to demonstrate a given fault to you, the passenger, the driver should not be asked to perform any test that will violate any aspect of road safety legislation. At all times the *Highway Code* must be observed.

## PROGRESS CHECK 2

1. The Act that covers the condition of a motor vehicle is:
(a) Motor Vehicle MOT Regulations 1985
(b) Motor Vehicle Environmental Regulations 1985
(c) Road Vehicles (Construction & Use) Regulations 1986
(d) Road Vehicles (Condition & Operation) Regulations 1986.

2. A 'type approval' certificate issued by the Department of Transport is required when:
(a) the engine is changed
(b) the vehicle is annually taxed
(c) a new vehicle is made for sale
(d) the age of the vehicle is more than three years.

3. You are asked to modify the braking system of a vehicle. Before undertaking this work you should:
(a) consult the relevant European Union directive
(b) ensure that the modification does not make the vehicle illegal
(c) obtain a written statement from the owner to accept responsibility
(d) check that the materials meet the environmental regulations.

4. An MOT certificate is required when a vehicle:
(a) is to be taxed
(b) becomes five years old
(c) steering system is renewed
(d) is fitted with new brake pads and linings

5. Which one of the following is not part of an MOT test?
(a) Body corrosion
(b) Seat security
(c) Engine power output
(d) Door mirror condition.

6. Which one of the following statements is correct?
(a) A qualified road tester can exceed the speed limit for a period of less than two minutes
(b) A person carrying out a roadtest must always observe the highway code
(c) Qualified testers are permitted to carry out all roadtests without fastening their seatbelts
(d) A driver, accompanied by a qualified tester, is permitted to demonstrate a fault even if the driver has to contravene the highway code.

# Materials and processes

# 3

# *Materials*

Since motor vehicles are made of many metal and non-metal materials, it is necessary that you identify the main materials used for component parts in order that you may carry out suitable repairs. After studying this chapter you should be able to understand the main qualities of common metals, the behaviour of each metal, together with the various methods available to the engineer to alter its properties.

## 3.1 Properties of materials

A number of terms and expressions are used to describe the properties of materials. You will recognise terms like strength, hardness and toughness, but others are not so obvious. The main ones are covered here to allow you to use the engineering language as applied to materials.

*Strength*   This is the ability of a material to withstand a load without breaking. Strength of a metal is stated as the *ultimate stress*. Stress is the resistance of a material to deform when a load is applied to it, i.e. its resistance to being pulled apart. The effect of a load on the material

depends on the cross-sectional area of the metal that is resisting it, so the larger the area the lower the stress. Figure 3.1.1 shows the main types of stress.

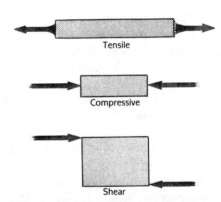

**Fig. 3.1.1** Main types of mechanical stress

*Elasticity*   When loads are applied to a component there is some deformation (change of shape); this is called *strain*. If the strain disappears on removing the load the material is said to be *elastic*, i.e. *elasticity* is the property by which a material is able to regain its original size and shape after being deformed by a load. Most materials are elastic up to the *elastic limit*; but when loaded beyond this limit there will be some *permanent strain* on removing the load. A bolt that has been overloaded by strain will be longer than a new bolt.

*Plasticity*   The property of a material to retain a deformation after the load is removed.

***Ductility*** A material which is plastic under tensile loads is said to be *ductile*. Materials having this property can undergo considerable stretching without breakage. Ductility is important in processes involving bending and pressing and in the manufacture of wire products.

***Malleability*** A material which is plastic under compressive loads is said to be *malleable*. Thus malleability is the property by which a material can undergo considerable permanent deformation without breaking when hammered or rolled.

***Brittleness*** Some materials break with little or no deformation. These are said to be *brittle*, and are particularly liable to break under suddenly applied (or 'shock') loads.

***Toughness*** The resistance of a material to fracture, measured by the amount of energy required to break a standard specimen. It is applied particularly to the ability to resist breaking under shock loads.

***Hardness*** The resistance of a material to penetration or scratching of the surface. Hard materials resist wear. Hardness is commonly measured by applying a load to a very small area of surface by means of a small piece of very hard material, such as a hard steel ball or a pointed diamond and measuring the size of the depression formed by a given load.

***Softness*** The reverse of hardness. Soft materials are easily shaped by cutting operations such as turning in a lathe, drilling etc., though other properties such as strength and ductility are also important. Many components which must resist wear must be softened to enable them to be made and must subsequently be hardened.

In some cases other properties such as *thermal* or *electrical conductivity, magnetic properties, resistance to corrosion* and *appearance* are important

### Some commonly used materials

Materials may be grouped into a number of different types such as:

- *Metals*, which can be further sub-divided into *ferrous* metals and *non-ferrous* metals;
- *Plastics*, which now form a very large group having a wide range of properties;
- *Timber* i.e. wood;

- *Ceramics*, which originally applied to materials made of some kind of clay, but is now generally used for a wider range of materials.

Each type of material has special properties which make it suitable for particular uses.

## 3.2 Metals – ferrous and non-ferrous

### Ferrous metals

These are metals in which the chief constituent is iron. Metals are seldom used in their pure state but are generally combined with other materials (usually other metals) to form *alloys* which modify the properties of the chief constituent. Possibly the most important single addition to iron is carbon which, although present only in relatively small amounts, causes important alterations in the properties of the metal.

The properties of all metals can also be influenced by heat treatment; this is a controlled heating and cooling of the metal in its solid state, with the object of obtaining particular properties in the metal.

***Cast Iron*** As its name implies, this is iron which has been melted and poured into a suitably shaped mould (usually made of sand) in which it is allowed to solidify. This is a simple and relatively inexpensive method of making complicated shapes, and one of the reasons for the use of iron in this way is the manner in which the molten metal will flow into quite complicated moulds. Some metals cannot be satisfactorily cast in this way.

Cast iron may contain up to 5% carbon; some of this is combined with the iron and the remainder is in a free state to form tiny flakes of graphite. Besides carbon there are small amounts of other materials; some of these are impurities which are costly to eliminate while others may have been deliberately added to improve the properties of the iron. The properties may also be modified, to some extent, by suitable heat treatment.

The tensile strength and shear strength of cast iron are fairly low, but the compressive strength is about five times the tensile strength.

***Steel*** Steel is fundamentally an alloy of iron and carbon in which the carbon content is usually less than about 2%; all the carbon is combined with the iron. Steels are commonly divided into groups, according to the carbon content. These are: low carbon steels (including mild steels), medium carbon steels and high carbon steels.

Low carbon steels are the most ductile and are used for making pressed steel components. They have

**REMEMBER**

**Carbon content of steel**

- low carbon    0.05–0.25%
- medium carbon  0.25–0.55%
- high carbon    0.55–0.90%

relatively low tensile strength (about 300–450 MN/m$^2$) and cannot be hardened to any useful extent by heat treatment, although there is a process called *case hardening* by which the carbon content of the outer skin can be increased. This enables a hard surface to be produced, but the core remains soft and ductile.

Medium carbon steels have a greater tensile strength (about 450–800 MN/m$^2$) and this can be improved by suitable heat treatment. The steels are rather less ductile than the low carbon type, but are capable of being hardened by heating followed by rapid cooling (quenching); this process further reduces the ductility.

High carbon steels give the greatest hardness, though the strength may not be much greater than that of medium carbon steels. Both strength and hardness depend upon suitable heat treatment, the more severe quenching causing improvements in these directions but reducing the ductility to the point of brittleness. This brittleness can be reduced to some extent by a process called *tempering*, which follows the quenching process and consists of reheating to a relatively low temperature and again quenching.

***Alloy steels***  Steels in which the distinctive properties are due mainly or solely to the carbon content and suitable heat treatment are called *carbon steels*. The addition of other alloying elements produces important modifications to some properties and steels of this kind are called *alloy steels*.

**Non-ferrous metals**

Below are given brief details of some of the commonly used metals of this type.

***Aluminium***  For motor vehicle work aluminium has two attractive properties. It is light, having a density less than half that of iron or steel; and it is a much better conductor of heat. In its pure state, it is soft and ductile, is resistant to atmospheric corrosion, but has a low tensile strength (about 80 MN/m$^2$). It is seldom used in the pure state, but is usually alloyed with other metals such as copper, silicon and magnesium to produce metals with much better strength and hardness, though its resistance to corrosion is impaired.

***Copper***  This metal is very ductile, malleable and soft, but easily *work hardens* (i.e. becomes hard when bent or stretched). Its outstanding property is perhaps its high electrical conductivity which has led to its almost universal use for electric wiring. It was commonly used for fuel and other pipes but its relatively high cost has led to its replacement for this purpose by steel and plastics. It is resistant to corrosion and easily soldered.

***Brass***  This is an alloy of copper and zinc. It is harder than copper and is commonly used for small fittings.

***Bronze***  This is an alloy of copper and tin and has found extensive use as a bearing metal.

***Zinc***  This is a soft metal having a low melting point which is easily cast. It is used for fittings such as door handles, and also for carburetter and fuel pump bodies.

Table 3.2.1 compares various properties and uses of non-ferrous metals.

## 3.3  Heat treatment

**Steel**

The main difference between iron and steel is the amount of carbon contained in the *composition* of the metal. Up to about 1.5% of carbon can be combined with pure iron (or *ferrite*, which is its chemical name) but above this percentage the carbon remains in an uncombined or free state. The point at which this free carbon or *graphite* appears is the dividing line between steel and iron – less than about 1.5% the material is steel, and above that point it becomes cast iron. A typical cast iron has a carbon composition of about 3 or 4%, so a large amount of free carbon exists in cast iron.

Carbon has a most important influence on steel: as the carbon content is increased the metal becomes harder and tougher. When the carbon percentage exceeds about 0.3% it is possible to alter the mechanical properties of the steel by heat treatment.

Other *impurities* are present in steel, in addition to carbon, namely, silicon, manganese, sulphur and phosphorus. To obtain a good quality steel, the amount of each impurity contained in a steel must be controlled.

| Metal | Chemical symbol | Melting point (°C) | Main properties | Uses |
|---|---|---|---|---|
| Aluminium | Al | 657 | Very light, soft, ductile malleable, good resistance to corrosion, good conductor of heat and electricity | Rarely used in pure state. Lightweight alternative to steel in alloy form |
| Copper | Cu | 1088 | Soft, ductile, malleable, good conductor of heat and electricity | Electrical cables. Fuel and oil pipes |
| Tin | Sn | 232 | Ductile and malleable | Coating for steel sheets (tin plate) |
| Lead | Pb | 327 | Soft, plastic, malleable almost non-elastic, unaffected by most acids | Battery plates |
| Zinc | Zn | 419 | Ductile and malleable Non-corrosive in air | Coating for steel (galvanised sheet) |

**Table 3.2.1** Properties and uses of non-ferrous metals

**Critical points**

When heat is applied at a constant rate to steel, it is noticed that there are one or more periods when the temperature does not rise. These 'temperature pauses' are called critical points, and during these periods the internal structure of the material is changed. A similar effect takes place when a steel is cooled; if gradual cooling is provided whilst the metal passes through the critical range, the steel will return to its original pre-heated state.

By quenching a medium or high carbon steel from a temperature higher than the critical range, the structural changes will be prevented and increased hardness will result. In all *heat treatment* operations the important factors are:

● temperature of quenching
● speed of quenching, i.e. rate of cooling.

The heat treatment processes applied to medium and high carbon steel are: hardening, tempering, annealing, and normalizing.

*Hardening* This treatment is performed to give the steel the ability to withstand scratching, wear, abrasion or indentation by harder objects. The steel is heated to a temperature above the critical range and quenched. For general purposes the *quenching temperature* is estimated by the colour. In the case of hardening, the steel is heated to a 'cherry red'; this represents a temperature of about 800°C. The liquid used for quenching is either water or oil; the latter gives a slower rate of cooling and reduces the risk of cracking.

*Tempering* Hardening a steel makes it very brittle and destroys its resistance to impact or shock. To improve these qualities, it is necessary to sacrifice hardness by tempering the steel; the final properties are governed by the temperature at which the process is performed. The steel is heated to the *tempering temperature* and quenched. The tempering temperature is set to suit the conditions to which the steel will be subjected (Table 3.3.1). Tempering at 200°C considerably reduces the brittleness, and tempering at 300°C decreases the hardness to a large extent. Most hand tools are tempered within 200–300°C range. Estimation of the temperature can be obtained by the colour of the oxide film which forms on a polished steel surface.

| Temper colour | Temperature (°C) | Tool |
|---|---|---|
| Pale straw | 220 | Scrapers |
| Dark straw | 240 | Taps, dies |
| Brownish purple | 260 | Twist drills |
| Dark purple | 280 | Cold chisels |
| Blue | 300 | Springs |

**Table 3.3.1** Tempering temperatures

Some medium carbon steels used for motor vehicle components are toughened by tempering at 600°C. Any excessive heat applied by a mechanic to these components makes the material brittle and weak.

*Annealing* The purpose of annealing is to soften the steel and increase its ductility; it also relieves *internal stresses*. The steel is heated to a 'cherry red' and cooled as slowly as possible. Slow cooling is achieved by covering the steel with sand, ashes or lime.

*Normalizing*  The object of this process is to restore the grain structure of a steel to a strong form after it has been either hot or cold worked. When steel is kept at a red-hot state for a long period of time (e.g. welding), the grain becomes large and coarse. Also when it is cold-worked (e.g. bent without heating), the internal structure becomes deformed and stressed. The steel is heated to a 'cherry red' and allowed to cool freely in air.

*Case hardening*  Components such as gudgeon pins and camshafts demand a hard surface to resist wear and a tough core to absorb shocks, so these and many other components are case hardened.

Low carbon steel is used since this ductile material can be made to absorb carbon when it is heated in contact with a carbon-rich substance. The extra carbon absorbed into the steel allows the surface to be hardened by the normal hardening process; the *carburizing* time governs the depth of hardness. For lightly loaded parts the depth is only about 0.25 mm, but in cases where large wear is expected, the depth is about 1.5 mm.

The methods used for carburizing are:

1) *Box process*  Steel parts are packed in a box containing a carbon-rich substance such as charcoal or bone dust, and heated to about 900°C for a period of 3 or 4 hours.
2) *Cyanide process*  Parts are immersed in molten sodium cyanide.
3) *Open-hearth*  Parts are heated to red-heat and dipped into a special compound. By reheating and dipping three or four times, a case-hardened surface of about 0.1 mm is obtained.

After carburizing, the part should be:

1) allowed to cool slowly to anneal;
2) heated to a 'bright cherry red' and quenched in oil to refine the grain;
3) heated to a 'dull cherry red' and quenched in oil or water to harden the surface.

Most case-hardened parts use a steel which contains a small amount of nickel. This material gives a more gradual change of hardness between the skin and core and reduces the risk of the hardened skin 'flaking-off' when in service. *Nitriding* is a low temperature case hardening process used on a special alloy steel and gives an extremely hard case. The machine-finished articles are packed, for a period of up to 90 hours, into a tank which is supplied with ammonia gas at a temperature of 500°C. Since a low temperature is used and quenching is unnecessary, distortion is minimised.

### Hot and cold working of steel

*Cold working*  Cold working is conducted below a temperature of about 600°C (dull red heat). When steel is bent or worked the crystal structure is distorted and this makes the steel harder and more brittle. Assuming the material has not cracked, it can be restored to a serviceable condition by annealing.

*Hot working*  Hot working occurs above the critical temperature range. Shaping a component by *forging* is an example of hot working. Forging produces a good grain flow by the shaping and a fine grain by the hammering, so components made in this manner are very strong (Figure 3.3.1).

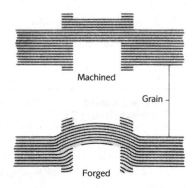

**Fig. 3.3.1** Grain flow in a crankshaft

### Annealing of copper

Bending or hammering of copper causes it to become hard and brittle, i.e. it *work hardens*. Also copper has the property of *age hardening*, i.e. it becomes harder with time. To restore the material to its ductile and soft state, it is heated to a dull red heat (650°C) and quenched in water.

## 3.4  Alloying elements

The materials used for motor vehicle construction must meet many requirements, including the following:

- strength
- elasticity
- ductility
- malleability
- brittleness
- toughness or shock resistance
- hardness
- relative density (weight)
- conductivity (heat and electrical)
- cost.

Some basic materials are able to satisfy a particular requirement, but where this is not possible other elements are often added and an alloy is formed.

### Steel alloys

Many vehicle components are made from steel alloys: these are formed by adding an alloying element to a low or medium carbon steel. In practice, alloy steels contain more than one element – a typical composition of one steel suitable for an engine crankshaft is:

carbon 0.35–0.44%
silicon 0.10–0.35%
manganese 0.50–0.80%
chromium 0.90–1.20%
molybdenum 0.20–0.35%
sulphur and phosphorus 0.05% maximum.

The effect of various additives in carbon steel is described in Table 3.4.1.

### Non-ferrous alloys

By combining together a number of non-ferrous metals, a material can be formed to suit a given application. The main alloys are given here.

*Aluminium alloy* Pure aluminium is rarely used because of its softness and low strength, but these drawbacks are overcome when it is alloyed with other metals. Many light alloys use aluminium as a base.

Some light alloys have the property of age-hardening; in the case of duralumin, a soft, workable condition is only retained for a few hours after heat treatment. Annealing is performed by heating to about 375°C and allowing the metal to cool in air, water or oil. (Heating by a flame causes ordinary engine oil applied to a metal surface to turn black at about 375°C so this may be used to indicate the temperature.) Two common alloys of aluminium are described in Table 3.4.2.

| Element | Approximate composition (%) | Properties which are improved | Typical application |
|---|---|---|---|
| Nickel | 1–5<br>3–5 | Toughness, elasticity<br>Case hardening – resistance to 'flaking' | Steering and suspension members<br>Ball and roller bearing races |
| Chromium | 12–20 | Resistance to corrosion (stainless steel) | 'Long-life' exhaust systems |
| Nickel<br>+<br>Chromium | 4<br>1 | Hardness, ductility, elasticity (can be hardened and tempered) | Shafts<br>High tensile bolts |
| Vanadium | 0.25 | Elasticity, toughness, fatigue resistance | Springs, spanners |
| Tungsten | 15 | Hardness at high temperature (high speed steel) | Metal cutting tools |
| Manganese | 12 | Strength, hardness and toughness | Axles, starter gears |
| Molybdenum | 0.2–1 | Hardness at high temperature, strength, does not become brittle during continuous heating | Crankshafts, gears |
| Aluminium<br>+<br>Chrome and Molybdenum | 1 | Hardening ability – allows steel to be case hardened by nitriding process (nitralloy) | Camshafts, crankshafts |

**Table 3.4.1**  Alloying elements added to low or medium carbon steel

| Alloy | Composition | Main properties | Uses |
|---|---|---|---|
| Duralumin | Aluminium, copper, manganese and magnesium | Good tensile strength | Engine parts which demand strength and lightness |
| 'Y' alloy | Aluminium, copper, nickel, magnesium and silicon | Light, strong, good heat conduction | Pistons, cylinder heads |

**Table 3.4.2**  Aluminium alloys

| Alloy | Composition | Main properties | Uses |
|-------|-------------|-----------------|------|
| Brass | Copper<br>Zinc | Great ductility, good strength, resistance to corrosion | Radiator parts, lamp fittings, chromium plated parts, light duty bushes, nuts |
| Bronze | Copper<br>Tin<br>(Phosphor bronze includes about 1% phosphorus) | Good bearing material – resistance to abrasion and low friction qualities | Plain bearings and bushes.<br>Worm-wheels |
| Copper–lead | Copper<br>Lead | High duty bearing material | Big end and main bearings |
| Lead–bronze | Copper<br>Tin and lead | Heavy duty bearing material | Heavily loaded engine bearings |

**Table 3.4.3** Copper alloys

***Copper alloys*** Brass and bronze are the main copper alloys and these are often used for engineering components: bronze is an excellent bearing metal. Copper alloy properties are described in Table 3.4.3.

***Tin alloys*** Solder and white metal bearing alloy are examples of tin alloys. Solder consists of tin and lead and the proportions used of these are governed by the application.

***Bearing alloy*** In the past, the white metal used for crankshaft bearings was Babbitt metal; this had a composition of tin, copper and antimony. Modern engines having high bearing loads demand a low friction material which is strong and resistant to the fatigue caused by surface deflection. Tin alloyed with aluminium is one modern material which combines strength with softness.

***Zinc alloys*** Many motor vehicle parts such as carburettors, hydraulic pump bodies, decorative fittings, are die cast, since this method produces a casting which has an excellent finish. The material used is normally a zinc-based alloy called Mazac – the name gives an indication of the composition – magnesium, aluminium, zinc and copper. Oxidation occurs with age, and the brittleness which results means that components made in this material must be treated with care.

## 3.5  Surface protection

Many metals, particularly steel, suffer *corrosion* when exposed to the atmosphere. The corrosion usually takes the form of oxidation of the exposed surface: in the case of steel the iron oxide formed in this way is called *rust*.

Corrosion of most metals is accelerated by exposure to dampness which, in the case of a motor vehicle is quite unavoidable.

Salt used by local authorities to melt ice and snow on the roads can be very corrosive to a vehicle. Water and salt together form an electrolyte, so if this solution connects two dissimilar metals then an electric battery is formed. An electrical current flowing in this way causes the metal to corrode rapidly.

Most materials are given protection from corrosion by coating their surfaces with a layer of some suitable material such as paint, or by an electro-plated coating of some corrosion-resistant metal such as chromium.

Many paints can be softened and ruined by substances such as brake fluid, acid or other general liquids used in a garage.

The frame and body structure of most cars is given a preliminary treatment such as *phosphating*. This consists of immersing the whole structure in a tank containing a liquid incorporating phosphoric acid, which converts the surface of the steel into iron phosphate. Not only does this, in itself, give some protection from corrosion but it also provides a surface to which paint will adhere strongly.

The underparts of a vehicle, which are liable to be abraded by grit and stones thrown up by the wheels, are usually given protection by a treatment known as *undersealing*. This takes the form of a sprayed-on coating of a rubber-based 'paint'.

## 3.6  Nature of stress

Earlier work showed that a load applied to a component caused the particles of the material to be deformed. The extent of this deformation is indicated by considering the load which acts on a given area. These two factors give the stress in a material, so

$$\text{stress} = \frac{\text{load}}{\text{area}}$$

If the load is in newtons and the area in square metres then

$$\text{stress} = N/m^2$$

Other units used for stress are: $N/mm^2$, pascal and bar. For conversion purposes:

$$1\,N/mm^2 = 10^6\,N/m^2$$
$$= 1\,000\,000\,N/m^2 \text{ OR } 1\,MN/m^2$$
$$1\,\text{Pa} \quad = 1\,N/m^2$$
$$1\,\text{bar} \quad = 10^5\,N/m^2 \text{ OR } 100\,000\,N/m^2$$

Direction of the loading indicates the type of stress; the main stresses are tensile, compressive and shear.

**Example**

A hand brake cable has a cross sectional area of 7 mm². Calculate the tensile stress in the cable when it is subjected to a force of 560 N.

$$\text{Stress} = \frac{\text{load}}{\text{area}}$$
$$= \frac{560}{7} = 80\,N/mm^2$$
$$= 80\,000\,000\,N/m^2 = 80\,MN/m^2$$

**Excessive loading on materials and components**

When a metal is subjected to a tensile load the material extends. Figure 3.6.1 shows the result obtained from a test on a ductile mild steel specimen. In common with

other metals, the extension of this steel varies with the load. Important parts of this graph are:

A–B: *Elastic range.* Extension is proportional to the load, i.e. Hooke's law applies. Provided the load does not exceed point B, the material will return to its original length when the load is removed. The working stress in a component should always be within this elastic range.

B–C: *Yield point.* Material yields and results in the material extending without further increase in the load. Once this point has been reached the plastic state of the metal produces a permanent deformation. (The yield of a metal can be felt when overtightening a bolt – when the yield point is reached, the bolt's resistance to rotation decreases and this causes a considerable reduction in its clamping ability.)

D: *Maximum load* (or ultimate tensile stress) taken by a material. Beyond this point the metal starts to break.

Consideration of the behaviour of a metal when subjected to a stress shows that overloading can cause breakage and the loss of elastic properties. To avoid these effects the material is given a *factor of safety*. This factor ensures that the working stress is a fraction of the metal's ultimate tensile stress. Tightening a bolt to a recommended torque gives a safe working stress and so reduces the risk of both under and overloading.

## 3.7   Non-metallic materials

**Plastics**

Materials of this type become plastic above a certain temperature (which may be as low as about 100°C in some cases) and in this state they can be squeezed in dies or moulds and made into any desired shape which they retain on cooling. There are two main classes.

*Thermosetting.* These undergo a chemical change during the moulding process and will not again become plastic on reheating. They can, therefore, be used in conditions where they may be subjected to relatively high temperatures. They are commonly used for covers in electrical equipment (distributor caps) and for decorative covers and mouldings. They are good electrical insulators.

*Thermoplastic.* These can be softened by heat repeatedly so that they cannot be used at temperatures much above the boiling point of water, and some become

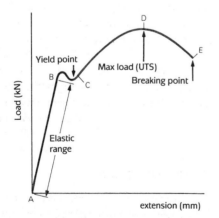

**Fig. 3.6.1** Load/extension curve for mild steel

plastic at even lower temperatures. Many of them are transparent (celluloid, cellulose, acetate, perspex) and most can be coloured as desired by the addition of suitable pigments. Brief details of some of the commoner types are given below.

*Polythene* is tough, slightly flexible has a strength of about 15 MN/m$^2$, but becomes plastic at temperatures not much above 100°C.

*Polyvinylchloride (PVC)* is flexible and rubber-like and is now almost universally used for insulating electrical cables. It can be coloured as desired and is completely resistant to oil and water. It is also available in sheet form and is used for upholstery.

*Polytetrafluorethylene (PTFE)* is rather similar to PVC. Its chief characteristic is that when used on itself or on most metals it has very low friction.

*Nylon* can be made into fibres and woven into a fabric, but can also be moulded. It is tough, has a tensile strength of about 60 MN/m$^2$ and low friction against metals. It is used for certain bearings and for small gear wheels (e.g. speedometer drive gears).

## Timber

Wood was at one time commonly used as the framework of motor car bodies (it has even been successfully used for vehicle chassis frames) but it is now almost completely eliminated from the motor car. Almost its only use in the modern car is for decoration e.g. instrument panels, window frames, and even here it is only found on a few makes of car.

It is still commonly used in certain types of commercial vehicle bodies, though even here it is gradually being replaced by metals.

Generally the *hardwoods*, produced by slow-growing trees such as oak, ash, beech and teak are used. The chief advantages of wood are its lightness compared with metals and the ease with which it can be cut and shaped. It is, therefore, very suitable for components which are made in very small numbers where expensive machines for manufacturing would not be justified.

Hardwoods have a tensile strength of about 40 MN/m$^2$ but are liable to rot if not adequately protected from wet.

## Ceramics

Almost the only use for materials of this kind on motor vehicles is the insulator of sparking plugs. These were at one time commonly made of a very fine natural clay called porcelain, but are now often made of aluminium oxide (corundum).

# PROGRESS CHECK 3

1. After being deformed by an applied load a material returns to its original size and shape. Materials which behave in this manner are called:
(a) elastic
(b) ductile
(c) plastic
(d) malleable.

2. A material which breaks with little or no deformation is called:
(a) ductile
(b) tough
(c) elastic
(d) brittle.

3. A ferrous metal is one which contains:
(a) iron
(b) carbon
(c) steel
(d) copper.

4. When two or more metals are combined, the metal formed is called:
(a) non-ferrous
(b) an alloy
(c) brass
(d) bronze.

5. Which one of the following metals applied to the statement: 'the metal is brittle and is often used for exhaust manifolds'?
(a) Low carbon steel
(b) Medium carbon steel
(c) High carbon steel
(d) Cast iron.

6. The type of heat treatment carried out on low carbon steel to alter its properties is:
(a) case hardening
(b) hardening and tempering
(c) quenching
(d) rapid cooling.

7. The most suitable material for a general purpose bolt is:
(a) low carbon steel
(b) high carbon steel
(c) cast iron
(d) iron.

8. Which one of the following has the highest thermal conductivity and highest thermal expansion?
(a) aluminium
(b) brass
(c) cast iron
(d) steel.

9. Which one of the following is the carbon composition of medium carbon steel?
(a) 0.05–0.25 per cent
(b) 0.25–0.55 per cent
(c) 0.55–0.9 per cent
(d) 0.9–4 per cent.

10. A high carbon steel is heat treated to improve its ability to withstand scratching and indentation. This process is performed by heating the steel to a 'cherry red' and:
(a) cooling as slow as possible
(b) quenching in oil or water
(c) placing it into hot sand
(d) plunging it into a special compound.

11. Steel at a temperature of 800°C has a colour described as:
(a) white hot
(b) cherry red
(c) dull red
(d) black heat.

12. The effect of annealing a material is to:
(a) reduce its hardness
(b) reduce its softness
(c) increase its resistance to wear
(d) increase its resistance to indentation.

13. Which one of the following oxide colours indicates the temperature at which quenching is necessary for a cutting tool subjected to severe impact or shock?
(a) Pale straw
(b) Dark straw
(c) Dark purple
(d) Blue.

14. After hardening a steel cutting tool the material is too brittle to use, so to improve its shock resistance the tool is:
(a) annealed
(b) tempered
(c) normalized
(d) case hardened.

15. The process in which a steel is heated to a 'cherry red' and then allowed to cool as slow as possible is called:
(a) hardening
(b) case hardening
(c) tempering
(d) annealing.

16. If a component, such as a gudgeon pin, needs a tough core and a wear-resistant surface, then the heat treatment required is called:
(a) hardening
(b) tempering
(c) annealing
(d) case hardening.

17. The process in which special alloy steel components may be surface hardened by heating in contact with ammonia gas is called:
(a) nitriding
(b) box
(c) cyanide
(d) open hearth.

18. The effect of overheating a clutch spring is that it will:
(a) make it harder
(b) make it more brittle
(c) increase the thrust that it applies on the plate
(d) decrease the thrust that it applies on the plate.

19. Which one of the following is a non-ferrous alloy?
(a) brass
(b) copper
(c) nickel-chrome steel
(d) chrome-vanadium steel.

20. A strip of copper is heated to a dull red heat and quenched in water. This process causes the copper to become:
(a) harder
(b) more brittle
(c) more ductile
(d) less ductile.

21. Which one of the following is a common alloying element that is used to improve the toughness of a steel?
(a) brass
(b) nickel
(c) bronze
(d) Y metal.

22. Which one of the following is an alloying element that improves the resistance of a steel to corrosion?

(a) vanadium
(b) tungsten
(c) manganese
(d) chromium.

23. Bronze is an alloy consisting of copper and:
(a) aluminium
(b) zinc
(c) tin
(d) lead.

24. A load of 400 N acts on a rod having a cross-sectional area of 200 $mm^2$. The stress is:
(a) $0.5 \text{ N/mm}^2$
(b) $1 \text{ N/mm}^2$
(c) $2 \text{ N/mm}^2$
(d) $80 \text{ kN/mm}^2$.

25. A load of 400 N acts on a rod having a cross-sectional area of 200 $mm^2$. The stress is:
(a) $0.5 \text{ MN/m}^2$ or 0.5 MPa
(b) $1 \text{ MN/m}^2$ or 1 MPa
(c) $2 \text{ MN/m}^2$ or 2 MPa
(d) $80 \text{ GN/m}^2$ or 80 GPa

26. Corrosion has reduced the diameter of a circular brake rod by 50%. During brake application the stress in the rod will be:
(a) half the original stress
(b) twice the original stress
(c) four times the original stress
(d) eight times the original stress.

27. 'Provided the load on a steel bolt does not exceed the _____, the material will return to its original length when the load is removed'. The words needed to complete this sentence are:
(a) yield point
(b) breaking load
(c) factor of safety
(d) ultimate tensile load.

28. A plastics material which can be softened by heat is called:
(a) thermosetting
(b) thermoplastic
(c) thermosoft
(d) thermohard.

29. The insulator of a sparking plug is often made of material called:
(a) PVC
(b) PTFE
(c) nylon
(d) ceramic.

30. A steel has a surface which consists of iron oxide. This means that the surface has:
(a) been painted with an iron oxide paint
(b) been electro-plated
(c) been phosphated
(d) rusted.

# 4

# *Tools and equipment*

A good technician needs a good set of hand tools that are suitable for the tasks that have to be undertaken. At an early stage of your training you must be aware of the main tools you will need so that you can assemble your own kit of tools. Remember that your tools will be in constant use, so you must carefully consider the quality of the tool and the long-term cost before you make your purchase.

Also in this chapter you will cover some of the special tools and items of equipment found in the average workshop. As with all tools, good practice and skill is acquired with experience and understanding of the correct method of use.

## 4.1  Hand tools

Tools play an important part in the efficient repair of a motor vehicle. Unless a suitable tool is available, the repair task becomes very difficult; in some cases you will be unable to carry out a task without causing further damage to the vehicle.

In addition to the general tools owned by you, the company must provide a full range of *safety equipment* to give protection to your eyes, ears, hands and lungs; **these must be used as appropriate**. Also the company will stock a range of specialist tools and equipment that is needed for repairs likely to be undertaken by the company. This equipment extends from special tools designed to perform specialised repairs on a particular vehicle to expensive items such as hoists, hydraulic jacks and electronic test equipment.

### Care of tools and equipment

Tool care is important and time is saved if your tools are kept in good condition. This includes cleaning after use, regular maintenance such as sharpening, and returning the tool to its proper place after use. Time searching for a tool is expensive, so you should adopt a simple system to avoid the aggravation associated with the loss of a special tool. This situation is most annoying when you remember that the tool was left in a customer's car.

It is essential that care is exercised when you use special tools and equipment provided by the company. After use you should return the tools to their correct place, most probably a shadowed tool board mounted in a prominent position. If a tool is found to be damaged, you should report it immediately to the person responsible for the equipment. If everybody does this, the workshop will run smoothly.

### Tool cabinet and contents

For location and security purposes you will need a suitable tool cabinet or chest to hold your personal tools. Today these containers range from a small, lockable tool box to a large transportable cabinet similar to that shown as Figure 4.1.1. Some of the common general tools are described below.

*Ring spanners*  Figure 4.1.2 shows the most common type of wrench used on motor vehicles. The widespread use of ring spanners is mainly due to the positive grip the ring provides around the complete nut. The rings on heavy duty spanners are hexagonally shaped, but for general use the bi-hexagonal ring is preferred because it allows small nut movements of 30°. Good ring spanners are drop forged and made of chrome vanadium; this is polished to give a smooth hand grip surface and cranked to give clearance. Sets of spanners cover the main sizes of nut; today the metric system is in common use, but A/F (across flats) spanners are still available for older vehicles. The size stamped on a metric wrench is the distance

**Fig. 4.1.1** Steel cabinets provide a secure, tidy, mobile means for holding a technician's personal tools. Cabinets can be wheeled to the work area or stored againt the workshop wall.

*Ford Motor Co Ltd*

**Fig. 4.1.2** Ring spanner

> ## Good practice
>
> - Wrenches should be **pulled** and not **pushed**
> - When a wrench slips, an injured hand often results

between the jaws. Each end of the wrench has a different size and the length of the spanner is set to give the required leverage. Typical metric sizes range from 6–24 mm and A/F spanners, 1/4–1 inch.

***Open-ended spanners*** This type (Figure 4.1.3) is used where there is insufficient clearance to use a ring or socket spanner. The standard open-ended spanner has the opening set at 15° to the wrench body; this allows the spanner to be inverted to facilitate engagement for most nut positions. Sizes normally cover metric and A/F

**Fig. 4.1.3** Open ended spanner

applications. Sets of spanners are sold which have a ring at one end and open-ended jaws at the other. This is called a *combination spanner*. This is useful because it saves having to carry two separate sets of spanner to a job.

***Socket wrenches*** Sockets, with their assortment of drives and handles, are very popular because they make the job easier and faster. Developed from the tubular box spanner, the range of sockets is very large; also sets of sockets are made to fit many types of bolt (Figure 4.1.4). The standard sockets used on cars have a 1/2 in square drive, but smaller versions with a 1/4 in and 3/8 in square drive are available for light work. Special deep, thin-walled sockets are made for sparking plugs. These fit in the deep cylinder head recesses and, to reduce the risk of damage to the plug insulator, the socket is lined with a rubber insert.

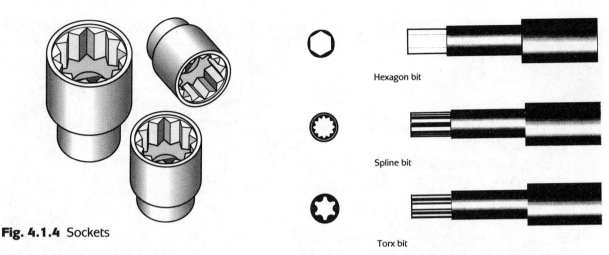

**Fig. 4.1.4** Sockets

**Fig. 4.1.6** Socket bits for recessed bolt heads

*Handles for sockets*   A variety of accessories (Figure 4.1.5) such as a T-bar, ratchet handle, speed handle (spinner), and extensions are made to suit the various applications. The angle of drive can be varied by using universal joints and wobble units; converters are made to connect the different sized drives.

*Socket bits*   The increased use of bolts having recesses in the bolt-head for key engagement has meant that the socket set has been enlarged to meet this requirement.

Special sets of interchangeable bits are made to cover hexagonal, spline and Torx® applications (Figure 4.1.6).

*Adjustable spanners*   This type of wrench (Figure 4.1.7) is designed to fit any nut within the range of its adjustment. The wrench size is given by its length and opening capacity of the jaws. The drop forged chrome vanadium types are supplied in sizes that range from a length of 100 mm (capacity 13 mm) to 380 mm (capacity 46 mm). In use this type of spanner does not maintain its adjustment; as a result it is likely to slip on the nut and damage the corners. The adjustable spanner should not be confused with a stillson-type wrench; this type has spring loaded jaws with teeth designed to grip objects such as pipes.

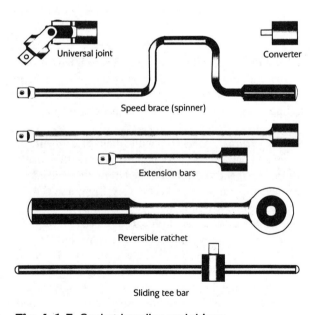

**Fig. 4.1.5** Socket handles and drives

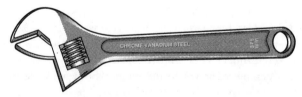

**Fig. 4.1.7** Adjustable spanner

**REMEMBER**

An adjustable wrench should be used as a last resort

*Impact wrenches* Although the standard type of socket is strong enough for hand use, it will break if it is impacted with a power driver such as an electric or pneumatic gun. For this type of power use, special toughened steel sockets and extensions are made (Figure 4.1.8). For strength purposes hexagonal sockets are used and these can usually be identified by their black heat-treated surface finish.

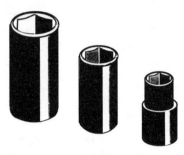

**Fig. 4.1.8** Impact wrenches

*Impact driver* A power driven impact tool is designed to save time when loosening and tightening nuts; this feature has persuaded many technicians to own their own power tool. Prior to using an impact tool to tighten a nut, the torque setting should be adjusted (Figure 4.1.9) to avoid over-tightening and possible breakage. It is recommended that nut tightness should be checked with a separate torque wrench in cases where vehicle safety is concerned.

## SAFE PRACTICE

Over-tightening with an impact driver is just as dangerous as under-tightening

*Torque wrench* When nuts and bolts are under-tightened, the low clamping load allows slight movement of the parts and increases the risk of the bolt working loose. Conversely, an over-tightened bolt can cause stripping of the thread or breakage of the bolt. In both cases there is a risk of danger because although the fixing appears to be

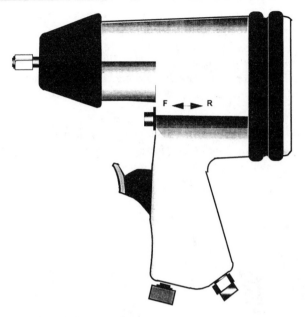

**Fig. 4.1.9** Impact driver

secure, the bolt can fail when it is stressed. In the past the skill and experience of the mechanic was relied on to indicate bolt tightness, but nowadays the use of new bolt materials has made this task more difficult. To eliminate guesswork the manufacturers publish the torque loading for most nuts and bolts; to measure this load a torque wrench is used (Figure 4.1.10).

Although many different types are in use, most use a spring-loaded ratchet that is adjusted by turning a key or the handle to the required setting. Wrenches are classified by the drive size and torque range; a typical wrench has a 1/2 in square drive and a torque range of 40–200 Nm (30–150 lbf ft). For accuracy purposes the wrench should be checked periodically. Before it is used

## REMEMBER

A torque wrench ensures that nuts and bolts are not under- or over-tightened

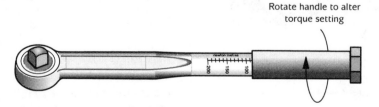

Rotate handle to alter torque setting

**Fig. 4.1.10** Torque wrench

the thread of the bolt should be checked for damage, because this can alter the loading.

***Special-purpose wrenches*** Some tasks on vehicles are difficult to perform with the standard range of wrenches; in these cases special tools have been developed. These include:

● *Drain plug keys* These are used for female sockets on sump drain plugs. Normally the body of a key, as shown as Figure 4.1.11, is rotated by using a 14 mm sparking plug socket.

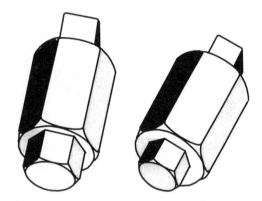

**Fig. 4.1.11** Drain plug keys

● *Oil filter removers* The task of removing a tight canister is made easy by using a strap, band or chain type wrench (Figure 4.1.12).

**Fig. 4.1.12** Oil filter remover

● *Specially shaped spanners* Spanners are made for special vehicle applications; these include wrenches of many shapes, ring spanners with sections cut out of the ring for pipe work, extra thin types, and ring spanners with built-in ratchets. These, and many others, are designed either to save time or make it possible to do some difficult task.

***Screwdrivers*** The purpose of a screwdriver is to tighten or loosen a screw; the standard type is not intended to be used as a chisel, punch or pry bar. Screwdrivers are classified by the shape of the blade and length of the shank and blade. Types include:

● *Blade screwdrivers* Figure 4.1.13 shows an engineer's screwdriver designed to fit a slotted screw. A number of drivers are needed to cover the different

**Fig. 4.1.13** Blade-type screwdriver

screw sizes; a typical range of blade widths and lengths is from 3.0 × 75 mm to 9.5 × 250 mm. Various lengths of shank are made for special purposes; these include the very short *chubby*, the *extra long shank* and *offset* types (Figure 4.1.14). Some high torque screw-

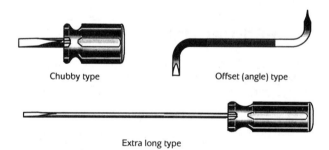

Chubby type    Offset (angle) type

Extra long type

**Fig. 4.1.14** Types of blade screwdriver

drivers have square section shanks and handles; this type allows a spanner to be used for extra leverage. To avoid damage the shape and size of the blade should fit and fill the screw slot; this means that the blade should be sharpened correctly (Fig. 4.1.15).

● *Multi-slot screwdrivers* The slots of these screwdrivers centre the tip so as to prevent it slipping off the screwhead; this feature makes them particularly suited for power driving. Various shapes of screwhead are used, so it is necessary to identify the slot type to avoid

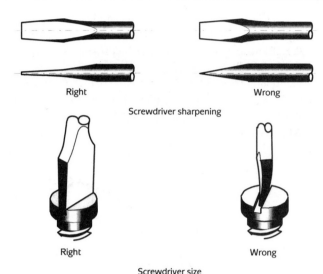

Screwdriver sharpening

Right                                    Wrong

Screwdriver size

**Fig. 4.1.15** Screwdriver blade details

**Fig. 4.1.18** Torx screwdriver

is eliminated. The positive grip makes the screw suitable for loading to a given torque.

---

## Good practice

The size of screwdriver bit should completely fill the recess in the screwhead

---

damaging the screw by using the incorrect tip. The main types are:

- *Crosshead*    Screws with X-slots cut into the head form a good seat for the screwdriver; that is assuming the correct size and shape of driver is used and all foreign material has been cleaned from the slot. The crosshead type shown in Figure 4.1.16 has sharp corners. An alternative type having a curved surface between the slots is known as a Phillips-type screwdriver. The X-slot size is numbered 0,1,2,3,4 etc., the smallest being No. 0, so a screwdriver classified as 3 × 150 mm has a shank length of 150 mm and an X-point to fit a No. 3 slot.

**Fig. 4.1.16** Crosshead screwdriver

- *Pozi-drive*    A Pozi/Supadriv screwdriver has a tip as shown in Figure 4.1.17, which is intended to give a better grip than the normal crosshead type.

**Fig. 4.1.17** Pozidrive screwdriver

- *Torx*®    Screws of this type have six parallel flutes cut into the side of a deep recess in the screwhead (Fig. 4.1.18), so slippage between the screw and driver

*Pliers*    Pliers are used to grip, bend or hold a part. They are not intended to be used as a wrench to unscrew a nut, because this bad habit results in 'round nuts'. Types of pliers include:

- *Combination pliers*    As the name suggests this type does many jobs; besides the main gripping jaws, cutting surfaces are provided for side cutting and wire chopping. Nowadays the handles are often sleeved with a plastic covering to provide a better hand grip. Various lengths are made; Figure 4.1.19 shows a typical 175 mm sleeved pair of pliers.

**Fig. 4.1.19** Combination pliers

- *Side cutters*    Sometimes called diagonal pliers, the type shown as Figure 4.1.20, is primarily used for cutting materials such as wire and for removing split pins. The size is determined by the length.

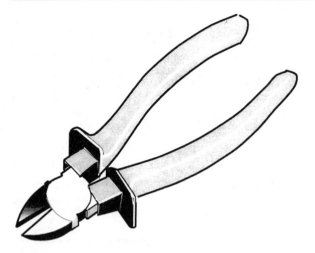

**Fig. 4.1.20** Side cutters

- *Radio pliers*   The *pointed*, or *needle pliers* shown as Figure 4.1.21 are very useful for fine work on instruments, radios and other electrical and electronic

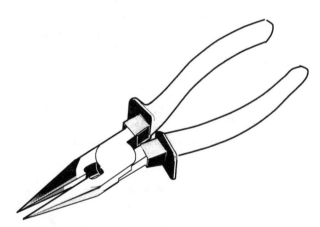

**Fig. 4.1.21** Long nose (radio) pliers

equipment. Besides being made in different lengths, pliers with various jaw dimensions are available. Some have very long jaws with blunt ends and others come to a sharp point. Radio pliers are most useful both for recovering small parts that have dropped into inaccessible places and for positioning small parts.

---

### Good practice

Pliers should not be used in places where a spanner can be applied

---

- *Circlip pliers*   These are made to simplify the task of removing and fitting spring-type circlips. Figure 4.1.22 shows one type having $90°$ tips with provision for the handles to be reversed to suit both internal and external circlips. To cover the many shapes and sizes of circlip, you will need either a number of separate pliers with different tips, or one pair of pliers with a range of detachable tips.

**Fig. 4.1.22** Circlip pliers

- *Slip-joint pliers (or water pump pliers)*   Used for gripping purposes, these pliers are made in different lengths and jaw shapes to suit many applications. By opening the handles of the straight jaw type shown as Figure 4.1.23, the pivot point can be adjusted to alter the opening but still keep the jaws parallel to each other.

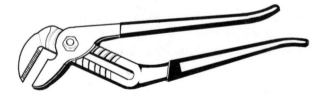

**Fig. 4.1.23** Slip-joint pliers

- *Crimping pliers*   Most electrical terminals are solderless and use detachable connections which are crimped (pinched) onto the cable. Figure 4.1.24 shows a type in common use.

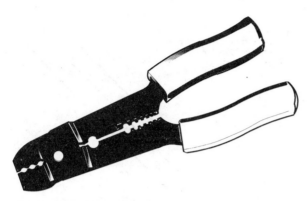

**Fig. 4.1.24** Crimping pliers

*Self-grip wrenches* The locking feature of this tool provides a vice-like grip to securely hold a part in position during either the dismantling operation or repair process. Adjustment is by means of a screw on the handle and a self-locking feature enables the handle to be snapped over-centre to secure the setting. From the original straight jaw type, many other shapes of jaw have been introduced (Figure 4.1.25).

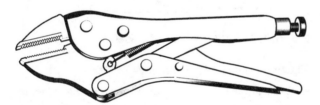

**Fig. 4.1.25** Self-grip pliers

The serrated jaws of a self-grip wrench leave an impression (as is the case with most pliers) so care must be exercised to avoid damage to a finished surface.

*Hammers* Various hammers are needed for auto repair work, the most common being the ball pein type (Fig. 4.1.26).

**Fig. 4.1.26** Engineer's hammer

- *Ball pein hammer* Classified by the weight of the head, the common sizes for general work are 450 g and 900 g. Mounted on a hickory or glass fibre shaft, the head has two faces: the 'flat' face, for normal hammering, and the pein which is made in different shapes to suit various craft trades and applications. Historically the ball pein was preferred by engineers, because the ball was useful for riveting work.
- *Soft-faced hammers* When a hammer blow is likely to damage the surface of a part, it is necessary to use either a soft drift (punch) or a soft-faced hammer head. These hammers have faces made of materials such as hide, plastic, rubber or copper.

## Good practice

A hammer used by an unskilled person can cause serious damage to the work piece

*Pry bar* There are many occasions when leverage is required; in these cases it is handy to use a pry bar (Fig. 4.1.27). When using this tool, care must be exercised to avoid damage or breakage of the part being levered.

**Fig. 4.1.27** Pry bar

*Other general tools* In addition to the forementioned tools, it will be necessary for you to own other tools such as:

- chisels
- feeler gauges
- files
- hacksaw
- marking-out tools (dividers, rule, scriber, square)
- oil can
- punches (pin, centre and drifts)
- snips
- trimming knife
- twist drills
- wire brush.

In addition it is expected your basic kit of tools will be supplemented by other tools needed for the jobs you are asked to do; e.g. if you do a large amount of electrical work, you will have your own multimeter. For obvious reasons it is suggested that this tool is kept for your use only.

## 4.2   Cutting tools

Whenever you undertake metal cutting or grinding, the appropriate safety equipment provided by your company **must** be used.

There are many occasions when you need to cut, grind or shape metal; to perform this work a number of hand and power tools are available to you. Some small tools will be part of your basic kit, but the larger and more specialised items will be provided by your company. Cutting tools include: chisels, files, drills, shears and hacksaws.

### Chisels

You will need a range of chisels that includes chisels of different diameters and lengths as well as various cross sections and point shapes.

*Chisel types*   The *flat chisel*, often called a *cold chisel*, is the most commonly used type; its flat cutting edge makes it suitable for general chipping work such as removing rivet heads. The main types of chisel are shown in Figure 4.2.1. A chisel needs a hard cutting edge and a tough, softer shank to absorb impact with the hammer; this is achieved by heat treatment.

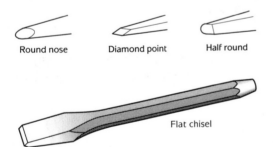

Round nose     Diamond point     Half round

Flat chisel

**Fig. 4.2.1** Chisel types

*Cutting action*   Chisels, files, drills, and hacksaw blades cut by forcing a sharp wedge into the surface to cause the top layer to break or chip off (Figure 4.2.2). You will obtain an efficient tool (one that requires the minimum effort to cut the metal) when the tool is:

1) made of a suitable good quality material;
2) correctly heat-treated to give a hard cutting edge and tough shank;
3) sharpened to an angle that suits the metal being cut.

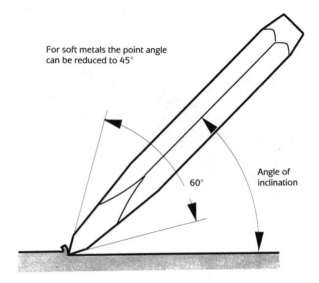

For soft metals the point angle can be reduced to 45°

60°

Angle of inclination

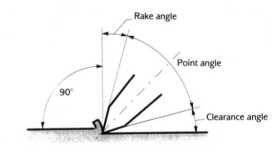

Rake angle

Point angle

90°

Clearance angle

**Fig. 4.2.2** Cutting angles of chisel

The two main cutting angles are:

- *Clearance angle*     This keeps the cutting edge in contact with the work and ensures that the force applied to the tool is concentrated at the cutting edge.
- *Rake angle*     This is the angle between the cutting face and the work. It is affected by the point angle of the chisel and the angle that it is held at. A small point angle allows the tool to cut into the metal easily, but the points of tools having this shape are weak and soon become damaged.

*Sharpening*   You should grind the point angle of a flat chisel to an angle of 60° for general work on steel, but the angle can be reduced when it is used on softer materials. For safety reasons you should grind the head periodically to prevent it mushrooming (Figure 4.2.3).

---

## SAFE PRACTICE

Before using a chisel make sure there is nobody in the line of fire

Your body will be protected, their body may not

---

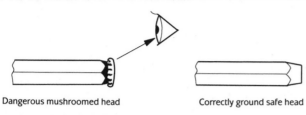

**Fig. 4.2.3** Chisel care

Dangerous mushroomed head

Correctly ground safe head

### Files

A steel file consists of a series of hardened cutting teeth which are used for removing or smoothing metal. Files are classified by length, grade of cut, shape of file and type of cut; e.g. a typical general-purpose engineer's file is a 200 mm, 2nd cut hand file having double-cut teeth. You will need a range of files similar to those shown in Figure 4.2.4. For safety reasons make sure your file is fitted with a good handle before using it. Today a plastic handle is often moulded to the file tang.

### Drills

You will need a set of twist drills covering the range 2–12 mm, preferably in steps of 0.5 mm. A drill gets very hot in use even when it is cooled with a good supply of

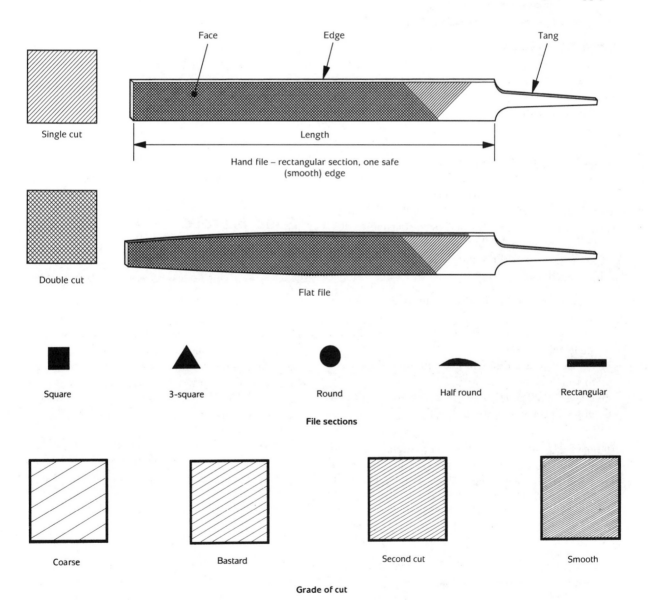

**Fig. 4.2.4** Types of file

cutting oil, so to maintain a sharp cutting edge a good material such as high speed steel (HSS) is needed.

In addition to the helical fluted drill shown in Figure 4.2.5, other types of drill bit are made for special applications: e.g. when you use a standard type of twist drill on thin metal, you will need to take special care when it breaks through the surface; for this type of work special drill bits are made that have either no flutes, or flutes having little or no helix.

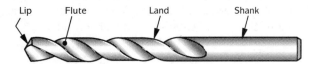

**Fig. 4.2.5** Twist drill

There are two types of drilling machines in common use; the portable drill (electric or pneumatic) and the fixed drilling machine mounted on a pillar or fixed to the bench.

*Sharpening drills* Periodically you must sharpen your drills, because if a drill is in poor condition it will cut slowly, drill an oversized hole or break. For general work you should grind a standard twist drill to the angles shown in Figure 4.2.6. You will need skill and practice to achieve these angles, but the task is made easier by using a jig. After grinding you should make the following checks:

a) *point angle*: you can check this with two nuts (Figure 4.2.7)
b) *web angle*: this gives an indication of the clearance angle
c) *clearance angle*: a drill will not 'bite' into the metal if this angle is too small
d) *length of each cutting edge*: if the lengths are unequal, the drill will cut an oversize hole (Figure 4.2.8).

*Using drills* Prior to drilling, you should mark the position of the hole with a centre punch; this prevents the drill from wandering. When a hole has to be

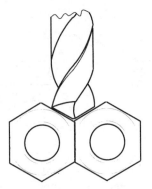

**Fig. 4.2.7** Checking point angle with two nuts

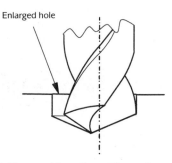

**Fig. 4.2.8** Unequal length cutting edges

## Good practice

When drilling make sure the work is clamped securely

accurately drilled through a polished or painted surface, damage can be prevented by using a strip of masking tape to cover the area around the hole. When you have to cut a large hole, a pilot drill (of diameter slightly larger than the web of the large drill) should be used. The use on sheet metal of large diameter twist drills should be avoided; this operation is best carried out with a *tank cutter*.

Maximum tool life and time saving are achieved when you use the correct *drilling speed* and *feed*. Spindle speeds on bench drilling machines can be varied to suit

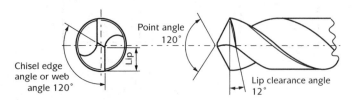

**Fig. 4.2.6** Twist drill angles

| Drill dia (mm) | Type of metal | |
|---|---|---|
| | **Mild steel** | **Aluminium, brass and copper** |
| 3 | 3185 | 6365 |
| 5 | 1910 | 3820 |
| 6 | 1590 | 3180 |
| 8 | 1195 | 2390 |
| 10 | 955 | 1910 |
| 11 | 870 | 1740 |
| 13 | 735 | 1470 |

**Table 4.2.1** Typical drilling speeds (rev/min)

the work material as well as the size and type of drill, but this is not always possible with portable drills. To overcome this drawback many modern portable drills incorporate either a 2-speed or variable speed feature.

Often the recommended spindle speeds are shown on the machine, but where this is not so, you can use the speeds shown in Table 4.2.1 as a guide.

*The drilling feed* is the distance that the drill advances into the work per revolution. This is normally controlled by you, the operator, either by moving the feed handle or, in the case of a portable drill, by the force that you apply to the drill. As a general guide a HSS drill is given a feed of:

*0.02 mm per revolution per 1 mm of drill diameter.*

---

### Good practice

1. Centre-punch before drilling a hole
2. A pilot hole is needed for a large drill

---

### Hacksaws

You will need two hacksaws, together with a variety of blades, for your work on vehicles: a standard 305 mm (12 in) adjustable type and a 'junior' 152 mm (6 in). The HSS type of blade is recommended for good blade life, and a selection of blades is required that cover the range from 18 to 32 teeth per unit (25 mm). You will use the coarse blades for soft metals and the fine blades for metal that is either hard or very thin (e.g. exhaust pipes).

### REMEMBER

A hacksaw blade is fitted so that it cuts on the forward stroke

## 4.3 Workshop equipment

Your company provides a range of workshop equipment such as hoists, axle stands, compressors, oxy-gas heating and similar machinery as well as specialist tools and equipment that you will need to repair particular vehicles. If your company offers MOT test facilities, it will have the equipment as specified by the Department of Transport.

In this chapter the general items of workshop equipment are considered.

### Cleaning facilities

Companies provide various cleaning facilities in which the complete vehicle, or the component parts, can be cleaned. Many different types are used which include:

*Drive-through wash* Often situated on the forecourt, these wash systems allow for either the vehicle to be driven through the wash, or the wash system to pass over the stationery vehicle. Customers can vary the wash programme to suit their requirements. The basic sequence gives an initial water soak with powerful jets of water, a soap/detergent spray and a final rinse.

*Portable high pressure water wash* This equipment consists of a portably-mounted, electrically-driven water pump that supplies a jet of water at high pressure (68 bar or 1000 lbf/in$^2$). Care must be exercised when you use this type of washer in view of the high pressure.

*Steam cleaning* This type is useful for cleaning components and assemblies that are heavily soiled with oil and dirt. Sometimes it is used with a proprietary solvent which chemically breaks down the main dirt or oil deposit on the component. You must take care to prevent steam coming into contact with electronic units, because water and heat easily damages these parts.

Often the wax coating, applied on new vehicles for protection during delivery, is removed by steam cleaning.

*Component cleaning* Various solutions are used in workshop cleaning baths. The cleaning application

### REMEMBER

Damage will occur if steam is directed onto any electronic control unit

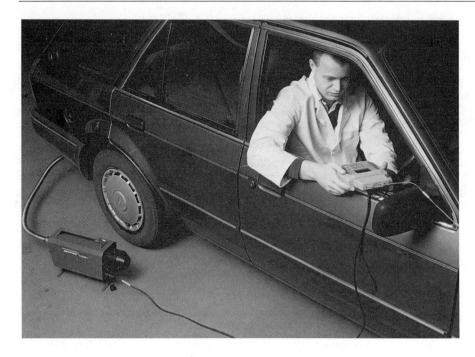

Only approved test equipment must be used in MOT Test Centres. As the annual test becomes more severe, new equipment, such as an emission smoke tester for diesel-type cars, is needed.

*Crypton*

governs the solution used; these include caustic soda, paraffin and proprietary makes of cleaning solution.

You must be careful to select a solution that is safe to use, cheap to operate and suitable for the purpose. Typical cases of unsuitability are: paraffin on clutch, brake parts and electrical equipment; caustic on aluminium alloy components.

### Nut and stud removal

*Nut removal*    A corroded nut is difficult to remove and unless you take care at an early stage, the bolt or stud will break; this will involve extra work and expense. If a nut refuses to move after it has been sprayed with a **penetrating oil** (such as WD40) and left to soak, you should use one of the following techniques:

1) *Shock enlargement*      You hold a heavy hammer on one face of the nut for support and strike the opposite face of the nut with a lighter hammer. After using a number of blows on as many faces as possible, you will find that the slight enlargement will allow the nut to be removed.
2) *Heat expansion*      After taking the necessary precautions, you can carefully heat the nut; this causes it to expand to allow removal.
3) *Nut splitter*      This is a quick way to remove a corroded nut. A typical nut splitter tool is shown as Figure 4.3.1. You clamp this around the nut and then tighten it to force a chisel bit into the nut to cut it

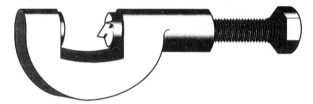

**Fig. 4.3.1** Nut splitter

open. Before using this method make sure you have a new nut!

*Stud removal*    You can use two nuts tightened together to form a lock-nut. A quicker way is to use a *stud setter* or *extractor* as shown as Figure 4.3.2. The stud is gripped by the wedging action produced by the offset knurled wheel of the tool.

A stud that has broken off can be removed by using a *stud extractor* as shown as Figure 4.3.3. The method is to centre-pop the stud accurately and then drill a hole to the size stated on the extractor; this leaves a thin walled shell into which the extractor can be screwed.

### Good practice

Before drilling-out a broken stud make sure the drill is central

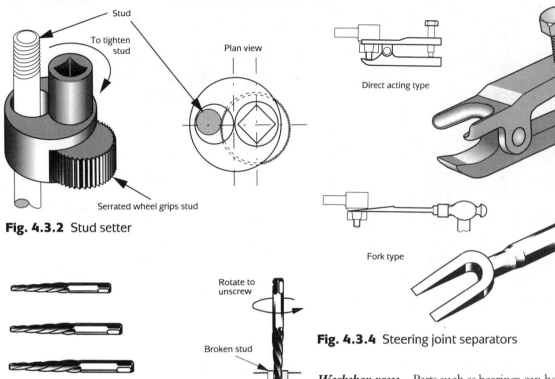

**Fig. 4.3.2** Stud setter

**Fig. 4.3.3** Broken stud extractor

**Fig. 4.3.4** Steering joint separators

## Special-purpose tools

There are many occasions when you use a tool to perform a given task; this may apply to a spanner or some other item of equipment.

In cases where a standard spanner cannot be used specially shaped tools are made. You will use these spanners for brake adjusting, timing belt tensioning, pipe nuts and drain plugs.

*Separators*  An example of a tool designed to do a special task is a *steering joint separator* (Figure 4.3.4). Although you can remove the tapered part of a ball joint by striking the side of the well-supported female member with a hammer, you will find that a special tool can save time.

*Pullers*  Every repair workshop must have a range of pullers and extractors to enable parts such as bearings and hubs to be removed. This range varies from the simple mechanical two- and three-legged pullers to the more powerful hydraulic types. A selection of pullers is shown in Figure 4.3.5.

*Workshop press*  Parts such as bearings can be damaged if they are hammered into position; to avoid this you should use a press. The size of press depends on the work it has to do; for general light work a bench-mounted press of capacity 50 tonne will suffice, but for heavier work a floor-mounted unit capable of giving a maximum force of 100 tonne is needed. The majority of presses are hydraulically operated to give the required mechanical advantage.

## Heating equipment

Normally you will use oxy-gas welding equipment when a source of intense heat is required. The ease of its use can lead to many dangerous practices, so the main hazards must be known before the flame is lit. A naked flame must not be used in the following situations unless the area is rendered safe.

1) *Fuel tanks*  Vapour remaining in a fuel tank is highly explosive. Even after repeated flushing with water the risk is still high.
2) *Flammable substances*  Paint, underseal, body trim, fuel lines, etc., are a fire hazard.
3) *Plastics*  Many plastic materials give off toxic gases when they are heated.
4) *Confined spaces*  Poor ventilation in places like workshop pits collect petrol vapour; a naked flame can cause an explosion.

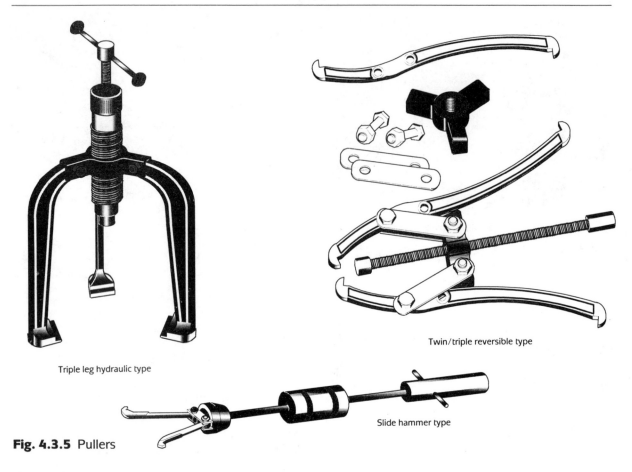

Triple leg hydraulic type

Twin/triple reversible type

Slide hammer type

**Fig. 4.3.5** Pullers

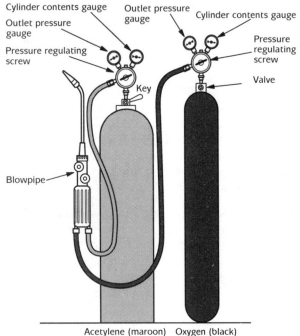

Cylinder contents gauge
Outlet pressure gauge
Outlet pressure gauge
Cylinder contents gauge
Pressure regulating screw
Pressure regulating screw
Key
Valve
Blowpipe

Acetylene (maroon)   Oxygen (black)

**Fig. 4.3.6** Oxy-gas heating and welding equipment

***Oxy-acetylene equipment*** The equipment shown as Figure 4.3.6 uses two gases, oxygen and acetylene, (oxygas) which are stored in separate steel cylinders.

Whereas oxygen can be easily stored at a pressure of 172 bar, the unstable and explosive nature of acetylene makes it necessary to dissolve the gas in liquid acetone

---

## SAFE PRACTICE

### Oxy-gas storage and handling

DON'T:

- mishandle or drop cylinders
- bump valves
- heat cylinders or hoses
- use oil or grease on any fitting
- leave gas on when not being used
- use naked flame to check for leaks (detect leaks with soapy water)
- leave flame unattended
- leave flame on when setting-up work
- use without suitable protective clothing

## REMEMBER

**Oxygen**

- painted black
- right-hand threads

**Acetylene**

- painted maroon
- left-hand threads
- store vertically

for storage in a cylinder at a pressure of 15 bar. This means that the acetylene cylinder should be kept vertical with the valve at the top.

*Pressure regulator*   Each cylinder is fitted with a regulator to reduce the pressure to 0.6 bar or less to suit the quantity of heat required; this is controlled by altering the size of nozzle.

*Lighting-up flame*    The sequence of lighting-up is:

1) Select the size of nozzle you want to suit the heat requirement.
2) Open both cylinder valves about half turn; leave key in acetylene valve.
3) Adjust regulator pressures to the setting for the nozzle size. When doing this, open the appropriate nozzle

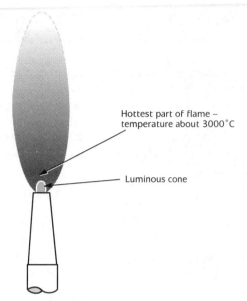

Hottest part of flame – temperature about 3000°C

Luminous cone

**Fig. 4.3.7** Neutral flame

valve prior to setting the regulator. Close each valve after the pressure has been set.
4) Turn on the acetylene and ignite the gas. If the flame is smoky, open the valve more until a smoke-free flame is obtained.
5) Open the oxygen valve slowly until a neutral flame (Figure 4.3.7) is obtained.
6) On shutting down, turn off the acetylene blowpipe valve first.

## PROGRESS CHECK 4

1. The inner shape of the ring of a standard ring spanner is:
(a) hexagonal
(b) bi-hexagonal
(c) 8-sided
(d) 16-sided.

2. Heavy duty ring spanners are:
(a) 6-sided
(b) 8-sided
(c) 12-sided
(d) 16-sided

3. The material used for a good quality ring spanner is:
(a) chrome-vanadium
(b) nickel-chrome
(c) high tensile steel
(d) nickel plated steel.

4. A metric wrench is stamped 12 mm. This dimension refers to the:
(a) length of the jaws of the wrench
(b) distance across the flats of the nut
(c) distance across the corners of the nut
(d) diameter of the bolt it is intended to fit.

5. A combination-type wrench:
(a) is adjustable
(b) has a self-lock feature
(c) can be varied in length
(d) embodies a ring and open-ended construction.

6. A deep thin-walled socket is lined with a rubber insert. This socket is intended for the removal of:
(a) drain plugs
(b) sparking plugs
(c) nuts made of plastics
(d) bolts fitted in deep recesses.

7. A Torx-type socket bit is a:
(a) hexagonal key
(b) part of a torque wrench
(c) 5-sided key that fits into a special bolt
(d) key that fits a Torx  bolt.

8. An adjustable wrench should be used:
(a) in confined spaces
(b) on square nuts
(c) as a last resort
(d) on nuts having rounded corners.

9. An impact socket is made for use with a:
(a) hammer
(b) power driver
(c) impact-type spinner
(d) hammer-action 'T' bar.

10. A chubby-type screwdriver is:
(a) extra short in length
(b) used on very small screws
(c) a type having a large diameter handle
(d) used for screws having a chubby-type slot.

11. Which one of the following screw heads is most suitable to load with a torque screwdriver?
(a) X-slot
(b) Torx-type
(c) Phillips-type
(d) Posi-drive.

12. Another name for a flat chisel is:
(a) cold chisel
(b) cross-cut chisel
(c) roughing chisel
(d) second-cut chisel.

13. One cause of a drill cutting an oversided hole is:
(a) web angle too small
(b) point angle too large
(c) unequal clearance angles
(d) unequal length cutting edges.

14. The name of the twist drill angle that can be checked with two nuts is:
(a) web
(b) rake
(c) point
(d) clearance.

15. A spindle speed of 955 rev/min is recommended to cut mild steel with a 10 mm drill. This speed is decreased when drilling:
(a) brass with a smaller drill
(b) mild steel with a larger drill
(c) copper with a smaller drill
(d) aluminium with a smaller drill.

16. Damage will occur if steam from a cleaner is applied to:
(a) brake levers
(b) electronic control units
(c) aluminium alloy parts
(d) copper alloy components.

17. The colour of an oxygen cylinder and the direction of the threads used to connect the oxygen equipment is:
(a) maroon and left-hand
(b) maroon and right-hand
(c) black and left-hand
(d) black and right-hand

18. Leakage of gas from oxy-gas equipment can be traced by using:
(a) oil
(b) grease
(c) powdered graphite
(d) soapy water.

19. Which one of the following should NOT be used on oxy-gas equipment?
(a) Oil or grease
(b) Powdered graphite
(c) Soapy water
(d) Acetone.

20. An acetylene cylinder should be kept in an up-right position with the valve at the top to:
(a) prevent the cylinder overheating
(b) avoid kapoc entering the regulator
(c) enable the valve to be shut off quickly
(d) prevent liquid acetone entering the pipe lines.

# 5

# Measurement

## What is covered in this chapter:

→ measurement methods
→ micrometer
→ vernier caliper

Often during the repair of a motor vehicle, you will need to use various measuring tools either to ascertain the amount of wear or make some adjustment to set the parts in accordance with manufacturers recommendations. Unless you are accurate in this work, the vehicle will not perform correctly. In this chapter you will study some of the common instruments in use in motor vehicle workshops. By using the book, in conjunction with practice with the actual tools, you will be able to understand how and where the tools are used.

## 5.1 Measurement methods

Rectification work on motor vehicle units and components requires the use of many measuring instruments; these range from a comparatively cheap steel rule to numerous precision instruments that are very costly. Before you handle and practise with these instruments, you must appreciate that they can be easily damaged, so treat them carefully; do not drop them and always place them back in their box after use. When you have finished with precision instruments you should wipe and oil them to neutralise the corrosive action caused by moisture from your hands.

### Rules and calipers
*Engineer's rule* A rule is used to measure any flat surface, for example the length of this page, but is unsuitable for direct reading of an object such as a steel ball. The straight edges of the rule are also utilised for alignment purposes or for checking a flange for distortion.

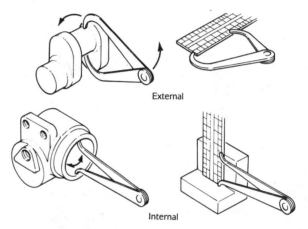

**Fig. 5.1.1** Using calipers for external and internal measurements

*Calipers – internal and external* Figure 5.1.1 shows two dimensions which can be conveniently taken by calipers; the external caliper is used for the crankpin and the internal caliper for the brake cylinder. The sketch shows the manner in which they are used. Holding one leg on the crankpin, the other leg of the external caliper is slid over the pin to locate the largest dimension. A similar method can be used for the internal caliper; the setting may be checked by rocking the instrument in the direction of the arrow. Whenever the caliper has to be set to a given distance, the final adjustment is obtained by tapping one leg (Figure 5.1.2).

Calipers are not used only for round surfaces. The thickness of a key may be checked with an external caliper, while the width of the keyway is measured with an internal caliper.

### Gauges
*Feeler gauge* Consisting of several strips of thin steel, each marked with its thickness, this gauge is used to measure the clearance between two components.

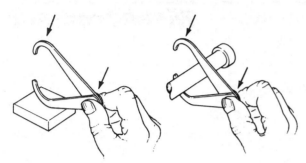

**Fig. 5.1.2** Fine setting of measurement with calipers

Although measurement of valve clearance is the most common application (Figure 5.1.3), it is also used to check the end float of camshafts, crankshafts, and so on. Whenever feeler gauges are used to check the fit of circular items such as pistons, the width of the gauge should be stated.

**Fig. 5.1.3** Using feelers to measure valve clearance

The precise clearance can only be obtained after experience has been gained as to the effort required to slide out the blade. For this reason gauges used for piston clearance sometimes incorporate a spring balance.

*Clock gauge* This dial test indicator, often abbreviated to d.t.i., is used to measure small linear movements. It consists of a clock gauge, finely calibrated in Metric units of length and a number of mounting attachments (Figure 5.1.4).

To mount the gauge to a component, assemble the required attachments and leave all attachment screws loose until the gauge is correctly positioned. Remember to preload the gauge plunger away from its outer stop, and ensure that the movement to be measured is not greater than the stroke of the gauge plunger.

The gauge will stick if the plunger is oiled.

*Cylinder gauge* Similar to the d.t.i., this instrument consists of a clock gauge and a linkage incorporated in the handle. Various distance pieces are provided to give a

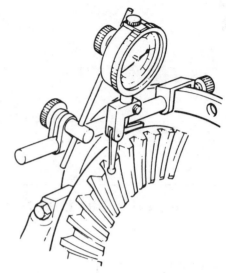

**Fig. 5.1.4** Mounting arrangement for clock gauge measurement

large range of measurement. It is sometimes called a comparator because it can only compare one distance with another.

Figure 5.1.5 shows the gauge being used to determine the size of a cylinder. Rocking the gauge in the direction shown enables the smallest reading to be found and rotation of the bezel ring allows the gauge to be set to zero. After the number of revolutions of the needle (sometimes registered on a separate small dial) has been noted the instrument is placed in an external micrometer and the actual distance determined.

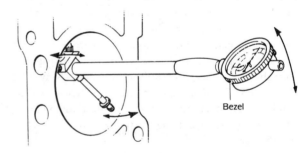

**Fig. 5.1.5** Cylinder gauge measurement

## 5.2 Micrometer

### Standard (external) micrometer

This is a development of the caliper which enables linear measurements to be determined to an accuracy of at least 0.01 mm.

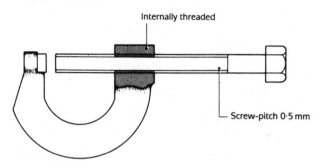

**Fig. 5.2.1** Principle of the micrometer: one turn of the screw closes gap by 0.5 mm

The principle can be shown by the diagrammatic sketch (Figure 5.2.1). This represents a screw which engages with an internal thread of pitch 0.5 mm in the frame. Rotating the screw one revolution causes the screw to advance 0.5 mm. If the head of the screw is divided into fifty parts then each division will represent 0.01 mm. Therefore turning the screw to the extent of $3\frac{7}{50}$ turns will move the screw to the extent of:

$$3 \times 0.5 = 1.5 \text{ mm}$$
$$7 \times 0.01 = 0.07 \text{ mm}$$
$$\overline{\text{Total} = 1.57 \text{ mm}}$$

Figure 5.2.2 shows the layout of a typical external micrometer. The frame carries an anvil and opposite this is an internal thread which engages the spindle. A

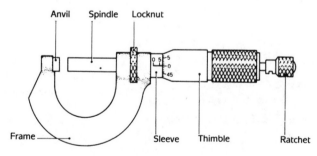

**Fig. 5.2.2** Typical external micrometer

thimble, locking up on a taper, allows the spindle to be rotated. Also attached to the frame is a scaled sleeve which is divided into 0.5 mm intervals: vertical scale markings above the horizontal datum line are spaced at 1 mm intervals whereas vertical markings below the datum indicate the 0.5 mm positions. The following examples show the manner in which the scale is read.

**Example**

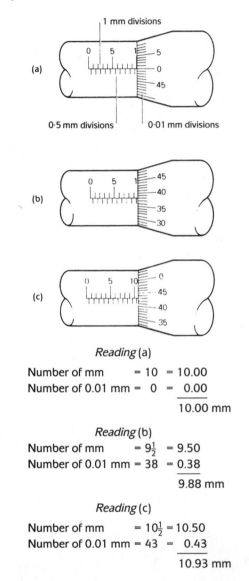

*Reading* (a)

| | | | |
|---|---|---|---|
| Number of mm | = 10 | = 10.00 |
| Number of 0.01 mm = | 0 | = | 0.00 |
| | | | 10.00 mm |

*Reading* (b)

| | | | |
|---|---|---|---|
| Number of mm | = $9\frac{1}{2}$ | = 9.50 |
| Number of 0.01 mm = 38 | | = 0.38 |
| | | | 9.88 mm |

*Reading* (c)

| | | | |
|---|---|---|---|
| Number of mm | = $10\frac{1}{2}$ | = 10.50 |
| Number of 0.01 mm = 43 | | = | 0.43 |
| | | | 10.93 mm |

Care must be exercised not to overtighten the thimble. Since the actual reading depends on the tightness, a ratchet is provided.

Normal type micrometers have a scale range of 25 mm so a number of micrometers are needed to cover the measurements of motor vehicle components. If, for example, a crankpin of 54 mm diameter is to be checked, then a 50–75 mm micrometer is needed. There are, however, some micrometers which can be fitted with a distance piece to enlarge the range.

If a micrometer is replaced in its box when not in use, it seldom requires adjustment, but the accuracy should be checked periodically. In the case of a 0–25 mm micrometer this is accomplished by checking that the reading is zero when the spindle contacts the anvil. Larger instruments are checked against a test piece of standard length or diameter.

Three adjustments are normally provided:

a) *thread adjustment* – to compensate for thread wear a split nut is provided.
b) *thimble adjustment* – the thimble is pulled up on a taper by a screw, so the position of the thimble scale may be set to the correct position.
c) *sleeve adjustment* – rotating the sleeve with a 'C' spanner allows minute adjustment of the scale.

### Internal micrometer

This micrometer measures the distance between two internal surfaces. Figure 5.2.3 shows the instrument being used to determine the bore of an engine cylinder.

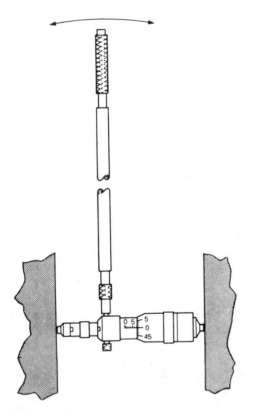

**Fig. 5.2.3** Typical internal micrometer

The most common type has a length of 50 mm and a scale range of 10 mm. The smallest hole which it can measure is 50 mm and distance pieces of length 10, 20, 40, 60 mm, and so on, enable a wide range of sizes to be covered.

Whenever a micrometer is used, it is important to ensure that the faces are clean. Small grit traps, cut in the distance pieces of an internal micrometer, collect the dirt when the distance piece is rotated before clamping.

When this micrometer is being used, it must be rocked in the direction shown in the diagram until the correct feel is achieved. Remember that you have great leverage on the instrument and that it will be damaged if it is forced.

Since the scale is limited to 10 mm the length of distance piece must be added to the scale reading to obtain the actual dimension.

## 5.3 Vernier caliper

This instrument enables a wide range of linear measurements to be determined. It gets its name from the type of scale used. Figure 5.3.1 shows that the instrument consists of two main parts:

1) the fixed jaw or body on to which is engraved the main scale;
2) the sliding jaw which contains the vernier scale.

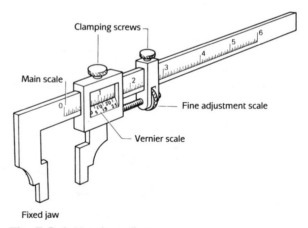

**Fig. 5.3.1** Vernier caliper

Positioned adjacent to the main scale, the vernier scale divisions are slightly smaller than those used for the main scale (Figure 5.3.2 shows an enlargement of the scale).

This arrangement uses a vernier scale having 25 divisions and these are spaced over a main scale length of 12 mm. Each division on the vernier scale equals

$$\frac{1}{25} \text{ of } 12 \text{ mm} = 0.48 \text{ mm}$$

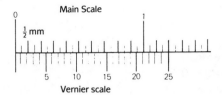

**Fig. 5.3.2** Enlargement of main and vernier scales of a vernier caliper

When the jaws of the instrument are opened and the first division on the vernier scale lines up with the first division on the main scale, the distance moved by the jaw is equal to the differences in size between the division on the main scale and the division on the vernier scale. The small divisions on the main scale represent 0.5 mm, so

$$\text{distance moved} = 0.50 - 0.48 \text{ mm} = 0.02 \text{ mm}$$

So each vernier division represents 0.02 mm

The measurement is obtained by adding to the main scale reading the value indicated by the line on the sliding scale which is level with a division mark on the main scale.

## Example

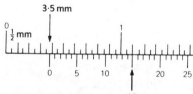

**Fig. 5.3.3** Example

Reading (see Figure 5.3.3)

| | |
|---|---|
| top scale | = 3.5 |
| bottom scale (15 × 0.02) | = 0.30 |
| total | = 3.8  mm |

## Example

Reading (see Figure 5.3.4)

| | |
|---|---|
| top scale | = 27.5 |
| bottom scale (7 × 0.02) | = 0.14 |
| total | = 27.64 mm |

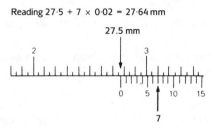

**Fig. 5.3.4** Example

## Other vernier scales

Not all verniers use 25 divisions on the scale; some use 50 and others 10, but the principle of each type is the same.

## Example

*Scale with 50 divisions:*  The main scale has divisions of 1 mm, and the vernier scale spreads over 49 mm.

$$1 \text{ vernier scale division} = \frac{1}{50} \text{ of } 49 \text{ mm}$$

$$= \frac{49}{50} = 0.98 \text{ mm}$$

$$\begin{pmatrix} \text{Distance moved by jaw} \\ \text{from zero to line-up} \\ \text{first vernier scale division} \end{pmatrix} = \begin{pmatrix} \text{difference between} \\ \text{top and bottom} \\ \text{divisions} \end{pmatrix}$$

$$= 1.00 - 0.98$$

$$= 0.02 \text{ mm}$$

## Example

*Scale with 10 divisions:*  The main scale has divisions of 1 mm and the vernier scale spreads over 9 mm.

$$1 \text{ vernier scale division} = \frac{1}{10} \text{ of } 9 \text{ mm}$$

$$= \frac{9}{10} = 0.9 \text{ mm}$$

$$\begin{pmatrix} \text{Distance moved by jaw from} \\ \text{zero to line-up first} \\ \text{vernier scale division} \end{pmatrix} = 1.0 - 0.9$$

$$= 0.1 \text{ mm}$$

One division on vernier scale represents 0.1 mm.

*Internal measurements*  By reducing the ends of the jaws to a given width, internal measurements can be taken. This width is normally stated on the jaw and must be added to the scale readings.

# PROGRESS CHECK 5

1. The pitch of a metric micrometer thread is:
(a) 0.05 mm
(b) 0.5 mm
(c) 1.0 mm
(d) 1.5 mm.

2.

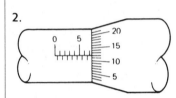

The micrometer reading shown above is:
(a) 7.12 mm
(b) 7.62 mm
(c) 5.32 mm
(d) 52.12 mm.

3.

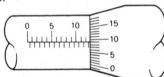

The micrometer reading shown above is:
(a) 10.09 mm
(b) 12.09 mm
(c) 12.59 mm
(d) 13.09 mm.

4.

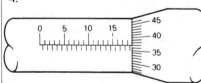

The micrometer reading shown above is:
(a) 18.37 mm
(b) 18.43 mm
(c) 18.87 mm
(d) 18.97 mm.

5. A vernier scale has 10 divisions spaced over a main scale length of 9 mm. The distance represented by each division on the vernier scale is:
(a) 0.1 mm
(b) 0.2 mm
(c) 0.9 mm
(d) 1.0 mm.

6. A vernier scale has 25 divisions spaced over a main scale length of 12 mm. The distance represented by each division on the vernier scale is:
(a) 0.01 mm
(b) 0.02 mm
(c) 0.12 mm
(d) 1.20 mm

7. A vernier scale has 50 divisions spaced over a main scale length of 49 mm. the distance represented by each division on the vernier scale is:
(a) 0.01 mm
(b) 0.02 mm
(c) 0.49 mm
(d) 4.90 mm

8.

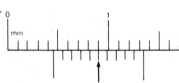

The vernier reading shown above is:
(a) 0.5 mm
(b) 4.5 mm
(c) 5.9 mm
(d) 9.0 mm.

9.

The vernier reading shown above is:
(a) 7.70 mm
(b) 5.27 mm
(c) 52.70 mm
(d) 59.00 mm.

10.

The vernier reading shown above is:
(a) 12.57 mm
(b) 15.00 mm
(c) 125.70 mm
(d) 132.00 mm.

11.

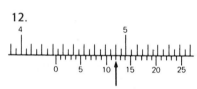

The vernier scale above has 25 divisions. The reading shown is:
(a) 1.68 mm
(b) 2.40 mm
(c) 3.09 mm
(d) 6.00 mm.

12.

The vernier scale above has 25 divisions. The reading shown is:
(a) 4.90 mm
(b) 43.10 mm
(c) 43.24 mm
(d) 49.12 mm

13.

The vernier scale above has 25 divisions. The reading shown is:
(a) 14.23 mm
(b) 16.50 mm
(c) 122.23 mm
(d) 122.46 mm.

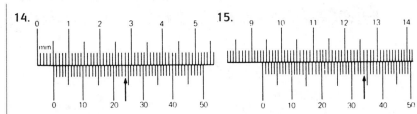

**14.** The vernier scale above has 50 divisions. The reading shown is:
(a) 0.74 mm
(b) 2.80 mm
(c) 5.24 mm
(d) 5.48 mm.

**15.** The vernier scale above has 50 divisions. The reading shown is:
(a) 9.64 mm
(b) 93.34 mm
(c) 93.68 mm
(d) 126.00 mm.

# 6 Metal jointing and fastening

## What is covered in this chapter:

→ types of joint and jointing materials
→ screw threads
→ locking devices
→ soft soldering
→ adhesives

Much of your work will involve the removal and replacement of vehicle components. This will require a knowledge of the methods employed, and the techniques used, to secure one part to another. The fastening method and type of joint that you make will be either permanent or detachable; the latter intended for disconnection at some future date if disturbance of the system is necessary.

## 6.1 Types of joint and jointing materials

Most motor vehicle components are securely bolted together. Where a joint between the faces of the two parts is subjected to air or fluid pressure, a seal is provided to prevent leakage. You must understand the main features of sealing devices so that you can make an effective leakproof joint. This is necessary because the engine and other systems will not function correctly if they leak. Also you will be unpopular if a poor seal allows fluid leaks – customers do not like to see a pool of oil under their cars after they have had it serviced.

### Joint classification

Although nut and bolt jointing is the most common, an inspection of a vehicle shows that this is not the only method. When considering either the type of jointing system, or the technique to be used, the following factors must be taken into account:

● strength of joint required;
● size, type and thickness of materials to be joined;
● nature of joint, i.e. whether the joint is to be permanent or not;
● nearness of joint to other parts and possibility of damage to these parts – this is important when accessibility is a problem or when heat is needed to make the joint.

The types of joint and fasteners used on vehicles are shown in Table 6.1.1.

### Jointing materials and compounds

Joints and gaskets are used to provide a seal between two metal surfaces. These are necessary because manufactur-

| PERMANENT | fusion welded | metal arc, resistance (spot), oxy-gas |
| --- | --- | --- |
| | non-fusion welded joints | soft soldering, hard (silver soldering), brazing, bronze welding |
| | riveted | solid rivets, iron, copper, brass and aluminium alloy, tubular rivets (pop) |
| | adhesive | epoxy, phenolic, elastomeric, shellac, anaerobic |
| FIXED JOINT (able to separate) | threaded | nut and bolt, stud and nut, set bolt, set screw, metal-thread screw, self-tapping |
| | pinned | parallel, taper and tubular |
| FLEXIBLE JOINTS | couplings | universal joints |

**Table 6.1.1** Types of joint

ing cost dictates that a component be made with comparatively generous limits and tolerances. This means that the surface flatness and alignment of two clamped components containing either a gas or liquid would be too poor to provide an effective seal. Also joints and gaskets compensate for any distortion caused by changes in temperature of the components.

The type of joint and liquid sealing compound is governed by the application. Where two components operate at a different temperature, considerable distortion takes place; in these cases a thick joint is often used. As the components heat up, slight relative movement between the component faces takes place, so the joint must slip to allow for this. In this instance the joint is made 'dry', but if surface irregularities prevent a good seal, a non-setting (flexible) type of sealant is used. Since there are many other factors that must be considered, you are advised to refer to the manufacturer's recommendations for the jointing material. Today, joints and gaskets are sold with the new components, so the only thing you will have to decide is the choice of jointing solution; reference to the manual will solve this.

Table 6.1.2 shows the main types of jointing material.

### Making a joint

When you separate two parts, a non-metallic jointing material normally breaks because it sticks to both surfaces, therefore make sure you have a new joint component before you start the job.

*Preparation* The separation of the parts requires skill and not brute force, since many parts are damaged during this process. Use of a soft faced hammer is recommended in preference to wedging a screwdriver between the faces, because the latter 'technique' damages the sealing surfaces and often results in a broken flange. A wide scraper is used, without digging-

in the surface, to clean the joint faces and the regions around the holes and studs. On many parts, especially those using a thicker joint or gasket, bolt over-tightening causes the flanges to distort. Before making a new joint you are advised to check for distortion by using a straight edge.

> ## *Good practice*
>
> **Fitting joints and gaskets**
>
> - remove old joint, de-burr and clean faces
> - apply suitable jointing compound (if recommended)
> - fit new joint or gasket to one face and check alignment of all holes
> - mate parts
> - pull down evenly and diagonally
> - do not under- or over-tighten
> - use torque wrench if possible
> - when engine is hot, check for leaks

*Reassembling* After removing all burrs and dirt from the faces, the jointing compound, if used, is applied to both faces. The joint component is then placed on the part that is best suited to hold it in place during reassembly. Check that the joint is fitted the correct way and that no holes are covered up or misaligned. During the tightening operation the securing nuts and bolts should be pulled down diagonally and evenly to the correct torque loading.

## 6.2 Screw threads

A screw thread is based on the principle of an inclined plane or wedge. This can be demonstrated by wrapping a triangular piece of paper around a cylinder (Figure

| Type of material | Amount of heat | Use |
|---|---|---|
| Copper, steel, aluminium alloy, copper asbestos | large amount | cylinder head, sparking plug, exhaust manifold, exhaust pipe |
| Cork, synthetic rubber | small amount | rocker cover, sump, transmission covers |
| Vellumoid-type | small amount | systems in contact with petrol |
| Fibre, compressed paper | small amount | general sealing |

**Table 6.1.2** Types of jointing material

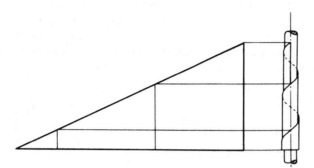

**Fig. 6.2.1** Wedge action

6.2.1). The helical form produced provides a compact form of wedge. *Screw thread terms* include:

- *Pitch* The distance between the crests of adjacent threads.
- *Lead* The amount the nut advances for one complete turn. In the case of a single start thread, pitch = lead.
- *Core diameter* The diameter of the thread measured at the root.

***Conventional representation*** British Standards Institution recommends in their standard (BS 308) that screw threads are represented in the form shown as Figure 6.2.2.

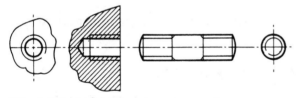

**Fig. 6.2.2** Screw thread representation

**Types of thread**
In the past many different types of thread were used. This caused difficulty because a nut with one thread profile could not be used on a bolt having a different shape of thread. Today modern vehicles built in this country use the metric type of thread.

***Metric threads*** The International Standards Organisation (ISO) recommend the thread form shown in Figure 6.2.3. This type is made in either fine- or course-pitch to suit the application, e.g. a fine thread resists vibration better and is easier to tighten, but is inferior in strength when it is cut in a soft material.

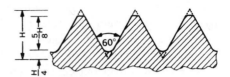

**Fig. 6.2.3** Metric thread profile

The method used to dimension a thread on a drawing indicates the main details of the thread, e.g. M8 × 1.25. This indicates:

M  = ISO metric thread
8   = diameter of bolt (mm)
1.25 = pitch of thread (mm)

Table 6.2.1 gives details of some screw thread sizes often used on motor vehicles.

| Bolt diameter (mm) | Pitch (mm) | |
|---|---|---|
| | Course | Fine |
| 8 | 1.25 | 1 |
| 10 | 1.5 | 1.25 |
| 12 | 1.75 | 1.25 |
| 14 | 2 | 1.5 |
| 16 | 2 | 1.5 |

**Table 6.2.1** Metric thread and bolt sizes

***Non-metric threads*** Many vehicles made in the USA do not use metric threads; instead they use the *unified national fine* (UNF) or *unified national course* (UNC) threads. For a few years prior to conversion to the metric system these threads were used in this country; before that many other thread profiles, as shown in Figure 6.2.4 were used; these included:

- British Standard Whitworth (BSW)
- British Standard Fine (BSF)
- British Standard Pipe (BSP)
- British Association (BA)

**Core diameter**
When an internal thread is to be formed in a piece of metal, the size of the hole must not be larger than the core diameter (Figure 6.2.5). Screw thread tables give the actual size of tapping drill to use to suit a given thread type. If a table is unavailable, then the approximate size may be determined by either:

1) finding the largest drill which passes through a new nut which matches the size and thread type, or

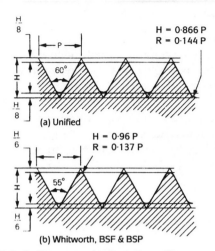

**Fig. 6.2.4** Non-metric thread profiles

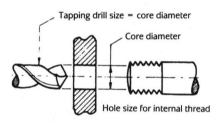

**Fig. 6.2.5** Drilling size

2) measuring the core diameter of the thread cut on a taper tap.

**Thread damage**
Often the re-assembly of a part is delayed by a damaged thread; this can be the result of corrosion during service or burring during the dismantling process. Naturally you should avoid damaging a thread; steps you will take include exercising care when removing parts and using protection sleeves to shield the threads. The following methods are used to renovate a damaged thread.

**Die nut** External threads are cut with a die. A die nut is a hexagonally shaped nut that has internally cut teeth that are hardened. The nut removes burrs when it is wound down a damaged thread.

**Tap** An internal thread is cut with a tap. Shaped like a fluted screw and hardened to cut steel, a tap cuts a thread into a hole that has been drilled to a size equal to the core diameter of the thread. A tap used to cut a new thread is tapered to give good alignment, but a tap with no taper

(bottoming tap) is needed to clean the thread in a blind hole. Between the taper and bottoming taps, a tap is made with only the first three threads tapered; this is called a plug type and is useful for cleaning most internal threads.

**Thread restorer** Sometimes called a *thread file* or *chaser*, this tool is similar to a square file with teeth at the end of each face to suit different thread pitches. It is handy to use in places where a die nut is not available or space is limited.

> **REMEMBER**
>
> **Burred and damaged threads cause:**
>
> - cross-threading
> - low clamping load
> - difficult nut removal
> - broken bolts and studs
> - incorrect torque loading
> - damage to nuts, bolts and studs

**Thread insert kit** This tool is used to renovate a stripped thread. It is an alternative to drilling and tapping a larger hole to take an oversized bolt. The kit contains suitably sized drills and special taps to cut a thread to accept a steel threaded insert. On some light alloy parts, thread inserts are used as original equipment.

## 6.3 Locking devices

Motor vehicles are subject to vibration and one effect of this is to cause securing devices such as nuts and bolts to work loose. The loss of a nut could cause either a serious accident or extensive component damage or both, so an effective locking device should be provided to reduce this risk.

**Types** Figure 6.3.1 shows some of the main types.

a) *Spring washer* Made of spring steel the washer digs into the nut to prevent the nut unscrewing. Various forms are in use:
   (i) single coil
   (ii) double coil
   (iii) shake-proof.

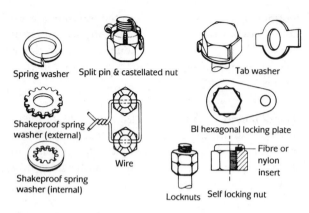

**Fig. 6.3.1** Types of locking devices

b) *Split pin* A mild steel pin fitted in a hole in a bolt engages with slots in a nut which is either:
  (i) slotted – slots cut in a standard thickness nut
  (ii) castellated – standard thickness nut + castellations.

Split pins, or cotter pins as they are sometimes called, should:
  • be the correct diameter and length
  • only be used once
  • be fitted as shown in the diagram
  • not move in the nut when fitted.

c) *Wire* Used to retain a nut to a stud and also prevents the stud from unscrewing.

d) *Tab washers* Made of mild steel, a tab washer has a tongue or tab to resist rotation and one or more external tabs which can be forced against the flat of the nut. Two or more tab washers are sometimes joined together to form one large locking tab.

e) *Locking plate* Generally a bi-hexagonal plate which fits over the nut.

f) *Lock nuts* Two nuts screwed up against each other. The first nut is tightened and then the second nut is pulled up against the first to take up the slackness in the thread. This action means that the thread of the second nut resists the main load.

g) *Self-locking nuts* Many different types are used. Normally they have some arrangement which increases the friction between the threads. The examples shown in Figure 6.3.1 are:
  (i) fibre or nylon insert
  (ii) split

Special liquid compounds can be applied to the threads of a standard nut to provide a locking action.

## 6.4 Soft soldering

### Soldering process

Solder is an alloy consisting mainly of tin and lead which has a melting point about 200°C. The low melting point of solder makes it most suitable for joining materials such as steel, copper and brass in situations which are not subject to excessive heat or vibration and where great strength is not required.

Figure 6.4.1 shows the main equipment required to join two pieces of thin steel sheet. The essential items are:

• *Soldering iron* the means for preheating the 'work' and melting the solder:
• *Flux* a substance to keep the surfaces chemically clean after dirt, grease, paint and oxide have been removed by mechanical methods, i.e. file, scraper, emery cloth, etc;
• *Solder* the lead/tin alloy which forms the metallic bond.

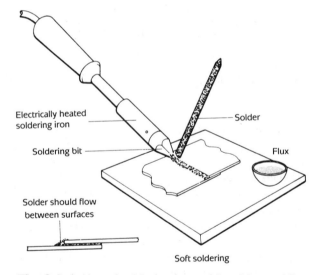

**Fig. 6.4.1** Use of soldering iron with solder and flux

Large heat loss by conduction must be avoided if the metal in the region of the join is to reach the temperature at which the solder melts. For the job shown in Figure 6.4.1, wood is suitable to use as a heat insulator.

When the item to be soldered forms part of either a large area or large mass, preheating by a flame is often necessary to compensate for conduction within the material. On the other hand electrical devices such as diodes are damaged by heat, so the method used for soldering in these special cases is to conduct the heat

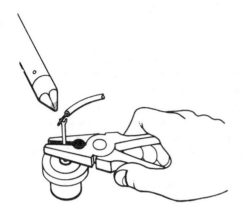

**Fig. 6.4.2** Use of pliers to conduct heat away from sensitive electric diode

away before it reaches the sensitive regions by using pliers as shown in Figure 6.4.2.

Referring back to the enlarged view of the joint shows that the solder has crept between the surfaces of the parent metal. This is called *capillary flow* and is necessary where strength is required. An overlap or seam joint as shown in Figure 6.4.1 will be weak if:

a) edges only are soldered;
b) thickness of solder between the metal sheets is not kept to a minimum.

**Soldering irons**
The main part of a soldering 'iron' is a mass of copper called a *bit*, which is generally heated by an electric element. Copper is a material capable of 'storing' a large quantity of heat for its size and also it is able to conduct heat easily – these two properties make it a suitable material for a soldering bit. See Figure 6.4.1.

**Flux**
Many materials absorb oxygen from the atmosphere and this process is increased when the material is heated. The oxide 'skin' acts as a barrier between the solder and the metal, thereby preventing a metal-to-metal join. To prevent this happening a substance called flux is applied to the metal immediately after the surfaces have been cleaned with emery or similar means.

On heating the metal, the flux coating prevents the air from contacting the metal and so keeps the surface 'chemically clean'. When the solder melts it flows under the layer of flux and on to the oxide-free surface.

The tip of the soldering iron bit must also be free from oxide if the heat and solder are to flow freely from the iron. A practice called *tinning* is performed on the iron before commencing work. The tip is cleaned with an old file, coated with flux and then heated. As the temperature of the bit increases, solder is applied to the iron until the tip is completely covered.

To perform its task the flux must:

a) withstand the heat – it must not fully vaporise below the soldering temperature;
b) be suitable for the metal being soldered;
c) be suitable for the job being soldered – some fluxes are corrosive so they are unsuitable for certain jobs, e.g. electrical work requires a *resin flux*.

The most common fluxes which are suitable for general work are:

● *Zinc chloride (killed spirits)*      Made by dissolving zinc in hydrochloric acid (spirits of salts). POISONOUS to human beings. Corrosive – job must be washed in water after soldering.
● *Resin*      Supplied as paste or in the core of the solder stock. Particularly suitable for electrical work.
● *Proprietary brands*      Easily obtained since they are ready for use.

Other, less common, fluxes are:

● *Phosphoric acid* for stainless steel;
● *Sal-ammoniac* for copper;
● *Hydrochloric acid* for zinc;
● *Tallow* for lead.

**Solders**
*Soft solder* is an alloy of tin and lead with the addition of small amounts of other metals such as antimony and copper.

*Melting range* represents the temperature range over which the solder is 'pasty'; it is completely solid at the lower temperature and completely liquid at the higher temperature.

The rules to follow when soft soldering are:

1) Thoroughly clean the surfaces to be joined.
2) Use the correct flux.

| General name | Tin % | Lead % | Melting range °C | Uses |
|---|---|---|---|---|
| Tinmans | 50 | 50 | 185–215 | General work |
| Plumbers | 30 | 70 | 185–250 | Solder for filling bodies |

**Table 6.4.1** Types of solder

3) Apply adequate heat.
4) Use the correct solder.
5) Clean the surfaces to remove flux.

## 6.5 Adhesives

Up to about fifty years ago the main adhesives were animal glues. About that time, vegetable glues were introduced for binding porous materials such as paper. The major development in adhesives came in the 1930s with the introduction of synthetic resins. These early resin-based adhesives had an excellent resistance to moisture and to mould growth and were particularly suitable for bonding wood. When aircraft constructions changed from wood to metal, adhesives were developed for metal bonding and from these many others were developed to suit other materials. From the wide range of modern adhesives it is normally possible to find one which not only suits the materials to be joined but also meets the operational requirements.

*Advantages* of adhesive bonding include:

1) *Appearance*　　the joint hardly shows;
2) *Strength*　　shearing force is spread over a large area instead of acting in local spots as in the case of a rivet;
3) *Reduced distortion*　　excessive heating is unnecessary;
4) *Reduced corrosion*　　electrolytic action between dissimilar materials is reduced.

Also there are advantages associated with particular applications, e.g. compared with rivets a bonded brake pad or lining has a larger friction area; this results in a lower rate of wear and improved fade characteristics.

*Disadvantages* of adhesive bonding include:

1) *Health hazard*　　dangerous fumes are given off by many non flammable adhesives, so good ventilation is essential;
2) *Fire and explosive risks*　　some adhesives give off a flammable vapour which becomes explosive when used in a confined space;
3) *Temperature limitations*　　the bond will break when the temperature exceeds the recommended figure;
4) *Inspection difficulties*　　it is difficult to ascertain by visual inspection the strength of the bond;
5) *Cost*　　expensive equipment is necessary for some special bonding applications; consequently, the method is sometimes uneconomical.

*Technical terms applied to adhesives*　　The following terms are used in connection with adhesives:

- *Thermoplastic*: can be repeatedly softened by heat;
- *Thermosetting*: sets by the action of heat or a catalyst to a permanently hard state;
- *Impact type*: an adhesive which is applied to both surfaces and allowed to become tacky; contact between the surfaces produces the bond;
- *Cold set*: an adhesive which is cured or set at room temperature;
- *Hot set*: an adhesive which requires heating to a given temperature to complete the bond;
- *Structural adhesives*: suitable for applications where the bonded joint sustains continuous loads in service; thermoplastic adhesives are normally unsuitable for these applications since they soon fail under a continuous load.

---

### SAFE PRACTICE

**Take care when working with adhesives. Most of them are:**

- highly flammable
- give off dangerous and toxic vapours

---

### Types of adhesive

*Structural adhesives* are usually epoxy-based synthetic resins which are thermosetting

*Epoxy*　　Normally a syrupy liquid, which, when mixed with a hardener (a catalyst, curing agent) is rapidly transformed into a hard transparent solid. It bonds not only absorbent materials such as wood, but also adheres to metal and glass. Used for a wide range of motor vehicle work which involves the bonding of metals, ceramics, glass, rubber, plastics, wood, etc. Also used for glass fibre work.

*Phenolic*　　When mixed with epoxy or nitrile synthetic rubbers, these hot set resins have a high shear strength and withstand temperatures up to about 250°C. Used for heavy duty applications such as bonding the friction material to steel brake shoes, pads or automatic transmission clutches.

***Non-structural adhesives*** These include a range of *elastomeric* (rubber based) adhesives:

a) *Natural rubber* for bonding rubber to rubber (e.g. tyre repairs) and fabric and leather;

b) *Natural rubber latex* for bonding fabrics, leather, felt, paper etc;

c) *Synthetic rubber* for PVC, wood and glass;

d) *Rubber and resin* for bonding rubber, felt, cork, etc., to wood or metal;

e) *Synthetic rubber and resin* for laminated plastics, plywood, hardboard to metal or wood; particularly suitable for smooth surfaces.

*Shellac* is natural resin used as an engine jointing compound for metal-to-metal surfaces or fibrous gasket material to metal surfaces. It is resistant to hydrocarbons at high temperatures.

*Anaerobic adhesives* ('absence of air') include *acrylic acid*. One product sets when in contact with metal if oxygen is absent. Used as a 'liquid lock-washer' for bolts, it is capable of withstanding temperatures up to 200°C; above 250°C the material softens, so this feature is useful when breaking a joint.

# PROGRESS CHECK 6

1. During a repair that involves the jointing of metal, the possibility of damage to other parts could rule out the use of:
(a) heat
(b) rivets
(c) bolts
(d) adhesives.

2. Solder is an alloy consisting mainly of:
(a) lead and tin
(b) zinc and tin
(c) lead and zinc
(d) tin and copper.

3. The melting point of solder is about:
(a) 100°C
(b) 200°C
(c) 300°C
(d) 400°C.

4. Before starting a soldering job the tip of the soldering bit should be cleaned, fluxed and coated with solder. This operation is called:
(a) tinning
(b) tipping
(c) coating
(d) de-oxidising.

5. During soldering work the formation of an oxide film on the surface of the metal is resisted by:
(a) using adequate heat
(b) occasionally scraping the surface
(c) the action of a suitable flux
(d) the metal in the solder.

6. Which one of the following is a suitable flux when soldering electrical cables?
(a) resin
(b) zinc chloride
(c) killed spirits
(d) phosphoric acid.

7. The composition of a typical 'tinmans' solder is about:

| | tin % | lead % |
|---|---|---|
| (a) | 20 | 80 |
| (b) | 30 | 70 |
| (c) | 50 | 50 |
| (d) | 70 | 30 |

8. A joint is to be fitted between two parts that operate at different temperatures. The joint used should:
(a) be extremely thin
(b) allow the surfaces to slip
(c) be made of copper-asbestos
(d) be sealed on both surfaces with a rigid compound.

9. Many cylinder head gaskets are faced with:
(a) cork
(b) fibre
(c) copper
(d) vellumoid.

10. Two parts are sealed with a cork jointing material. Use of a torque wrench on the flange clamping bolts is recommended because:
(a) flange distortion is minimised
(b) flange leakage is likely to occur
(c) this type of joint must be more securely clamped
(d) this type of flange has to be tightened to a higher degree.

11. The pitch of a screw thread is the:
(a) diameter of the core of the screw
(b) length of the threaded part of the bolt
(c) difference between core and crest diameters
(d) distance between the crest of adjacent threads.

12. The angle between the faces of a metric thread is:
(a) 47.5°
(b) 55°
(c) 60°
(d) 65°.

13. The size of a metric bolt is M14 × 2.00. The 14 indicates the:
(a) bolt length
(b) bolt diameter
(c) thread depth
(d) thread pitch.

14. A thread has to be tapped in a hole. The size of the 'tapping drill' should:
(a) be equal to the pitch of the thread
(b) not be smaller than the crest diameter
(c) not be larger than the core diameter of the thread
(d) be slightly larger than the crest diameter of the bolt.

15. Which one of the following is a thermosetting synthetic adhesive?
(a) latex
(b) shellac
(c) epoxy
(d) anaerobic.

# Part C

# Drawing interpretation

# 7                                *Drawing principles*

## What is covered in this chapter:

→ projections and diagrams
→ dimensioning and sectional views
→ limits and tolerances
→ information channels

Technical information giving details of the vehicles on which you work, is vital if you are to carry out a satisfactory repair. Today manufacturers and product suppliers regularly send this information to their franchised dealers and request that it is communicated to the appropriate staff. Without this knowledge you would not know about any new product. Also you would be unaware of the operation and recommended method of repair of that product.

Information is normally conveyed by the written word, but diagrams and drawings are also used to make the subject matter easier to understand. This can only be achieved if the recipient understands simple drawing techniques, i.e. understands the 'language' used to graphically communicate some important point such as a dimension, repair sequence or modification.

You will waste valuable time unless everybody uses the same graphical language. For this reason British Standards Institution (BSI) recommend to the motor industry that they should use the drawing standard known as BS308.

## 7.1   Projections and diagrams

### Projection

Any manufacturer's service manual shows how widespread is the use made of drawings. Whether it indicates a form of construction or a suggested method of repair, a drawing reduces the written description and conveys ideas in a form from which the actual item can easily be recognised. The purpose of this section of the book is to clarify the layout of an engineering drawing.

Engineering components are three-dimensional; i.e. they possess length, breadth and depth, so the drawing should convey the detail of each dimension. In the majority of cases only three sides of the figure need be shown. These sides may be shown in one drawing (pictorial projection) or each side could be shown separately (orthographic projection).

The following methods of projection show the way in which a battery could be drawn.

***Pictorial projection***   Two forms are used by engineers: (i) Isometric; (ii) Oblique.

In an *isometric* drawing the component is viewed from the corner, and lines joining the corner of the battery are inclined at 30° to the horizontal as in Figure 7.1.1(a). All lines representing the length of the component are of equal length – this is the meaning of the term isometric.

In an *oblique* drawing the front face of the object is drawn to scale and the side is projected on an axis at 45° to the horizontal. The depth of the component is drawn half scale as in Figure 7.1.1(b).

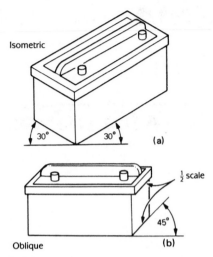

Fig. 7.1.1 Isometric and oblique projection

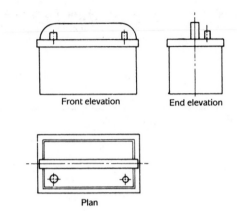

Fig. 7.1.2 1st angle projection

***Orthographic projection*** This method shows a separate view of each face of the object; the number of views necessary will be governed by the shape of the object. Rectangular solids normally require three views; a front elevation, end elevation and plan. If circumstances justify it a view of the base and the other end are also shown.

The position each view occupies on the paper is controlled by the projection angle used. Figure 7.1.2 is drawn in a form called 1st Angle. This is the common arrangement used in Europe. The American-favoured 3rd Angle projection system is also used in this country.

*1st Angle Projection.* To determine the position each elevation of the object should occupy on the paper consider the demonstration shown as Figure 7.1.3.

Using a matchbox to represent the object, lay the box on its side and draw the face you can see (front elevation).

2) Place the box on this drawing and move the box to the right by rocking it through one right angle. Draw the face you can see. This drawing is positioned on the side to which the box has moved; that is, the right-hand side in this case.

3) Return the box to the original position and again rotate the box through one right angle to move it towards the bottom of the paper. Draw the face you can see (plan).

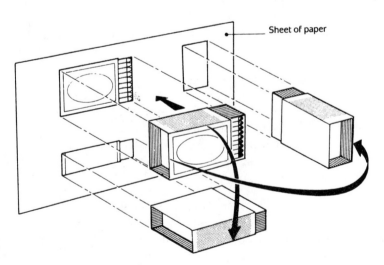

Fig. 7.1.3 Demonstration of 1st angle projection

To summarise: turn the box through one right angle and the position it occupies will indicate where the 1st angle elevation should be drawn.

*3rd Angle Projection.* Using the same matchbox demonstration, draw the faces you can see, but rotate the box through three right angles to show the position for each view. In this case it will be seen that the faces occupying the plan and end elevation positions are opposite those drawn in 1st angle projection.

Figure 7.1.4 shows a battery drawn in 3rd angle projection. Further views could be inserted in positions A and B if the three views did not enable the full details to be shown.

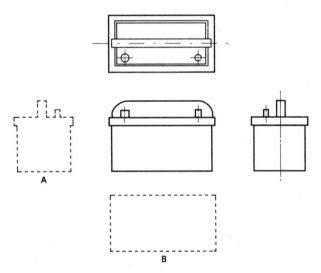

**Fig. 7.1.4** 3rd angle projection

### Types of line

BSI recommend the use of the following types of line for general engineering drawings:

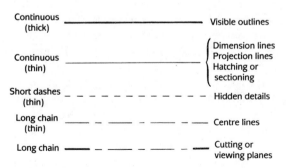

The purpose of a drawing is to convey information to other people so to avoid misunderstandings British Standard BS 308 is used; e.g. using this convention the cross in the square in Figure 7.1.5 represents a bearing.

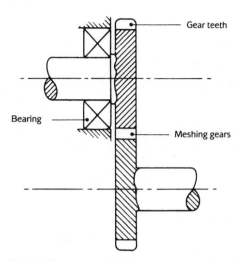

**Fig. 7.1.5** Example of BS symbols and styles for drawings

### Line diagrams

A line diagram is a diagrammatic or schematic form of drawing which shows the main arrangement without unnecessary detail. Many uses of this method of drawing are found in the Technology subjects especially in the earlier years. Figure 7.1.6(a) shows typical examples.

*Electrical circuits* are generally shown in line form; the cable shown by a straight line drawn either horizontally or vertically. Fig. 7.1.6(b) shows a circuit for a fuel gauge.

Line diagrams are used in conjunction with *block diagrams*. Fuel and lubrication systems are shown in this

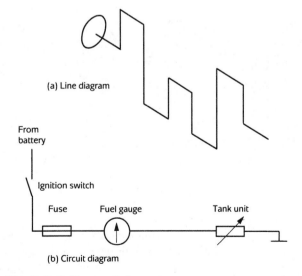

**Fig. 7.1.6** Types of diagram

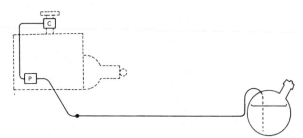

**Fig. 7.1.7** Line and block diagram

way. The component is shown by a block or box (here shown dotted) and the piping is represented by a line (Figure 7.1.7).

## 7.2 Dimensioning and sectional views

### Dimensioning

A dimension is provided on a drawing to give some other person information about the size or shape of an object. It is essential that this guidance can be easily understood, so rules are laid down in BS 308 for the manner in which the dimension is shown.

Consider the dimensions shown in Figure 7.2.1. The dimension line should be a thin, full line terminating with an arrow head not less than 3 mm long. Arrow heads should just touch the projection line. This is a thin full line starting just clear of the outline and extending beyond the arrow head.

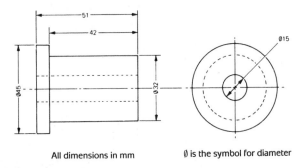

All dimensions in mm       Ø is the symbol for diameter

**Fig. 7.2.1** Dimensioning example

Centre lines should not be used as dimension lines. The end elevation in Figure 7.2.1 shows the dimension line moved around slightly.

If possible the dimension lines should be placed well away from the drawing with the largest dimension on the outside. The line may be interrupted for the dimension or this may be placed above the line. All

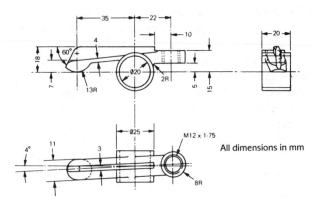

**Fig. 7.2.2** Dimensioning example

dimensions should be arranged so that they can be read from either the bottom or the right-hand side of the drawing. Figure 7.2.2 shows a dimensioned drawing.

### Sectional views

Technological work often deals with the detailed construction of components, so a drawing showing only the external view of a part has a limited use. The internal construction or hidden detail could be shown by a line of short dashes. However, in some cases the drawing could cause confusion. To overcome this drawback a sectioned view of the component is normally given. This shows the item either cut in half or cut through a plane which brings out some special feature of the design.

Figure 7.2.3 shows at the top an external view, front and end elevation, of a brake cylinder. The plan shows the cylinder sectioned through the centre line. Not only does this drawing show the advantage of a sectional view but it also indicates the main rules which apply to this method of representation:

a) The sectioned drawing shows the part that remains after the portion nearest the reader is cut away.
b) Material which is cut is indicated by section lining (cross hatching). These are thin lines, suitably spaced, drawn at an angle of 45° or some other angle to avoid the hatching running parallel with the outline. Adjacent sectioned portions should either be lined in different directions or at contrasting pitches.
c) The cutting plane, shown by a long chain line, is lettered and arrowed to show the direction in which the section is viewed.
d) When a cutting plane passes longitudinally through ribs, shafts, bolts, nuts, rods, rivets, keys, balls, rollers and split pins, the items mentioned are not sectioned.

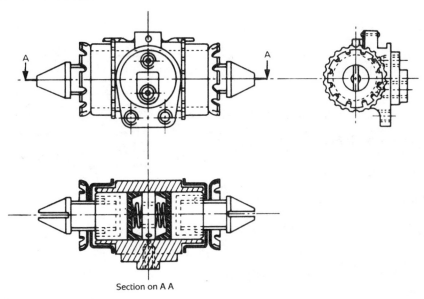

**Fig. 7.2.3** Example of sectional view

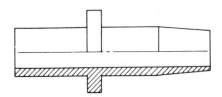

**Fig. 7.2.4** Example of half-sectional view

Components which are symmetrical about a centre line are normally drawn in half section (Figure 7.2.4).

## 7.3 Limits and tolerances

Consider the measurement of a stud which is stated to have a length of 50 mm. Although great care might have been exercised in its production it is most unlikely that the actual length of the stud is precisely 50 mm. A rule may indicate a size of 50 mm, but when the specimen is checked with a micrometer, it will most probably show that the length is not 50 mm. In a similar manner, if a micrometer was used to gauge the length during manufacture and more precise equipment is then used to check the length, it will once again show up a further inaccuracy.

This example shows that very few components could be made to a definite dimension and indicates how the accuracy of a product is influenced by the type of measuring instrument used.

The designer must decide on the accuracy required. His decision will be governed by the effect of any inaccuracy of a part on other mating parts and on the amount of interchangeability required. He will be aware that a high degree of accuracy causes high production costs and this means that the standard suggested should not be higher than necessary.

**Limits**
After fixing the nominal dimension, which in the case of the stud previously mentioned was 50 mm, the designer decides on the limits of size. He states the largest and smallest size which are acceptable and these limits could be shown in one of three ways:

$$50 \pm 0.05 \quad \text{or} \quad \begin{matrix} 50.05 \\ 49.95 \end{matrix} \quad \text{or} \quad \begin{matrix} 50.05 \\ -0.1 \end{matrix}$$

In this example the size of the part must fall between the limits 49.95 and 50.05. The largest and smallest size are called the upper and lower limit respectively. Limits do not always occur equally on each side of the nominal dimension; for example:

$$50 \begin{matrix} +0.05 \\ -0.1 \end{matrix} \quad \text{or} \quad \begin{matrix} 49.95 \\ 49.9 \end{matrix} \quad \text{or} \quad \begin{matrix} 49.95 \\ -0.05 \end{matrix}$$

In all cases the largest dimension is placed at the top.

## Tolerance

Tolerance is the acceptable size range into which the component must fall; in other words, the range between upper and lower limits. An item dimensioned $50 {\,}^{+0.12}_{-0.05}$ has a tolerance of:

Upper limit − lower limit = 50.12 − 49.95 = 0.17

The tolerance indicates the degree of accuracy required.

## REMEMBER

### Limits and fits

- limit – the largest and smallest size of a part
- tolerance – the difference between the largest and smallest size
- clearance fit – the difference in size between a shaft and a larger diameter hole
- interference fit – the difference in size between a shaft and a smaller diameter hole

## Examples

1. What is the maximum size, minimum size and tolerance allowed for the following:

|  | Max. size | Min. size | Tolerance |
|---|---|---|---|
| (a) $11.5 \pm 0.005$ | 11.505 | 11.495 | 0.01 |
| (b) $13.2 {\,}^{+0.013}_{-0.004}$ | 13.213 | 13.196 | 0.017 |
| (c) $12.5 {\,}^{+0.007}_{+0.003}$ | 12.507 | 12.503 | 0.004 |
| (d) $16.3 {\,}^{0}_{-0.008}$ | 16.3 | 16.292 | 0.008 |
| (e) $11.7 {\,}_{-0.005}$ | 11.7 | 11.695 | 0.005 |

2. What is the maximum angle, minimum angle and tolerance allowed for the following:

|  | Max. angle | Min. angle | Tolerance |
|---|---|---|---|
| (a) $90° \pm 5°$ | 95° | 85° | 10° |
| (b) $^{45°}_{44°}$ | 45° | 44° | 1° |
| (c) $^{22° \, 0'}_{-0° \, 30'}$ | 22° | 21° 30' | 0° 30' |

## Types of fit

The relative size of two mating parts governs the fit. Figure 7.3.1 shows two basic types of fit.

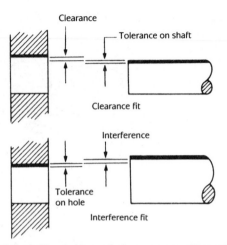

**Fig. 7.3.1** Illustration of clearance and interference fits

*Clearance fit*   The shaft is always smaller than the hole; the size difference between the shaft and hole is termed the *clearance*. Tolerance on the shaft and hole can cause the clearance to vary by a good deal. If the tolerance on the parts is large, then selective assembly is necessary if a specific clearance is to be obtained. This method of assembly entails the mating-up of a large shaft with a large hole, and so on.

Motor vehicle components such as pistons and crankshafts are examples of a clearance fit.

*Interference fit*   The shaft is larger than the hole; the difference in size is termed the *interference*.

The shaft is inserted in the hole by:

a) utilising force given by a press or hammer,
b) heating the female member,
c) cooling the male member.

This type of fit is often used to retain a part in position. Items such as a cylinder liner and flywheel ring gear are examples of an interference fit.

## 7.4   Information channels

Technical information is presented in a number of ways; these range from the traditional paper book form to sophisticated electronic mail techniques.

### Paper and books

In the past paper was used by manufacturers as a means for conveying technical information such as service manuals, service bulletins and parts books. This was sent by post to their dealers and then by hand to the appropriate department.

Modern vehicles are complicated to repair so all available technical literature should be used for reference

*Ford Motor Co Ltd*

The traditional repair manuals contain technical drawings, line and block diagrams and descriptions of workshop operations and repair schedules applicable to a given model. Also information is included on component setting and adjustments, e.g. ignition and fuel settings, torque loading of bolts, tyre pressures, etc. Without this valuable information the successful repair of a modern vehicle would be near impossible.

To function efficiently, the Parts Department needs a considerable amount of information material; this includes parts catalogues and current prices to enable the various parts to be identified, numbered and costed.

The major drawback of the 'paper system' is the difficulty associated with the task of keeping the material in good condition and up-to-date. Periodically the manufacturer supplies amendments and these must be incorporated in the appropriate manual; a laborious task for somebody to undertake. For this reason, other methods are used to speed up and simplify the system.

## Microfilm

The accommodation required by companies and libraries to store files in paper form, books and other written matter is large and costly to maintain. Further-more it often takes a long time to find a file that has been stored for a long time. The microfilm system was introduced to overcome these problems. The roll of negatives obtained by photographing the material is a fraction of the size of the original, so the contents of a large book can be retained in a small container for storage. When the material is required, the film is placed in a special projector; this enlarges the selected page and back-projects the image onto a screen.

*Microfiche*   This system is a development of the microfilm system and was used initially in the industry by the Parts Department to replace the *parts book* and *price list*.

Used in this way 'micro' means small, and 'fiche' is a French word for an index card, sheet or slip. These two words are appropriate to name a system that uses a sheet of negative film (the size of one quarter of this page) that contains a large number of pages of information. Enlargement is by means of a bench-mounted projector; this has a horizontal platform to hold the fiche and gives movement in two directions to allow the operator to locate the required page.

## Video and computer

Today these systems are commonly used for the storage, retrieval and communication of a wide range of industrial information. For many years the motor industry has used computers for the stock control of parts and vehicles. When they are connected on-line to the manufacturer, the network becomes an efficient way of ascertaining stock availability and ordering replacement parts. Within the company the computer is valuable for general administration and serves as a 'tool' for management to monitor and control the company's performance.

Some manufacturers use video tapes to convey to their dealer information such as repair instructions and vehicle modifications. The tapes are played back on a domestic-type VCR recorder.

*Compact disc (CD)*   A CD system is a convenient and economic way for the manufacturer to convey large amounts of information to its franchised dealers. The player, which may be separate or part of a modern computer system, allows viewers to quickly locate a given topic and then interact with the presentation to make it easier for them to comprehend the subject. Some manufacturers have developed the system to allow it to be used by a technician as part of a vehicle test programme.

# PROGRESS CHECK 7

1. A drawing which shows three separate views; front elevation, end elevation and plan, would be called:
(a) oblique projection
(b) isometric projection
(c) pictorial projection
(d) orthographic projection.

2. The term '1st angle' is one form of:
(a) oblique projection
(b) isometric projection
(c) pictorial projection
(d) orthographic projection.

3. The view obtained 'from looking down on an object' is positioned on the drawing paper under the front elevation. This projection is called:
(a) 1st angle
(b) 3rd angle
(c) isometric
(d) oblique.

---

4. A centre line on a drawing is represented in Figure PC7.1 by the number:
(a) 1
(b) 2
(c) 3
(d) 4.

5. A visible outline on a drawing is represented in Figure PC7.1 by the number:
(a) 1
(b) 2
(c) 3
(d) 4.

6. Hidden detail in a drawing is represented in Figure PC7.1 by the number:
(a) 1
(b) 2
(c) 3
(d) 4.

7. It is recommended that dimensions should be inserted in a drawing so that they can be read from either the:
(a) bottom or left hand side
(b) bottom or right hand side
(c) top or right hand side
(d) top or right hand side.

---

*Questions 8–11 refer to Figure PC7.2*

8. The component has an overall length of:
(a) 32 mm
(b) 42 mm
(c) 45 mm
(d) 51 mm.

9. The dimensions of the hole in the component indicate that the hole has a diameter of:
(a) 15 mm and a length of 51 mm
(b) 15 mm and a length of 42 mm
(c) 32 mm and a length of 42 mm
(d) 45 mm and a length of 51 mm.

10. The drawing uses a projection which is called:
(a) 1st angle
(b) 2nd angle
(c) 3rd angle
(d) 4th angle.

11. The drawing shows that the component has a boss of diameter 45 mm. What is the thickness of this boss?
(a) 9 mm
(b) 32 mm
(c) 42 mm
(d) 51 mm.

---

1 ——————————————

2 ——————————————

3 – – – – – – – – – – – –

4 —— – —— – —— – ——

**Fig. PC7.1**

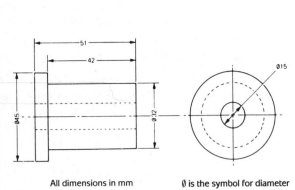

All dimensions in mm

Ø is the symbol for diameter

**Fig. PC7.2**

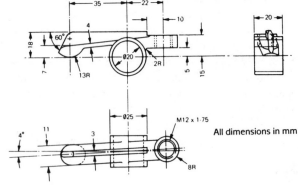

All dimensions in mm

**Fig. PC7.3**

*Questions 12–16 refer to Figure PC7.3*

12. What is the distance in mm between the centre line of the bush and the centre line of the threaded portion?
(a) 5
(b) 10
(c) 20
(d) 22.

13. A screw engaged in the female thread of the component is first moved to a position where all of the threads are in contact and then it is completely unscrewed. The minimum number of turns needed to remove the screw is:
(a) 1.25
(b) 5.72
(c) 8
(d) 8.57.

14. What is the length in mm of the hole of diameter 20 mm?
(a) 11
(b) 20
(c) 22
(d) 25.

15. What is the angle in degrees between the centre line of the large hole and the centre line drawn from the thread through the 3 mm thick web?
(a) 3
(b) 11
(c) 60
(d) 86.

16. The largest curved surface has a radius of:
(a) 8 mm
(b) 10 mm
(c) 12.5 mm
(d) 13 mm.

17. What is meant by the term 'limit' as applied to dimensions?
(a) The difference between smallest and largest acceptable size
(b) The difference between maximum and nominal sizes
(c) The variation from the nominal size
(d) The maximum and minimum size of a component.

18. What is meant by the term 'tolerance' as applied to dimensions?
(a) The range between upper and lower limits
(b) The maximum and minimum size of a component
(c) The difference between maximum and nominal sizes
(d) The difference in size between a shaft and hole.

19. The maximum size and tolerance for a component dimensioned $13.5 \pm 0.003$ are:
(a) 13.8 and 0.006
(b) 13.8 and 0.003
(c) 13.503 and 0.006
(d) 13.203 and 0.006.

20. The maximum and minimum sizes for a component dimensioned $22.1^{+0.006}_{-0.001}$ are:
(a) max 22.106
    min 22.009
(b) max 22.106
    min 22.099
(c) max 22.6
    min 21.9
(d) max 22.7
    min 22.

21. The maximum size, minimum size and tolerance, for a component dimensioned $44.7^{+0.009}_{+0.005}$ are:
(a) max 44.709
    min 44.695
    tolerance 0.014
(b) max 44.709
    min 44.705
    tolerance 0.004
(c) max 44.79
    min 44.75
    tolerance 0.04
(d) max 45.6
    min 44.2
    tolerance 0.4.

22. The maximum size, minimum size and tolerance for a component dimensioned $13.4^{-0}_{-0.006}$ are:
(a) max 13:394
    min 13.388
    tolerance 0.006
(b) max 13.4
    min 12.8
    tolerance 0.6
(c) max 13.4
    min 13.394
    tolerance 0.006
(d) max 13.406
    min 13.394
    tolerance 0.012.

23. What is meant by the term 'clearance' as applied to a shaft and bearing? The bearing is:
(a) larger than the shaft and the space between is the clearance
(b) smaller than the shaft and the space between is the clearance
(c) made the same size as the shaft and clearance is the wear
(d) made the same size as the shaft and the clearance is the tolerance.

24. What is meant by the term 'interference' as applied to a shaft and hole? The hole is:
(a) larger than the shaft and the difference in size is the interference
(b) smaller than the shaft and the difference is the interference
(c) made the same size as the shaft and interference is the wear
(d) made the same size as the shaft and the interference is the tolerance.

# Part D

# Science

# 8      *Mechanics and machines*

---

## What is covered in this chapter:

→ SI units
→ force
→ the moment of a force
→ principle of moments and centre of gravity
→ energy and work
→ power
→ friction and lubrication
→ friction clutches
→ centrifugal force and balancing
→ machines
→ velocity, acceleration and braking efficiency

---

A machine such as a motor vehicle operates in accordance with basic laws of science. These laws govern the manner in which a machine behaves when it is exposed to natural and unnatural conditions. For example, if a force is applied to an object, it generally moves, but in cases when it does not move, there must be some explanation. This chapter investigates the basic behaviour of objects and examines the reasons for any departure from the underlying principle.

Once you have mastered these aspects you will be able to apply this knowledge to understand the operation of engineering components and the behaviour of vehicles on the road. Also you will be able to offer a sound technical explanation and valid reason for a component failure.

## 8.1    SI units

If you have travelled out of this country you will appreciate the difficulties that arise when you try to communicate with people living in other lands. Many of these difficulties would be avoided if the traveller was able to speak the language of the country, but this requires considerable effort, intelligence and practice. Consider the advantages that would be gained if we all spoke one common language.

In the past this 'language difficulty' has applied to the various units which are used to represent such things as distances or quantities. Not only was it difficult to understand the units used in a country, but it often caused confusion – two examples of this are the 'ton' and the 'gallon'. An 'American ton' and 'American gallon' are quite different to their namesakes in Great Britain, and if France is included, then yet another value is obtained.

### Standard base units

With the increase in trade between nations an international body was set up to make recommendations for suitable standards. This body is called the International Standards Organisation (ISO) and in Britain the organisation associated with ISO is the British Standards Institute (BSI). At an international conference in 1960 it was recommended that everyone should use a metric system of measurement called 'Systeme International d'Unites' and this is normally abbreviated to SI in all languages. The system was based on six primary units.

## REMEMBER

### SI units

| metre | m | length |
|---|---|---|
| kilogram | kg | mass |
| second | s | time |
| ampere | A | electric current |
| kelvin | K | temperature |
| candela | cd | luminous intensity |

| Unit multiplier | Prefix | Symbol |
|---|---|---|
| One million or $10^6$ | mega | M |
| One thousand or $10^3$ | kilo | k |
| One hundredth or $10^{-2}$ | centi | c |
| One thousandth or $10^{-3}$ | milli | m |
| One millionth or $10^{-6}$ | micro | $\mu$ |

**Table 8.1.1**

*Metre, the unit of length* Distances are expressed in this unit. Originally the metre represented a part of the distance between the earth's pole and equator, and a bar of platinum was kept in Paris to form the standard length. Nowadays the need for greater accuracy has demanded a more stable standard, so in 1960 the metre was redefined as the length obtained by using the wavelengths of a certain type of light.

*Kilogram, the unit of mass* The standard kilogram is a certain cylindrical block of metal kept in France and was originally intended to represent a mass of 1000 cubic centimetres of water. The term mass is the quantity of matter in a body. When a mass of 1 kg is placed on one side of a simple balance, it will serve as a standard to compare other substances. For example, if 1 kg of grease is required, then this could be 'weighed' on a balance until the two masses are equal. When this occurs the earth's pull of gravity will give a force on the standard mass which will be the same as that acting on the grease.

*Second, the unit of time* You are aware that a day has 24 hours, one hour has 60 minutes, and one minute has 60 seconds. Before 1967 astronomical observations were used to check the special clocks housed at Greenwich, but since that date the second has been redefined as the time given by the action of a certain element in an atomic clock.

### Multiples and submultiples

The other base units will be discussed at a later stage in the book. Often the recommended unit is either too large or too small, e.g. the distance between London and Manchester is 297 000 metres and a typical gap for a sparking plug is 0.000 635 metres. To avoid this cumbersome presentation, multiples and submultiples of SI units are used and the following table shows the common prefixes used in our type of work.

Using this system the distance between London and Manchester is given as 297 kilometres and the sparking plug gap as 0.635 millimetre or in even shorter form as 297 km and 0.635 mm respectively. Since common practice is to use symbols, then both SI and BSI recommendations should be followed. The symbol 'm' already represents 'milli' and 'metre' so it is obvious that it cannot be used for a minute of time. In cases like this, the non-SI abbreviations are changed and this is the reason why expressions such as RPM should now be stated as rev/min.

The forementioned prefixes can be applied to all SI units.

### Example

$$220\,613 \text{ grams} = 220.613 \text{ kg}$$
$$0.02 \text{ second} = 20 \text{ ms}$$
$$0.0075 \text{ kilometre} = 7.5 \text{ m}$$
$$700 \text{ milliamperes} = 0.7 \text{ A}$$

These examples also show why the letter 's' should not be added to the symbol to form a plural. Where confusion is likely the unit should be written in full – in this case the plural can be used where appropriate.

The table of prefixes above is based on the metric system, which, as applied to the length unit, can be written as follows:

| | | |
|---|---|---|
| 10 millimetres (mm) | = 1 centimetre | (cm) |
| 10 centimetres | = 1 decimetre | (dm) |
| 10 decimetres | = 1 metre | (m) |
| 10 metres | = 1 decametre | (dam) |
| 10 decametres | = 1 hectometre | (hm) |
| 10 hectometres | = 1 kilometre | (km) |

Inspection of this table shows that some units have not been included in previous sections of this chapter. This is because in SI, certain units are preferred and these are shown in the table.

## Derived units

Many other units can be derived from the six primary units to form a system which is all linked together. Thus if two units are multiplied together the resultant quantity forms a new unit.

Some derived units are named after famous scientists; for example

joule (J) – energy
newton (N) – force
watt (W) – power

Prefixes are used in front of the basic unit to avoid writing in full a number which consists of many digits; e.g. it is easier to write 52 km than 52 000 m. These are the prefixes shown in Table 8.1.1, which are extended in Table 8.1.2.

**Area**   Unit of area is the square metre ($m^2$). Since there are 100 centimetres in a metre, there will be $100 \times 100$ square centimetres in 1 square metre. So:

$$10\,000 \text{ cm}^2 = 1 \text{ m}^2$$

**Volume**   Unit of volume is the cubic metre ($m^3$). Using the length measurement as a basis it will be seen that:

$$1 \text{ cm}^3 = 10 \times 10 \times 10 \text{ mm}^3 = 1000 \text{ mm}^3$$

In the past the symbol for a cubic centimetre was 'cc' and in many cases the total swept volume (swept volume of one cylinder × number of cylinders) of an engine was stated in cc (e.g. 250 cc).

**Capacity**   Unit of capacity is the litre (l). Originally this was stated as the volume occupied by a mass of 1 kg of pure water measured under stated conditions, but due to slight errors the litre was redefined in 1964 as equal to 1000 cm³. Although the litre is not a preferred SI unit, its general use makes it necessary to include it here.

Engine capacity is often stated in litres. Since 1000 cm³ = 1 litre, an engine having a capacity of 1500 cm³ would be called a $1\frac{1}{2}$ litre engine.

**Mass**   Unit of mass is the kilogram (kg). This primary SI unit comes from the metric table:

1000 mg = 1 gram (g)
1000 g  = 1 kg
1000 kg = 1 tonne

To avoid misunderstanding it is advisable to write tonne in full.

## 8.2  Force

We are all familiar with the fact that things have to be pulled or pushed to make them move. Pulls and pushes are examples of what we call force. This we cannot see or

| Prefix | Symbol | Standard Value | Value (written in full) |
|---|---|---|---|
| tera | T | $10^{12}$ | 1 000 000 000 000 |
| giga | G | $10^{9}$ | 1 000 000 000 |
| mega | M | $10^{6}$ | 1 000 000 |
| kilo | k | $10^{3}$ | 1 000 |
| hecto | h | $10^{2}$ | 100 |
| deca | da | 10 | 10 |
| deci | d | $10^{-1}$ | 0.1 |
| centi | c | $10^{-2}$ | 0.01 |
| milli | m | $10^{-3}$ | 0.001 |
| micro | $\mu$ | $10^{-6}$ | 0.000 001 |
| nano | n | $10^{-9}$ | 0.000 000 001 |
| pico | p | $10^{-12}$ | 0.000 000 000 001 |
| femto | f | $10^{-15}$ | * |
| atto | a | $10^{-18}$ | * |

\* Expressed as a 'power of 10' the value is much shorter to express; it would need a much wider page to write in full the value of 'femto' and 'atto'. The number that indicates the power to which 10 is raised is called an 'index' (plural, indices).

**Table 8.1.2** SI prefixes

touch but we are aware of its existence from its effects, so from these effects we can say:

> *force is that which changes a body's state of rest or of uniform motion in a straight line*

This statement is a technical expression of facts which are generally known. Translating it more into simple words:

1) If an object is stationary it will remain stationary. A force must be applied to move it.
2) When an object is moving then it will continue to move in the given direction and speed unless a force is applied to it.

In order to investigate this subject more fully we must consider some more basic terms. Firstly, let us look at the object or body onto which the force is acting. The quantity of matter in the object is its *mass* and this would be expressed in kilograms.

Assuming that the object or mass is free to move, the application of a force will cause the object to move in the direction that the force is acting. At first the object will move slowly, but all the time the force acts the velocity of the object will increase.

> *The rate of increase in velocity is called acceleration*

Let us assume that the velocity increases by 2 metres/second for every second that the force is acting:

After 1 second the velocity would be 2 metres/second
After 2 seconds the velocity would be 4 metres/second
After 3 seconds the velocity would be 6 metres/second
After 4 seconds the velocity would be 8 metres/second.

In each second of time, the velocity has increased by 2 m/s, so the acceleration is said to be 2 metres per second, per second, which in symbol form is 2 m/s/s or more correctly stated as $2 \text{ m/s}^2$.

Now let us return to the force which was accelerating the object and consider the unit of force. SI adopts a unit which is directly linked (coherent) to the base units and honours the work of Sir Isaac Newton.

> *The SI unit of force is the newton and is given the symbol N*

Referring to the definition of a newton (illustrated in Figure 8.2.1) which is:

> *1 newton is required to accelerate a mass of 1 kg at a rate of 1 m/s²*

then it is possible to state that: 9.81 N is required to accelerate a mass of 1 kg at a rate of $9.81 \text{ m/s}^2$. The effect

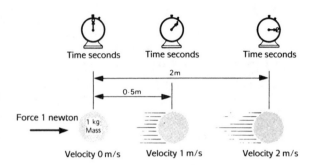

**Fig. 8.2.1** Example of acceleration at 1 m/s$^2$

of the earth's gravity causes a mass of 1 kg to give a force of about 9.81 N, Figure 8.2.2, i.e.

> *Force of gravity on mass of 1 kg $\simeq$ 10 N*

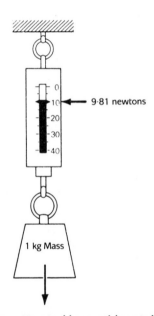

**Fig. 8.2.2** Mass attracted by earth's gravity

### Example
A 4-wheeled vehicle has a mass of 2000 kg. What force acts between the tyre and road assuming the force on each wheel is equal?

$$\text{Mass acting on each wheel} = \frac{2000}{4} = 500 \text{ kg}$$

1 kg gives a force of 9.81 N

$$\text{so } 500 \text{ kg} = 500 \times 9.81$$
$$= 4950 \text{ N} = 4.905 \text{ kN}$$

(Check – answer should be about 10 times larger than the mass acting on each wheel).

Prior to the introduction of SI, the unit of mass in Britain was the pound (lb) and the gravitational force on this mass was 'one pound force', which was written as 1 lbf. Using this convention, a mass of 1 kg had a gravitational force of 1 kgf. Introduction of the newton as the SI unit of force has made redundant the units 'lbf' and 'kgf', but it is expected that the reader will encounter these units for some time.

To convert to SI units the following can be used:

$$1 \text{ lbf} \simeq 4.45 \text{ newtons}$$
$$1 \text{ kgf} \simeq 9.81 \text{ newtons}$$

(You will note that when the name of a person is used as a unit, small letters are used for the name of the unit and a capital letter used for the symbol).

*One newton is the force which, acting on a mass of one kilogram, gives to that mass an acceleration of one metre per second per second.*

$$1 \text{ newton} = 1 \text{ kg} \times 1 \text{ m/s}^2$$

### Weight and gravity

The force with which we are most familiar is that produced by the earth's gravity since any object on or near the surface of the earth is attracted towards the centre of the earth. This force of gravity is proportional to the amount of material the object contains; in other words its mass in kilograms. In everyday language the force of gravity on a mass is called weight but this term has technical limitations due to the:

1) variation in gravitational attraction in different parts of the earth's surface;
2) lack of gravity when the object is away from the earth, i.e. in space.

These limitations show that the weight of an object depends on its location, so to overcome these drawbacks the term mass is preferred: this will remain the same irrespective of the location of the object.

In various problems given in this book the term 'mass' has been used to indicate the 'size' of an object. However the reader must expect to see the word 'weight' applied to many vehicle applications since apart from a few exceptions it is expected that the normal motor vehicle will operate within the earth's gravitational field.

Accepting the fact that any large mass produces a gravitational force, then it follows that if an object is dropped from the top of a tall building, it will fall towards the ground at a velocity which increases with time, i.e. the mass will accelerate due to the force of

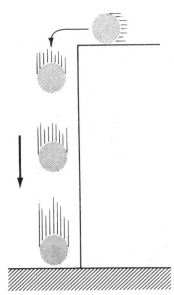

**Fig. 8.2.3** Earth's gravity causes object to accelerate at 9.81 m/s²

gravity as in Figure 8.2.3. Taking accepted values for an object falling in a vacuum:

*g or gravitational acceleration is 9.81 m/s².*

This acceleration applies to objects big and small – they all accelerate at the same rate.

## REMEMBER

| force | newton | N |
| mass | kilogram | kg |
| acceleration | metres/second² | m/s² |

**Weight** is the force of gravity on an object

**Force of gravity** on mass of 1 kg is about 10 N

## 8.3   The moment of a force

If we want to make something turn, or rotate, we must support it at the point about which we want it to turn. This is to ensure that it cannot move at this point, but can turn around it.

There are many situations where the mechanic can confirm this fact, e.g. any attempt to apply a force to a spanner to unscrew the nut shown in Figure 8.3.1 is not very successful – the whole thing floats away in the direction of the arrows. The mechanic's answer is to clamp the bolt in a vice. Now the force acting on the

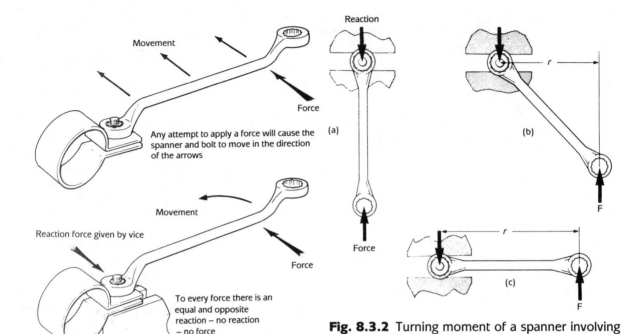

**Fig. 8.3.1** Clamping showing moment of force and turning movement (torque)

**Fig. 8.3.2** Turning moment of a spanner involving force and distance

spanner is resisted by the vice and this provides an equal and opposite force to that exerted by the mechanic.

### Torque

This example shows that a force cannot act unless there is a reaction or:

> ***To every force there is an equal and opposite reaction***

Let us examine some other facts about the use of this spanner. You are all aware that a force applied to a spanner as shown in Figure 8.3.2(a) would not have much effect on a tight nut. The line of action of the force given by the mechanic acts through the centre of the nut so no turning effect is obtained. Setting the spanner in the manner shown in Figure 8.3.2(b) is not much better but when it is repositioned to enable its full length to be used as in Figure 8.3.2(c) the maximum turning effect is obtained and the nut can be moved with the minimum of effort.

This example shows that the turning effect is governed by two things; the force $F$ and the distance $r$. The product of $F$ and $r$ is called the *moment of a force* and when this is applied to things that rotate, then terms such as *turning moment* or *torque* are used.

> ***Torque is a turning moment about a point and is the product of the force and the perpendicular distance between the point and the line of action of the force***

$$\textit{Torque} = \textbf{\textit{F}} \times \textbf{\textit{r}}$$

Referring to Figure 8.3.2 shows that when the spanner is positioned as in (a), the torque is zero. Moving the spanner as in (b) causes the distance $r$ to increase and this distance is a maximum in (c). This means that when a constant force is applied, maximum torque is produced in position shown in (c).

Torque is a product of a force, which is given in newtons, and distance which is expressed in metres, therefore:

> ***The newton metre is the unit of torque***

### Example

A spanner of length 0.4 m has a force of 80 N applied to its end as shown in the diagram (Figure 8.3.3). Calculate the turning moment given by this force.

$$\begin{aligned} \text{Turning moment} &= F \times r \\ &= 80 \times 0.4 \\ &= 32\ \text{N m} \end{aligned}$$

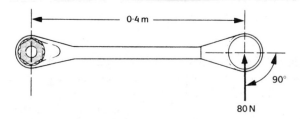

**Fig. 8.3.3** Illustration of turning moment

### Example

A connecting rod applies a force of 9.6 kN to a crank of length 50 mm when the crank is positioned to form a right angle to the connecting rod. Calculate the torque at this instant (Figure 8.3.4).

$$\text{Torque} = F \times r$$

Force is 9600 N and distance is 0.05 m

$$\begin{aligned}
\text{Torque} &= 9600 \times 0.05 \\
&= 96 \times 5 \\
&= 480 \text{ Nm}
\end{aligned}$$

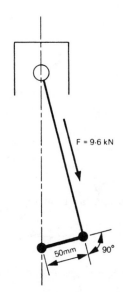

**Fig. 8.3.4** Example

### Measurement of torque

Occasions occur when the torque applied to a component must be measured. Figure 8.3.5 shows a spring balance applied to the flange of a final drive pinion to measure the bearing preload. Torque is obtained by multiplying $F$ by $r$. Special gauges are available for this job and these are calibrated in Nm.

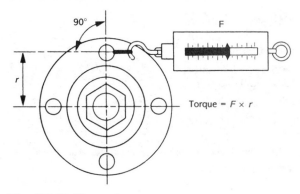

**Fig. 8.3.5** Measuring torque

Nuts and bolts of motor vehicles must be tightened the correct amount. Undertightening allows the item to move when it is loaded and can result in the nut working loose, whereas overtightening weakens the bolt and often leads to breakage.

Assuming the thread is undamaged, the tightness depends on the torque. Where a specific degree of tightness is essential the manufacturer states the torque to which the nut or bolt should be set and this is achieved by a *torque wrench* (Figure 8.3.6). Various designs are available; the type illustrated is used by setting the wrench to the recommended torque and then tightening the nut until the wrench indicates that the torque has been reached. Typical torque for the tightness of a sparking plug in a cast-iron head is 34 Nm.

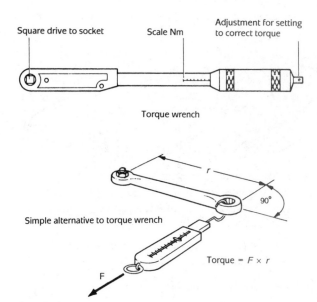

**Fig. 8.3.6** Setting torque values

## REMEMBER

**Torque** is

- a turning moment
- force × radius
- measured in newton metres (Nm)

A spring balance applied to a spanner is an alternative to a torque wrench.

## 8.4 Principle of moments and centre of gravity

The remarkable feat shown in Figure 8.4.1 illustrates the principle of moments. The car is in equilibrium, i.e. a state of balance, and in this position the sum of the turning moments which tend to rotate the car in a clockwise direction, equals the sum of the moments which tend to rotate the car in the anti-clockwise direction. Phrased in a more precise form:

*The principle of moments states that when a body is in equilibrium, then the clockwise moments about any point equal the anti-clockwise moments about the same point*

Taking moments about the jack:

anti-clockwise moments = $F_1 \times a$
clockwise moments = $F_2 \times b$
clockwise moments = anti-clockwise moments
∴ $F_1 \times a$ = $F_2 \times b$

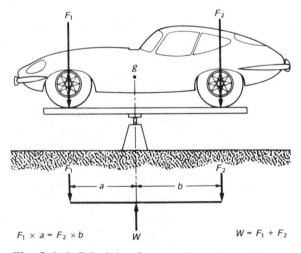

$F_1 \times a = F_2 \times b$ 　　 $W$ 　　 $W = F_1 + F_2$

**Fig. 8.4.1** Principle of moments

The jack is taking the whole weight of the car so:

$F_1 + F_2$ 　　　　　　 = total weight of car

In this case it is convenient to use the jack as the point around which the moments are taken, but the principle would apply if any other point were selected.

Suspending the car in Figure 8.4.1 by a wire attached to point 'g' would produce a state of balance irrespective of the initial position of the car. Point 'g' is the *centre of gravity* and is the theoretical point at which the total mass is considered to act. Instead of each separate mass, i.e. the engine, gearbox, etc., giving a number of individual moments, all the masses can be grouped together to give one mass which is concentrated at the centre of gravity.

### Example
A brake lever, Figure 8.4.2, has a force of 400 N applied at a distance of 80 mm from the pivot. What force will act on the rod which connects the lever to the brake?

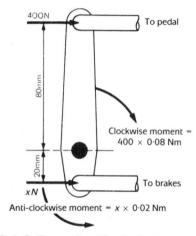

**Fig. 8.4.2** Example of brake lever

Take moments about the pivot and let $x$ = required force:

Clockwise moment = 400 × 0.08 Nm
(both moments must be in the same units)

Anti-clockwise moment = $x$ × 0.02 Nm
Anti-clockwise moment = clockwise moment
$x$ × 0.02 = 400 × 0.08
$$x = \frac{400 \times 0.08}{0.02}$$
$x$ = 1600 N

### Example
An 'inclined' force acts on a bell crank lever as shown in Figure 8.4.3. Calculate the force $F$.

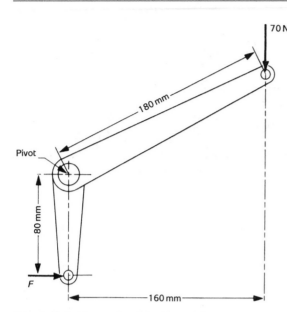

**Fig. 8.4.3** Example of bell crank lever

Taking moments about the pivot:

Clockwise moment    = 70 × perpendicular distance
                            = 70 × 160 N mm
Anti-clockwise moment = $F$ × 80 N mm
Anti-clockwise moment = Clockwise moment
$F$ × 80                = 70 × 160
$F$                      $= \dfrac{70 \times 160}{80} = 140$ N

***Torque at rear wheels*** Figure 8.4.4 shows a driving wheel onto which is applied a torque $T$ by means of an axle shaft. Torque is $F \times r$ so a force of $F$ is given at the

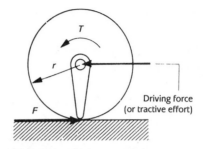

**Fig. 8.4.4** Example of driving wheel

road surface. Grip between the tyre and the road prevents the tyre from skidding and this results in a driving force being applied to the axle casing.

$$\text{Driving force (or tractive effort)} = \frac{\text{Torque (Nm)}}{\text{Wheel radius (m)}}\text{N}$$

***Couples*** When two parallel forces act in opposite directions a couple is formed. Figure 8.4.5 gives two examples of couples. The magnitude of a couple is:

> ***force × perpendicular distance between the forces***

### Centre of gravity

The centre of gravity is the theoretical point at which the total mass is considered to act. Any component which is suspended from this point would be in a state of balance or equilibrium (Figure 8.4.6).

The position of the centre of gravity (c.g.) has a considerable influence on the behaviour of a component, as the following examples show.

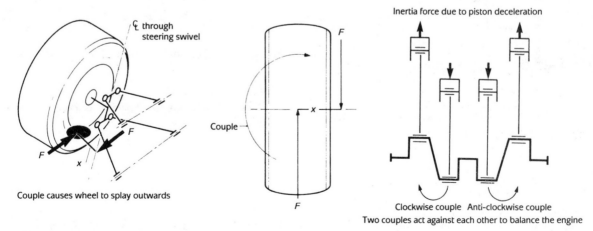

**Fig. 8.4.5** Different examples of couples

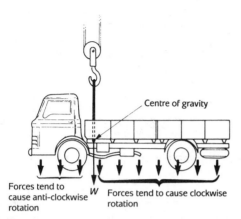

**Fig. 8.4.6** Vehicle will be in a state of balance if suspended from the centre of gravity

*Vehicle* The position of the centre of gravity of a vehicle is controlled by the location of its main components and occupants. The distances between the c.g. and the front and rear wheels control the load carried by the axles. In cases where the c.g. is towards the front of the vehicle, for example, in front wheel drive vehicles, the load taken by the rear wheels is small. This will influence such things as tyre inflation pressures and the degree of braking which can be provided by the rear wheels (Figure 8.4.7).

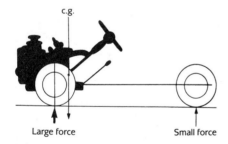

**Fig. 8.4.7** Displacement of centre of gravity

Height of the c.g. affects the *angle of roll* when a vehicle is cornering (Figure 8.4.8).

*Rotating components* Any part of a vehicle which revolves at speed (shafts, wheels, etc.) should have its c.g. on the axis of rotation (Figure 8.4.9). If this condition is not achieved, an out-of-balance force is produced which causes considerable vibration.

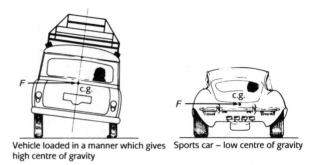

Vehicle loaded in a manner which gives high centre of gravity    Sports car – low centre of gravity

**Fig. 8.4.8** Effect of c.g. on angle of roll

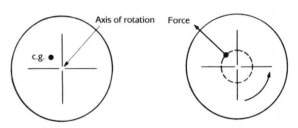

**Fig. 8.4.9** An out-of-balance force causes vibration if the c.g. does not coincide with the axis of rotation

**Example**

A wheel is supported by a pivot which is located at the wheel's axis of rotation (Figure 8.4.10). In this position an out-of-balance mass of 50 g acts at a radius of 327 mm. What mass must be placed on the rim at a radius of 150 mm to make the c.g. coincide with the wheel axis?

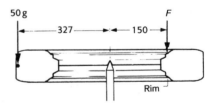

**Fig. 8.4.10** Example of out-of-balance wheel

When balance is correct (i.e., c.g. is on wheel axis) anticlockwise moments about pivot = clockwise moments about pivot. Therefore:

$$50 \times 327 = F \times 150$$
$$F = \frac{50 \times 327}{150}$$
$$F = 109 \text{ g}$$

A mass of 109 g placed on the rim diametrically opposite the out-of-balance mass will give *static balance*.

## REMEMBER

**moment** of a force (Nm)

   clockwise moments = anti-clockwise moments

**couple** (Nm)

   force × perp. distance between forces

**Centre of gravity**

theoretical point where mass is considered to act

## 8.5   Energy and work

**Energy**

As stated already:

> ### Energy is the capacity for doing work

There are many forms of energy; to name a few – chemical, heat, mechanical and electrical. These are all applicable to motor vehicles and in this book reference is made to these various forms of energy.

> ### Energy cannot be created or destroyed – it can only be converted from one form to another

Internal combustion engines act as a good example to illustrate this statement. Chemical energy enters the engine in the form of fuel; the fuel is burnt to produce heat energy; the heat increases the pressure of the gas and produces mechanical energy. The process does not stop here because the mechanical energy used to drive the car along the road is given back to the atmosphere (Figure 8.5.1).

*Work*   When a force overcomes a resistance and causes movement, work is done. Here we are concerned with work in an engineering sense and most probably this

## REMEMBER

**Energy** is

- capacity to do work
- expressed in joules (J)

**Work** is

- force × distance moved
- expressed in joules (J)
  or newton metres (Nm)

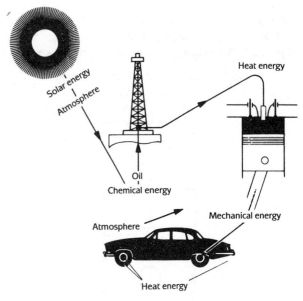

**Fig. 8.5.1** Demonstration of energy conversion cycle

differs from the average person's idea of work. Stated in a technical form:

> ### Work = force × distance moved

Force is measured in newtons; distance is in metres so the product of these two units is a newton metre (Nm).

> ### In SI the unit of work is the joule

$$1\,J = 1\,Nm$$

Sometimes it is convenient to state the unit of work as the newton metre – both the newton metre and the joule are acceptable units. Work is linked with energy; the unit of energy is the joule.

Figure 8.5.2 shows a vehicle being driven along a road at a constant speed by a force. The work done is the product of the force and the distance moved.

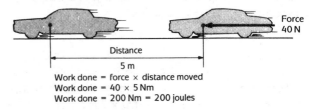

Work done = force × distance moved
Work done = 40 × 5 Nm
Work done = 200 Nm = 200 joules

**Fig. 8.5.2** Demonstration of work done

## Example

An engine having a stroke of 70 mm has an average force of 4 kN acting on the piston during the power stroke (Figure 8.5.3). Calculate the work done during this stroke.

$$\begin{aligned}
\text{Work done} &= \text{Force} \times \text{distance moved} \\
&= 4000 \times 0.07 \text{ Nm} \\
&= 40 \times 7 \\
&= 280 \text{ Nm} = 280 \text{ J}
\end{aligned}$$

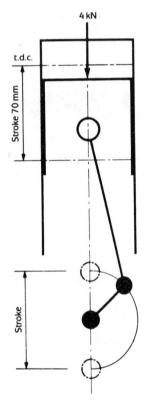

**Fig. 8.5.3** Example of work done

## Example

An engine of mass 50 kg is lifted through a vertical distance of 2 m. Calculate the work done against gravity. Take $g$ as 9.8 m/s$^2$ (Figure 8.5.4).

$$\begin{aligned}
\text{Force required to lift mass} &= 50 \times 9.8 \\
&= 5 \times 98 \\
&= 490 \text{ N}
\end{aligned}$$

$$\begin{aligned}
\text{Work done} \quad &= \text{Force} \times \text{distance moved} \\
&= 490 \times 2 \text{ Nm} \\
&= 980 \text{ J}
\end{aligned}$$

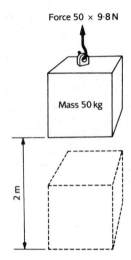

**Fig. 8.5.4** Example of work done

***Work done by a torque*** Work is done when a component is rotated under the action of a torque. A torque of $T$ newton metres may be produced by a force of $F$ newtons acting at a radius of $r$ metres from the centre of rotation. Then, in one revolution, the point of application of the force moves a distance of $2\pi r$ (Figure 8.5.5).

$$\begin{aligned}
\text{Work} &= \text{force} \times \text{distance moved} \\
&= F \times 2\pi r \quad \text{OR} \quad F \times r \times 2\pi
\end{aligned}$$

Since torque is $F \times r$ then:

$$\begin{aligned}
\text{Work done per revolution} &= T \times 2\pi \quad \text{OR} \quad 2\pi T \\
\text{Work done in } n \text{ revolutions} &= 2\pi n T
\end{aligned}$$

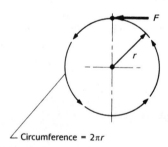

**Fig. 8.5.5** Work done by torque

## Example

A torque of 42 Nm is applied to a winch handle of radius 0.5 m (Figure 8.5.6). Calculate the work done: (i) per revolution; (ii) per minute when the handle is moved at the rate of 50 rev/min. (Take $\pi$ as $\frac{22}{7}$.)

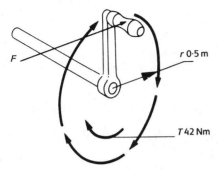

**Fig. 8.5.6** Example of work done by torque

(i) Work done per revolution $= 2\pi T$
$$= \frac{2 \times 22 \times 42}{7} \text{ Nm}$$
$$= 264 \text{ Nm} = 264 \text{ J}$$

(ii) Work done per minute $= 2\pi nT$
$$= 264 \times 50 \text{ Nm}$$
$$= 13\,200 \text{ Nm}$$
$$= 13\,200 \text{ J} = 13.2 \text{ kJ}$$

## 8.6 Power

The rate at which a machine or engine does work is called its power. Work at the rate of one joule per second is the unit of power – the watt.

*Power is the rate of doing work and is expressed in watts*

The diagram (Figure 8.6.1) shows an example of the use of the term power. It compares two vehicles: A, with a 'small' engine and B with a 'big' engine. Both vehicles

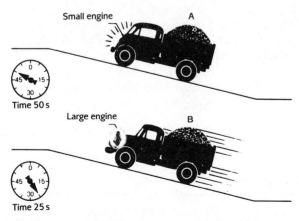

**Fig. 8.6.1** Vehicle B is twice power of vehicle A

are expected to climb the hill that is shown, but tests show that A will take a longer time – in this case vehicle B is more powerful than vehicle A. Assuming the mass of each vehicle is equal, the:

$$\text{work done by A} = \text{work done by B}$$

Since B can do this work in half the time then:

$$\text{power of B} = \text{twice the power of A.}$$

Hence:

$$\text{power} = \frac{\text{force} \times \text{distance moved}}{\text{time}}$$

or

$$\text{power} = \frac{\text{work done}}{\text{time}} \quad \text{i.e. work done in a given time.}$$

**Example**

A vehicle travels a distance of 1.8 km in a time of 2 minutes. If the tractive effort is 200 N, calculate the power used.

$$\text{Work done} = \text{force} \times \text{distance moved}$$
$$= 200 \times 1800 \text{ Nm in 2 minutes}$$
$$= \frac{200 \times 1800}{2 \times 60} \text{ Nm in 1 second}$$
$$= 3000 \text{ Nm/s} = 3 \text{ kNm/s} = 3 \text{ kJ/s}$$

1 J/s is 1 watt so power used = 3 kilowatts which is also written as 3 kW.

**Horsepower**

The Imperial unit of power is the horsepower which is given the symbol hp. This unit was introduced by James Watt to indicate to prospective buyers the power output of his steam engines. In that period the horse provided the power for transport purposes so Watt tested a number of horses and from these results he decided that:

*1 horsepower = work at the rate of 33 000 foot pounds per minute*

or $\qquad$ 1 hp = 33 000 ft lbf/min

For conversion purposes:

$$1 \text{ horsepower} \simeq 746 \text{ W}$$

Some German manufacturers still use horsepower as the unit of engine power. When translated the term horsepower becomes *Pferdestärke*, which is abbreviated to PS.

**REMEMBER**

**Power** is

- rate of doing work
- expressed in watts (W)

   1 watt = 1 joule/second
   1 kW = 1000 W

**Horse power** is

- the Imperial unit of power
- 1 hp is about 746 W
- Pferdestärke in German (PS)

## 8.7   Friction and lubrication

**Friction**

When a block is placed on a horizontal surface and a force is applied to it, the block will not move until the force reaches a value sufficient to overcome an opposing force called friction (Figure 8.7.1). the force required to initially cause sliding is termed the *limiting frictional force* and once this has been overcome a smaller force will keep the block moving.

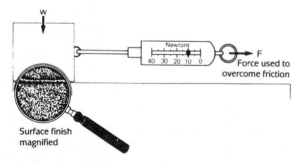

Surface finish magnified

**Fig. 8.7.1** Demonstration of frictional force

   Sometimes friction is a disadvantage, but if it did not exist many things that we do would be impossible, e.g. walking – no grip between the shoe and the ground would mean that a new method of propulsion would be needed.

   With motor vehicles it is possible to consider the effects of friction and group these effects into situations where friction is an advantage and a disadvantage. Situations where friction is usefully employed:

1) *clutch*    drive is made possible by the friction between the plates;
2) *brakes*    energy of motion is converted to heat by rubbing one surface against another;

3) *tyres*    the wheel rim drives the tyre by friction; the tyre 'grips' the road;
4) *fan belt*    drive to the fan and generator is made possible by friction;
5) *steering wheel*    friction between the driver's hand and the steering wheel.

Situations where friction is disadvantageous:

1) *piston*    for high efficiency the piston should slide easily in the cylinder;

2) *bearings*    shafts must turn as freely as possible – friction in bearings results in a reduction in the power applied to drive the vehicle; 'rolling friction' is much smaller than sliding friction, so ball or roller bearings are efficient types of bearing.

In cases where friction is essential the designer selects his material to give the appropriate grip between the surfaces. All the time this friction is maintained the component will perform its task, but if friction is decreased due to wear or other reasons then slip will occur.

   The *frictional resistance* between two surfaces depends on the:

a) the nature of the materials – there is more friction between asbestos substitutes  and iron than between steel and bronze;

b) the condition of the surfaces – smooth or rough, wet or dry;

c) the force pressing the surfaces together – friction is proportional to the force, i.e. when the force thrusting one surface against another is doubled, the friction force is doubled.

**Static and sliding friction**

A block is placed on a dry horizontal table and a force is applied to slide the block along. When the force is sufficient to overcome the interlocking action of the contacting surfaces, the block moves. As soon as it starts to move, the force required to keep it moving is less than that required to 'unstick it'. This shows that:

   *Sliding friction is less than static friction*

Motor vehicle applications of static and sliding friction are as follows.

1) *Braking*    a wheel skidding over a road surface produces a smaller braking action than a wheel held on the verge of skidding;

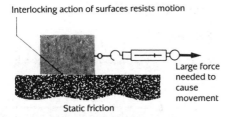

Interlocking action of surfaces resists motion

Large force needed to cause movement

Static friction

Only a small force is needed after block starts to move

Sliding friction

**Fig. 8.7.2** Sliding friction is less than static friction

2) *Crankshaft*   the torque required to initially turn a crankshaft is greater than that required to keep it moving: this fact shows up when new bearings and pistons have been fitted.

Sometimes the expression *stiction* is used to describe the effect of static friction.

**Coefficient of friction**
Investigation of the forces required to slide the block, Figure 8.7.2, along a horizontal surface reveals that a relationship exists between the force $F$ needed to overcome friction and the force $W$ pressing the surfaces together. The constant $F/W$ is called the coefficient of friction and is represented by the Greek letter $\mu$ (pronounced 'mu').

$$\text{Coefficient of friction} = \frac{\text{sliding frictional force}}{\text{force between surfaces}}$$

or

$$\mu = \frac{F}{W}$$

or

$$F = \mu W$$

In Figure 8.7.3 the value for $\mu$ is 0.5 and since it is a ratio no units are used. The coefficient of friction varies with different materials. Table 8.7.1 shows some typical values.

| Surfaces | $\mu$ |
|---|---|
| Tyre on normal road surface | 0.6 |
| Brake lining on cast iron drum | 0.4 |
| Clutch lining on cast iron flywheel | 0.35 |
| Metal on metal (dry) | 0.2 |
| Metal on metal (lubricated) | 0.1 |

**Table 8.7.1** Friction values

In some situations friction is useful but in many other cases it must be reduced by one or more of the following:

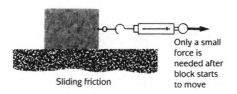

$W$ (newtons)

$F$ (newtons)

| $W$ (newtons) | $F$ (newtons) | $\dfrac{F}{W}$ |
|---|---|---|
| 4 | 2 | $^2/_4 = 0\cdot5$ |
| 6 | 3 | $^3/_6 = 0\cdot5$ |
| 8 | 4 | $^4/_8 = 0\cdot5$ |
| 10 | 5 | $^5/_{10} = 0\cdot5$ |
| 12 | 6 | $^6/_{12} = 0\cdot5$ |

**Fig. 8.7.3** Relationship between $F$ and $W$ ($F/W$ is equal to the coefficient of friction)

1) employing low-friction materials
2) lubrication
3) using ball or roller bearings since rolling friction is far less than sliding friction.

**Laws of friction**
Simple experiments show that friction between surfaces obeys the following laws:

1) The frictional force is proportional to the force pressing the surfaces together.
2) It depends on the nature of the surfaces.
3) It is independent of the area in contact.
4) It is independent of the speed of rubbing.

The nature of the surface means the type of material and condition of the surfaces, i.e. wet, dry, smooth or rough.

The simple tests (Figure 8.7.4) show that the area in contact does not affect the frictional force. In Test 1 the spring balance may be considered as pulling along four

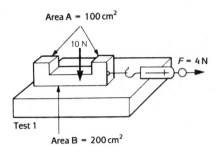

Test 1

Area A = 100 cm²

Area B = 200 cm²

10 N

F = 4N

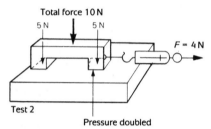

Total force 10 N

5 N    5 N

F = 4N

Test 2

Pressure doubled

**Fig. 8.7.4** Friction is independent of the area in contact

blocks; each one carrying a load of 2.5 N, whereas in Test 2 the balance is pulling two blocks each having a load of 5 N.

On a motor vehicle the friction law referring to area has to be applied carefully, since other factors often affect the result. These factors apply in the following ways.

*Brakes*    Increasing the lining width of a brake shoe does not increase the friction. However, the larger area gives a reduction in the rate of wear and also allows the lining to operate at a lower temperature – this is beneficial since the coefficient of friction decreases when a given temperature is reached.

*Bearings*    Increasing the diameter or length of a plain bearing does not increase the friction, that is, assuming that the bearing is operated in a dry condition. Normally bearings are lubricated, so the basic laws of friction do not apply. Instead *fluid friction* laws apply, and with these laws an increase in the bearing area produces a larger *oil drag*.

*Tyres*    A smooth tyre running on a smooth dry road has the same friction value as a similar tyre of wider section. Once again this is a situation which should not be found in practice. A tyre has a tread which cuts through the greasy, wet film on the surface and 'bites' into the road.

**REMEMBER**

**Friction** is

● affected by surface nature and condition
● expressed by the symbol '$\mu$'

$$\mu = \frac{\text{frictional force}}{\text{force pushing surfaces together}}$$

So if the area of tread is increased, the grip is generally improved.

**Effect of temperature on friction**

Most modern materials used as brake linings and clutch facings maintain a near-constant friction value for operating temperatures up to about 300°C. When this temperature is exceeded, the coefficient of friction decreases and *fade* is said to occur. As applied to brakes, fade results in an increase in the pedal force, and in cases where the brakes have become overheated, the driver experiences difficulty in stopping the vehicle.

Figure 8.7.5 shows the effect of temperature on two different materials. Tests are performed by the manufacturer to select a material which suits the particular vehicle, so if an inferior cheap substitute is subsequently used, fade may occur during normal brake operation.

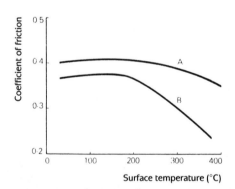

**Fig. 8.7.5** Effect of temperature on brake linings (lining A fades at a higher temperature than does B)

**Example**

A brake pad is pressed against a disc by a force of 400 N. If the coefficient of friction is 0.4 and the pad acts at a radius of 150 mm (Figure 8.7.6), calculate the frictional force and braking torque given by the pad.

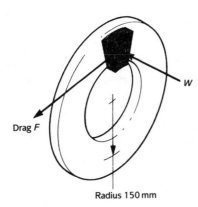

**Fig. 8.7.6** Brake pad example

$$\mu = \frac{F}{W} = \frac{\text{frictional force}}{\text{force between surfaces}}$$

$$F = \mu W$$
$$= 0.4 \times 400$$

Frictional force $= 160$ N

$$\text{Torque} = \text{force} \times \text{radius}$$
$$= 160 \times 0.15 \quad (\text{since } 150 \text{ mm} = 0.15 \text{ m})$$
$$= 24 \text{ Nm}$$

**Example**

When all wheels are locked on a vehicle of weight 8 kN, a force of 5 kN is required to drag it along a level surface. Calculate the coefficient of friction between the tyres and the road.

$$\mu = \frac{F}{W}$$
$$= \frac{5}{8} = 0.625$$

**Lubrication**

It is believed that friction is caused by the interlocking action of the two surfaces and also by the attraction of one material to another. Placing two surfaces together causes the load to be supported by small 'crests'. If one surface is now slid over the other, the crests will attain a very high temperature and will tend to weld the two materials together. Further movement will break these welds, 'tear' the surface, and cause rapid wear. A reduction in the energy lost to friction and longer component life can be obtained if the surfaces can be separated; this is achieved by lubrication.

A lubricant introduced between the surfaces may be considered as a series of globular liquid particles which easily slide over each other. Provided there is no metal-to-metal contact, any friction which exists will be caused by the resistance of one particle to leave its neighbour – this resistance is called the *viscosity* of a lubricant.

The type of lubricant is governed by the conditions under which it operates.

**Properties of oil**

Two important properties of oil are oiliness and viscosity.

*Oiliness* A spot of oil applied to a clean piece of metal soon runs into the small crevices in the surface and this results in a 'clinging action' or attraction of an oil to the metal surface. This action is called oiliness and the property varies with oils, e.g. vegetable-based oils have excellent oiliness qualities. A method which relies on the oiliness to provide an oil film is termed *boundary lubrication* (Figure 8.7.7).

*Viscosity* Oil particles tend to cling to each other. This produces a resistance to flow which is called viscosity, and is tested by an instrument such as a Redwood

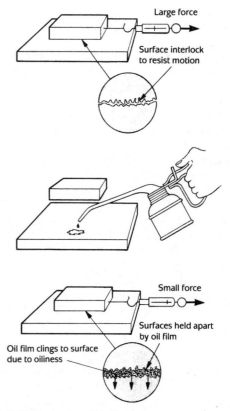

**Fig. 8.7.7** Boundary lubrication

**REMEMBER**

**Oil viscosity** is

● resistance to flow
● lowered when temperature is raised
● expressed by an SAE number e.g. SAE 20

viscometer, this measures the time in seconds for a given quantity of oil to flow through an orifice. Temperature affects the viscosity, so the test should be performed at specified temperatures.

The rating introduced by the American Society of Automotive Engineers (SAE) is universally adopted to classify oils according to their viscosities. This method is based on a test performed with a Saybolt viscometer at a temperature of 99°C (210°F). An engine oil having an SAE number of 50 has a higher viscosity or is thicker than a SAE 20 oil.

*Viscosity Index*  An oil gets thinner as the temperature increases, but this decrease in viscosity varies with different oils (Figure 8.7.8). To indicate the effect of temperature on the viscosity of an oil, an index based on the behaviour of two oils is used:

a)  Pennsylvanian oil – small viscosity variation – index 100;
b)  Gulf Coast oil – large viscosity variation – index 0.

By comparing other oils with these two it is possible to give each oil an index. Modern engine oils have a viscosity index of at least 80 and in some cases greater than 100.

*Multigrade Oils*  In the past the high viscosity oil used in an engine during the summer made engine cranking difficult in the winter, so different grades were specified for the two seasons. Nowadays special additives that reduce the change in an oil's viscosity with temperature are often used, and this has meant that the same grade can be used throughout the year. These oils are called multigrade, crossgrade or trade names which suggest that the viscosity remains constant.

An oil which has this small variation in viscosity is tested at two temperatures; the original SAE value of 210°F (99°C) and 0°F (−18°C). The letter W indicates that the rating is measured at the sub-zero temperature. Figure 8.7.9 shows how a multigrade oil is similar to SAE 20 at a low temperature and SAE 50 at a high temperature.

An oil having a viscosity of 10 000 Redwood seconds at −18°C and 70 Redwood seconds at 93°C would be classified as 10 W 40.

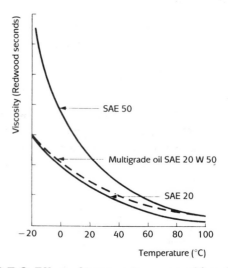

**Fig. 8.7.9** Effect of temperature on multigrade oil

*Transmission oils*  Gear oils are subjected to conditions different from that of the engine, so they are classified under a different specification.

Resistance to wear under severe loading and other necessary qualities of an oil are improved by using special *additives*.

**Grease**

Grease is used when it is difficult to retain a less viscous lubricant. The grease is usually manufactured by mixing a heavy oil to a substance called a base, which is selected

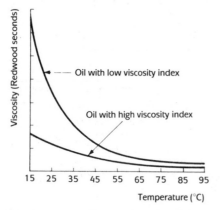

**Fig. 8.7.8** Change in viscosity with temperature

| SAE No. | Viscosity range (Redwood seconds at 200°F (93°C)) | |
|---|---|---|
| | Minimum | Maximum |
| 20 | 43 | 55 |
| 30 | 55 | 67 |
| 40 | 67 | 83 |
| 50 | 83 | 112 |

| **Multigrade Oil Classification** | | |
|---|---|---|
| SAE No. | Viscosity range (Redwood seconds at 0°F (−18°C)) | |
| | Minimum | Maximum |
| 5W | — | 3520 |
| 10W | 5250 | 10 560 |
| 20W | 10 560 | 42 000 |

**Table 8.7.2** Crankcase oil classification

to suit the operating conditions. The following bases are commonly used: limesoap for general work, bentone for hubs which are subjected to high temperature and lithium for resistance to corrosion.

Some grease bases do not mix, so it is advisable to follow the manufacturer's recommendations.

## 8.8 Friction clutches

The widespread use of a friction clutch to perform a number of tasks on a motor vehicle means that the basic principle of operation should be understood if accurate fault diagnosis is to be carried out.

One essential feature of a transmission clutch is that it should transmit the required torque without slipping. Whenever slip occurs, energy that would have been available for useful purposes will now be lost. An indication of the extent of this energy loss is shown up by the amount of heat generated at the clutch.

**Torque transmitted by a plate type clutch**
Figure 8.8.1 shows a pad which is pressed against a disc by a force $p$ newtons. When a spring balance is used to drag the pad across the disc, it is found that the reading increases up to the point where the pad slides. This occurs when:

$$\text{frictional force } F = \mu p$$

The frictional force $F$ may be considered as the force which acts at the centre of the block. This force is at

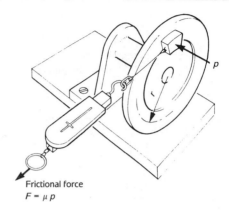

Frictional force
$F = \mu p$

**Fig. 8.8.1** Brake pad and disc

a radius of $r$, so the torque required to give slip is given by:

$$\text{torque} = \text{force} \times \text{radius}$$
$$T = F \times r$$
$$T = \mu p \times r$$
$$T = \mu p r$$

Replacing the pad with an annular ring (Figure 8.8.2) having the same width as the pad will not alter the torque, because friction is independent of the area in contact.

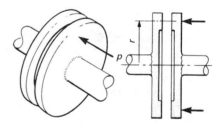

**Fig. 8.8.2** Brake discs

Sandwiching a friction disc between two driving surfaces (Figure 8.8.3) will double the torque required to produce slip, since this arrangement utilises the friction on both sides of the disc.

## REMEMBER

**Torque transmitted** by a plate-type clutch depends on

- number of contacts
- total spring thrust
- coefficient of friction
- mean radius

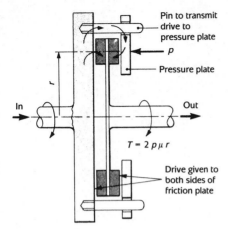

**Fig. 8.8.3** Fraction disc drive

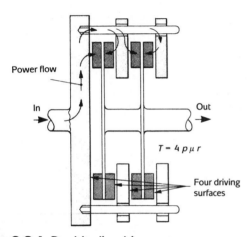

**Fig. 8.8.4** Double disc drive

If the construction shown as Figure 8.8.4 was used, the torque that could be transmitted before slip developed would be four times the original value. To summarise:

torque transmitted = $\mu pr$ × number of contacts

Symbols make this relationship easier to remember:

$$T = S p \mu r$$

where
$T$ = torque transmitted (Nm)
$S$ = number of contacts
$p$ = total spring thrust (N)
$\mu$ = coefficient of friction
$r$ = mean radius (m)

**Example**

Calculate the torque transmitted by a single plate clutch having a mean radius of 100 mm, total spring thrust of 1500 N and coefficient of friction of 0.3.

$$T = Sp\mu r$$
$$T = 2 \times 1500 \times 0.3 \times 0.1$$

(Note that a single plate clutch has two driving surfaces.)

$$T = 90 \text{ Nm}$$

## 8.9 Centrifugal force and balancing

### Centrifugal force

*Newton's first law of motion* states that a body remains in a state of rest or of uniform motion in a straight line unless it is acted on by some external resultant force. This statement shows that the natural path taken by a moving object is a straight line. To make the object depart from this path, a force must be applied. Let us consider the practical effects of this force.

Figure 8.9.1 shows a steel ball in position A moving at $v_1$ m/s. To change the direction of motion, a force is applied to the ball and this gives a movement as shown in position B.

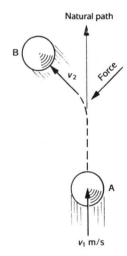

**Fig. 8.9.1** Ball in motion affected by force

If the ball is attached to a cord and rotated about a point (Figure 8.9.2), then the direction of motion will change continually. The diagram shows the motion of the ball at positions A and B, and from this it will be seen that an inward acting force must be applied by the cord if the ball is to move in a circular path. A force that acts towards the centre of rotation is called *centripetal force*.

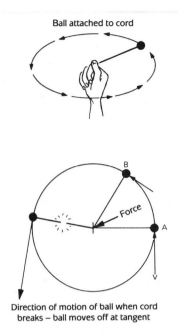

Ball attached to cord

Direction of motion of ball when cord breaks – ball moves off at tangent

**Fig. 8.9.2** Illustration of centrifugal force

*Newton's third law of motion states that to every acting force there is always an equal and opposite reactive force.*

When this law is applied to an object moving in a circular path, the reactive force is caused by the inertia of the body and acts in an outward direction. The force is called *centrifugal force* and exists whenever a centripetal force causes an object to move in a circular path.

Breakage of the cord in Figure 8.9.2 will cause the ball to fly off at a tangent to the circle: it moves off on its natural path, a straight line, because centripetal force is absent.

When the relationship between centripetal and centrifugal force is appreciated, the reader will discover many cases where the term 'centrifugal' is used loosely to describe the outward movement of a rotating item, e.g. governors, ignition timing controls, fluid couplings, etc. Centrifugal force is given by the formula:

$$F_c = \frac{mv^2}{r}$$

where    $F_c$ = centrifugal force (N)
   $m$ = mass (kg)
   $v$ = linear velocity (m/s)
   $r$ = radius (m)

### Balancing

Many motor vehicle components rotate at high speed, so severe vibration occurs if any unbalance exists. Some

**REMEMBER**

**Centrifugal force** is

● the outward force created when an object moves in a circular path
● the cause of vibration when a rotating component is out-of-balance

components, such as road wheels, are balanced by a mechanic, but many others are only balanced during manufacture. In the latter case, the mechanic should ensure that any part removed from a component is refitted in its original position.

Correction of out-of-balance components is achieved by either removing material from the heavy part or by adding material on the opposite side to the heavy spot, so as to give a counterbalance action (Figure 8.9.3).

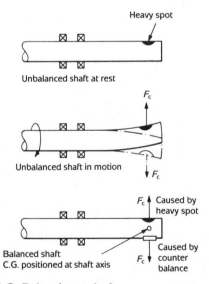

Heavy spot

Unbalanced shaft at rest

$F_c$

Unbalanced shaft in motion    $F_c$

$F_c$ Caused by heavy spot

Balanced shaft
C.G. positioned at shaft axis    $F_c$ Caused by counter balance

**Fig. 8.9.3** Balancing a shaft

*Static balance* When the force given by the counterbalance does not act in the same plane, another form of vibration occurs. In Figure 8.9.4 the wheel has good *static balance* but when it is rotated, the heavier parts exert a centrifugal force which produces an unbalanced couple.

To correct this, material must be added to produce an equal and opposite couple. Incorrect dynamic balance is particularly important in respect to road wheels, since

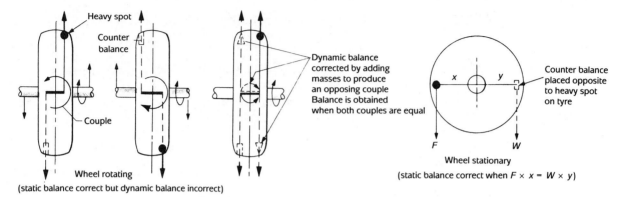

**Fig. 8.9.4** A balanced road wheel

the steering layout will allow the wheel to vibrate about the swivel axis or king pin at a frequency equal to the speed of wheel rotation. As stated previously, the force causing this disturbance greatly increases with speed, so at high vehicle speeds a severe 'flapping' of the road wheel (wheel shimmy) and oscillation of the steering wheel is experienced.

***Dynamic balance***   This also applies to crankshafts. The crankshaft shown in Figure 8.9.5(a) is not used because the couples are unbalanced – both tend to cause the engine to move in the direction shown. Rearranging the crank pins to the form indicated in Figure 8.9.5(b) improves the engine balance, and this is the arrangement used in a 4-cylinder in-line engine. This type of shaft can be improved still further by incorporating counter-balance masses as in Figure 8.9.5(c). These masses produce opposing couples which relieve both the stress acting on the shaft and the load taken by the centre main bearing.

**Stability**

Occasions sometimes arise where a vehicle is jacked up and the risk of overturning is present. An object overturns or falls over when the vertical line through the object's centre of gravity falls outside its base.

Figure 8.9.6 shows a loaded vehicle with a high centre of gravity. In the position shown the vehicle is on the verge of overturning so any action such as jacking-up the right-hand side will have an obvious result.

A p.s.v., such as the double-decker bus shown as Figure 8.9.7, must pass a stability or tilt test to ensure that the vehicle with the upper deck laden does not overturn when it is tilted to a specified angle.

---

**SAFE PRACTICE**

**A vehicle will overturn** when

a vertical line through the centre of gravity falls outside the roadwheels

---

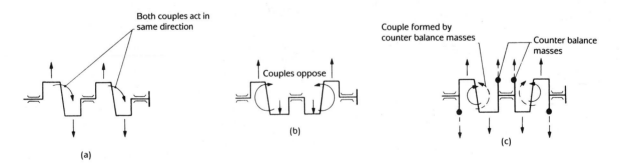

**Fig. 8.9.5** Crankshaft balance

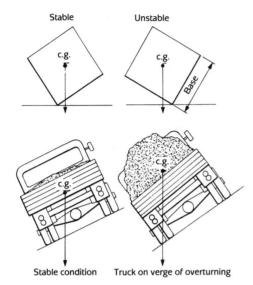

Stable    Unstable

Stable condition    Truck on verge of overturning

**Fig. 8.9.6** Vehicle stability

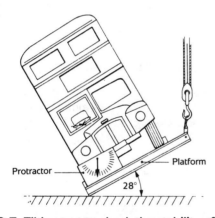

Protractor    Platform
28°

**Fig. 8.9.7** Tilting test to check the stability of a bus

## 8.10 Machines

A machine is a device for transmitting energy – in most cases it enables a large force to be given at the 'output' end of the machine when only a small force is applied at the 'input'. Some machines are extremely simple; and examples of these are the humble spanner, the hammer and various kinds of levers. Some are exceedingly complex, like some of the automatic machine tools used for making motor vehicle components. We consider here the basic principles of some of the simple types of machine. (Figure 8.10.1).

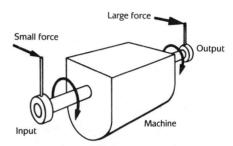

**Fig. 8.10.1** Multiplication of torque obtained from a machine

### The lever

The lever is essentially a bar, either straight or cranked (bent) which is pivoted at some point called the *fulcrum*. An *effort* applied at some point on the lever overcomes a *load* at some point on the lever. There are three basic types or orders of lever and Figure 8.10.2 shows these.

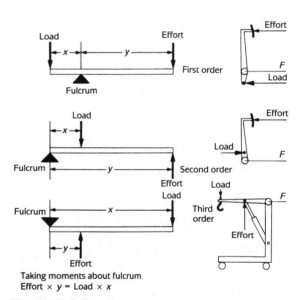

Taking moments about fulcrum
Effort × y = Load × x

**Fig. 8.10.2** The lever

Referring to Figure 8.10.2 this shows that:

$$\text{Load} \times x = \text{Effort} \times y$$

$$\therefore \quad \frac{\text{Load}}{\text{Effort}} = \frac{y}{x}$$

The ratio $\dfrac{\text{Load}}{\text{Effort}}$ is called the *force ratio* or *mechanical advantage*. To obtain a large force ratio with a lever, the distance '*y*' must be much longer than the distance '*x*'. At first it appears that we are getting 'something for nothing' but this idea is modified when we consider the movement of the effort in respect to the movement of the load. This relationship is called the *movement ratio* or *velocity ratio*. To summarise:

$$\textbf{\textit{Force ratio}} = \frac{\textbf{\textit{load}}}{\textbf{\textit{effort}}}$$

$$\textbf{\textit{Movement ratio}} = \frac{\textbf{\textit{movement of effort}}}{\textbf{\textit{movement of load}}}$$

If friction was not present in the machine then:

$$\text{Force ratio} = \text{movement ratio}$$

## Example

Figure 8.10.3 shows a lever which is acting as a brake pedal. Neglecting friction calculate: (a) the effort required to produce a force of 1.2 kN on the brake rod; (b) the movement of the rod when the pedal pad moves 84 mm.

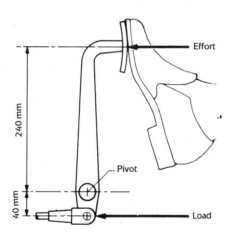

**Fig. 8.10.3** Brake pedal lever

(a) Taking moments about the pivot:

$$\text{effort} \times 240 = 1.2 \times 40$$

$$\therefore \text{effort} = \frac{1.2 \times 40}{240} = 0.2 \text{ kN}$$

The ratio $\dfrac{\text{distance between effort and fulcrum}}{\text{distance between load and fulcrum}}$ is sometimes called the leverage. Effort × leverage = load.

(b) Distance $z$ is proportional to the distance from the pivot (Figure 8.10.4).

Effort applied at point 240 mm from pivot
Load applied at point   40 mm from pivot

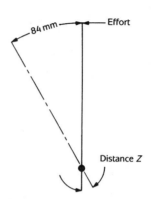

**Fig. 8.10.4** Lever example

$$\text{Movement ratio} = 6$$

$$= \frac{\text{movement of effort}}{\text{movement of load}}$$

$$6 = \frac{84}{\text{movement of load}}$$

$$\therefore \text{ movement of load} = \frac{84}{6} = 14 \text{ mm}$$

In this example it will be seen that:

$$\begin{aligned} \text{work input} \ &= \text{force} \times \text{distance moved} \\ &= 16.8 \text{ kN mm} = 16.8 \text{ Nm} \\ \text{work output} &= 1.2 \times 14 \\ &= 16.8 \text{ kN mm} = 16.8 \text{ Nm} \end{aligned}$$

If friction is neglected:

$$\text{work input} = \text{work output}$$

This is an assumption which is never justified in practice since friction always opposes movement.

## Efficiency

The effect of friction means that some of the work put into a machine is converted into heat and lost. So:

**Work output is always less than the work input**

To indicate the extent of these internal friction losses the term efficiency is used. This can be applied to give the expressions:

$$\textbf{\textit{efficiency}} = \frac{\textbf{\textit{work output}}}{\textbf{\textit{work input}}}$$

or

$$\text{efficiency} = \frac{\text{load} \times \text{movement of load}}{\text{effort} \times \text{movement of effort}}$$

$$= \frac{\text{load}}{\text{effort}} \div \frac{\text{movement of effort}}{\text{movement of load}}$$

$$= \frac{\dfrac{\text{load}}{\text{effort}}}{\dfrac{\text{movement of effort}}{\text{movement of load}}}$$

Expressed in this way, efficiency will have a value less than one. To express efficiency as a percentage, multiply above values by 100.

## REMEMBER

### Machines

- input force is called the effort
- output force is called the load

$$\text{movement ratio} = \frac{\text{distance moved by effort}}{\text{distance moved by load}}$$

$$\text{force ratio} = \frac{\text{load}}{\text{effort}}$$

$$\text{efficiency} = \frac{\text{force ratio}}{\text{movement ratio}}$$

### The screw jack

A lifting jack is normally a part of a vehicle's tool kit and Figure 8.10.5 shows one type; a screw jack. Effort applied by a spanner rotates the screw in the nut. Attached to the nut is an arm which engages in a socket welded to the frame of the car. Besides providing the lifting action, the arm prevents rotation of the nut. During a single revolution of the screw the nut will be moved a distance equal to the *lead* of the screw. With a single start thread the lead is equal to the *pitch*.

In one revolution of the screw, effort moves $2\pi r$, since:

$$\text{Movement ratio} = \frac{\text{movement of effort}}{\text{movement of load}}$$

$$= \frac{2\pi r}{\text{lead of screw}}$$

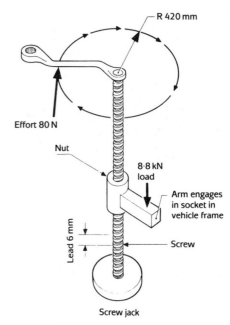

**Fig. 8.10.5** Lifting jack

### Example

The screw of a lifting jack has a lead of 6 mm and an effort of 80 N applied at a radius of 420 mm is just sufficient to move a load of 8.8 kN. Calculate the efficiency of the jack.

Force ratio $= \dfrac{\text{load}}{\text{effort}} = \dfrac{8800}{80} = 110$

Movement ratio $= \dfrac{2\pi r}{\text{lead}} = \dfrac{2 \times 22 \times 420}{7 \times 6} = 440$

efficiency $= \dfrac{\text{force ratio}}{\text{movement ratio}} = \dfrac{110}{440} = 0.25$ or 25%

This low value means that 75% of the work input is used to overcome friction in the machine. When the efficiency is less than 50% the machine is irreversible and the load is self-sustaining, i.e. the load on the nut will not rotate the screw.

### Gearing

Torque could be transmitted by pressing two smooth wheels together, but friction between the wheels would be insufficient to prevent slip when a high driving torque is applied. To obtain a positive drive, teeth are cut on the surface of the wheels to form gears. The teeth are formed above and below the curved surface of the smooth wheels so that the gears would have the same movement ratio as the wheels. The diameter of the wheel, which is

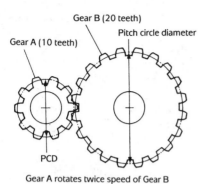

Gear A (10 teeth)
Gear B (20 teeth)
Pitch circle diameter
PCD
Gear A rotates twice speed of Gear B

**Fig. 8.10.6** Demonstration of gearing

equivalent to the diameter of the gear on this basis, is called the *pitch circle diameter* (p.c.d.).

The comparative diameters of two meshing gears governs the relative speeds, e.g. if the p.c.d. of gear B in Figure 8.10.6 is double that of gear A then the smaller gear will rotate twice as fast as gear B. This speed relationship is similar to movement ratio – it indicates the movement of the input relative to the output and is generally called the *gear ratio*.

$$\text{Gear ratio} = \frac{\text{revolutions of driver}}{\text{revolutions of driven}}$$

$$= \frac{\text{p.c.d. of driven}}{\text{p.c.d. of driver}}$$

$$= \frac{\text{number of teeth on driven}}{\text{number of teeth on driver}} \quad \text{or} \quad \frac{\text{driven}}{\text{driver}}$$

**Example**

A pinion with 26 teeth drives a gear wheel having 78 teeth. Calculate the speed of the output shaft when the input turns at 2700 rev/min.

$$\text{Gear ratio} = \frac{\text{driven}}{\text{driver}}$$

$$= \frac{78}{26} = 3$$

The ratio is stated as '3 to 1', meaning that three turns of the input are required to rotate the output shaft once. Hence:

$$\text{speed of output} = \frac{\text{speed of input}}{\text{gear ratio}}$$

$$= \frac{2700}{3} = 900 \text{ rev/min.}$$

**Example**

An output shaft of a gearbox consisting of a pair of gears turns 12 revolutions for every 9 revolutions made by the input shaft. If the p.c.d. of the driven gear is 75 mm calculate the p.c.d. of the other gear.

$$\text{Ratio} = \frac{\text{revolutions of driver}}{\text{revolutions of driven}} = \frac{9}{12} = 0.75:1$$

To drive the output faster the driving gear must be larger

$$\text{Ratio} = \frac{\text{p.c.d. of driven}}{\text{p.c.d. of driver}}$$

$$\text{p.c.d. of driver} = \frac{\text{p.c.d. of driven}}{\text{ratio}} = \frac{75}{0.75} = 100 \text{ mm}$$

A gear layout which causes the output shaft to rotate slower than the input would be called a *reduction gear*. Similarly an increase of speed is termed an *overdrive*.

**Torque ratio**

As applied to gearing the expression 'force ratio' is referred to as the *torque ratio*.

$$\text{Torque ratio} = \frac{\text{torque on output shaft}}{\text{torque on input shaft}}$$

When the efficiency is 100%, the:

*torque ratio = speed ratio = gear ratio*

**Example**

A gearbox provides a reduction of 4:1. What torque acts on the output shaft when the input torque is 70 Nm? (Neglect frictional losses).

Gear ratio = torque ratio = 4:1

Since the speed is decreased, the torque is increased.
∴ Torque on output shaft = input torque × ratio
= 70 × 4
= 280 Nm

**Gearing efficiency**

When the machine has an efficiency of 100% the power does not change. Examples show that the increase in torque is achieved by a sacrifice in speed, i.e.

*input speed × input torque = output speed × output torque when efficiency is 100%*

Previous problems on gearing have been based on the assumption that the gearbox is an ideal machine, i.e. a machine in which friction is not present. Such an arrangement does not exist in practice so we must accept that the work output is always less than the work input.

As in the case of the screw jack and lever, friction does not alter the movement ratio, it only affects the force ratio or torque ratio.

### Example

A gearbox providing a ratio of 8:1 has an efficiency of 80% when a torque of 200 Nm is applied to an input shaft rotating at 4000 rev/min. Calculate the output shaft (a) speed; (b) torque.

(a)
$$\text{Speed of output} = \frac{\text{Input speed}}{\text{ratio}}$$
$$= \frac{4000}{8} = 500 \text{ rev/min}$$

(b) When efficiency is 100%:

output shaft torque = input torque × ratio
$$= 200 \times 8$$
$$= 1600 \text{ Nm}$$

When efficiency is 80%, output torque is less:

$$\text{output shaft torque} = 1600 \times \frac{80}{100}$$
$$= 1600 \times 0.8 = 1280 \text{ Nm}$$

---

## REMEMBER

### Gearing

$$\text{gear ratio} = \frac{\text{driven}}{\text{driver}}$$

$$\text{movement ratio} = \text{gear ratio} = \text{speed ratio}$$

$$\text{force ratio} = \text{torque ratio} = \frac{\text{output torque}}{\text{input torque}}$$

$$\text{efficiency} = \frac{\text{torque ratio}}{\text{gear ratio}}$$

---

### Example

Figure 8.10.7 shows the layout of a gearbox. Calculate: (a) the gear ratio; (b) the output torque if the efficiency is 75%.

(a)
$$\text{Gear ratio} = \frac{\text{driven}}{\text{driver}} \times \frac{\text{driven}}{\text{driver}}$$
$$= \frac{60}{30} \times \frac{70}{20}$$
$$= 7:1$$

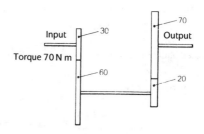

**Fig. 8.10.7** Example of gearing

(b)
$$\text{Efficiency} = \frac{\text{torque ratio}}{\text{gear ratio}}$$

torque ratio = efficiency × gear ratio
$$= 0.75 \times 7 = 5.25$$

since
$$\text{torque ratio} = \frac{\text{output torque}}{\text{input torque}}$$

then
output torque = torque ratio × input torque
$$= 5.25 \times 70 = 367.5 \text{ Nm}$$

Part (b) could also be solved by:

Output torque (when efficiency is 100%)
$$= \text{input torque} \times \text{gear ratio}$$
$$= 70 \times 7$$
$$= 490 \text{ Nm}$$

Output torque (when efficiency is 75%)
$$= 490 \times 0.75 = 367.5 \text{ Nm}$$

### Example

At an engine speed of 2025 rev/min, a torque of 96 Nm is supplied to the gearbox. If the gearbox and final drive ratios are 2:5 and 4:5, respectively, calculate: (a) the overall gear ratio; (b) the torque supplied by the differential to each road wheel (frictional losses may be neglected); (c) the speed of the road wheel.

(a) Overall gear ratio is the *product* of gearbox ratio and final drive ratio:

$$\text{Overall gear ratio} = 2.5 \times 4.5$$
$$= 11.25$$

(b) Since efficiency is 100% then:

$$\text{torque ratio} = \text{gear ratio}$$

so total torque output from differential
$$= \text{input torque} \times \text{torque ratio}$$
$$= 96 \times 11.25$$

The differential divides the torques equally between each driving wheel irrespective of speed, therefore:

$$\text{torque applied to each wheel} = \frac{1080}{2} = 540 \text{ N}$$

(c) $\quad$ Speed of road wheel $= \dfrac{\text{engine speed}}{\text{combined gear ratio}}$

$$= \frac{2025}{11.25} = 180 \text{ rev/min}$$

### Planetary (epicyclic) gearing

A small gear rolling on the circumference of another gear is the meaning of the term epicyclic. This type of gearing is commonly used in automatic gear boxes; the gear selection is obtained by applying a band brake or by locking a multi-disc clutch. Connecting the input shaft to different gear elements by clutches enables a number of different ratios to be obtained from one epicyclic gear train. When the advantages of this compact layout is linked with the ease and speed that the gear change can be effected, then the reasons for the use of this type of gearing will be apparent.

Figure 8.10.8 shows the main components of a simple gear train; the layout shown is that used when a large speed reduction is required.

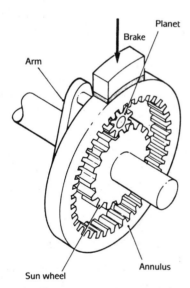

**Fig. 8.10.8** Simple epicyclic gear train

*Gear ratio* $\quad$ The gear ratio of a train arranged as a Figure 8.10.9 can be calculated from the formula:

$$\text{Ratio} = \frac{A + S}{S}$$

$$= \frac{80 + 20}{20} = \frac{100}{20} = 5{:}1$$

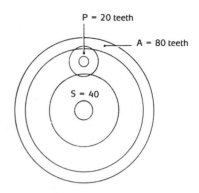

**Fig. 8.10.9** Gear ratio example

where $A$ = teeth on annulus, $S$ = teeth on sun.

Rearranging the layout by connecting the input shaft to the annulus and applying a brake to the sun, gives the ratio: $(A + S)/A$.

Using the same gear sizes as in Figure 8.10.9 will give a ratio of

$$\frac{80 + 40}{80} = 1.5{:}1$$

Figure 8.10.10 shows the variation which may be obtained by connecting up an epicyclic gear train in different ways.

## REMEMBER

**Planetary gear ratio**

$$\text{ratio} = \frac{A + S}{S}$$

when sun (S) is driving and annulus (A) is held

### Belt drives

The belt is still the most common method used for driving external engine auxiliaries such as the alternator, water pump, fan, pump for power steering, etc. During the past few years the introduction of the toothed belt has extended the application to include drives to camshafts and other components which demand non-slip features.

The vee belt relies on its wedging action (Figures 8.10.11) to provide the grip. This allows the torque applied by the driving pulley to produce a tensile force in

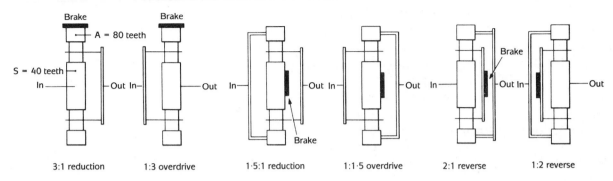

**Fig. 8.10.10** Epicyclic gear train

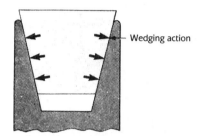

**Fig. 8.10.11** 'V' belt drive

the belt which in turn applies a torque to the driven pulley. Belt and chain drives are examples where rotary motion is converted into linear motion.

### Hydraulic machines

A vehicle braking system and various items of garage equipment use the principle of a hydraulic machine. Low friction losses make the system very efficient and when this is coupled with advantages gained by using flexible pipes instead of rigid linkages, then the appeal of hydraulic equipment can be appreciated.

Figure 8.10.12 shows the layout of a simple hydraulic lift. A small plunger pump displaces fluid to a large ram cylinder which in this case operates a vehicle lift. As with any machine, to obtain a large force ratio the movement of the effort is much greater than the movement of the load.

Liquid is incompressible, so operation of the plunger will move the liquid from the small cylinder to the ram cylinder. Since the load is acting against the ram piston, the liquid has a tendency to compress: the force acting on a fluid in this manner is called *pressure*. The area on which the force acts governs the pressure, so the definition used is:

*Pressure is the force acting on a unit of area*

The force is expressed in newtons, the area in square metres, so:

*Pressure is measured in N/m$^2$*

Other units of pressure will be experienced by the reader:

pascal (symbol Pa) is equal to 1 N/m$^2$
bar (symbol bar) is equal to 100 000 N/m$^2$ ($10^5$ N/m$^2$).

The Imperial system used 'pounds per square inch' as the unit of pressure: 1 lbf/in$^2 \simeq 7$ kN/m$^2$. To avoid confusion we shall use the basic derived unit; the newton per square metre.

Now returning to Fig. 8.10.12 consider the plunger produces a pressure in the operating cylinder of 700 kN/m$^2$ (7 bar). When friction is neglected, this pressure will act throughout the system so if the ram has an area of:

0.5 m$^2$ the thrust on the ram is 350 kN
1.0 m$^2$ the thrust on the ram is 700 kN.

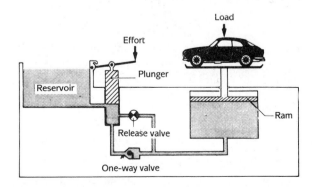

**Fig. 8.10.12** Hydraulic machine

From this we may conclude that a large force ratio is obtained when the area of the ram is much greater than the area of the plunger. Hence:

$$Force\ ratio = \frac{area\ of\ ram}{area\ of\ plunger}$$

### Example

A hydraulic press has a ram area which is 1000 times greater than the plunger area. Neglecting friction, what force will act on the ram when a force of 800 N is applied to the plunger?

$$
\begin{aligned}
Force\ applied\ at\ ram &= 800 \times 1000\ N \\
&= 800\,000 \\
&= 800\ kN
\end{aligned}
$$

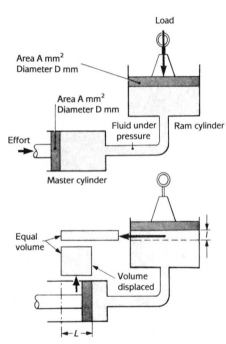

**Fig. 8.10.13** Simple hydraulic machines

Figure 8.10.13 shows the layout and principle of a simple hydraulic machine. The fluid displaced (pumped) from the master cylinder is used to move the ram, so if the latter has a larger diameter, its movement will be less. Therefore:

$$Movement\ ratio = \frac{movement\ of\ effort}{movement\ of\ load} = \frac{L}{l}$$

Since fluid displaced by master cylinder = fluid received by ram cylinder then area of master cylinder plunger ×

stroke = area of ram cylinder piston × ram stroke, or:

$$a \times L = A \times l$$

and

$$\frac{L}{l} = \frac{A}{a}$$

so

$$
\begin{aligned}
Movement\ ratio &= \frac{L}{l} \\
&= \frac{A}{a} \\
&= \frac{\pi D^2 / 4}{\pi d^2 / 4} = \frac{D^2}{d^2} \\
\end{aligned}
$$

$$Force\ ratio = \frac{load}{effort}$$

When efficiency is 100% force ratio = movement ratio. So:

$$force\ ratio = \frac{area\ of\ ram}{area\ of\ plunger}$$

when friction is neglected.

### REMEMBER

**Hydraulic pressure** is

- the force acting on area of 1 m$^2$
- measured in N/m$^2$, bar or pascal
- calculated from:

$$pressure = \frac{force}{area}$$

### Hydraulic braking system

The motor vehicle uses many hydraulic machines; these include systems for operating, or assisting in the operation of, the brakes, steering, automatic gearboxes, suspension and many power take-off auxiliaries.

Hydraulic operation is particularly suited for braking systems. Low friction losses in the system combined with the ease in which a hydraulic supply can be applied to the brake cylinders are major advantages. Furthermore, the fact that pressure cannot be applied to any brake until all clearances have been taken-up simplifies the task of brake adjusting and ensures that each brake starts to apply at the same time. Also, when the brakes do act, the pressure received by each one is the same, i.e. the self-compensating feature ensures that each brake receives its share of the applied effort. This feature can also cause problems; any leakage in the system will prevent any of

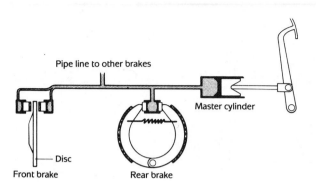

**Fig. 8.10.14** Hydraulic braking system

the brakes from functioning, so to avoid this, a tandem cylinder or dual layout is used.

A hydraulic machine will not function efficiently if air is present in the system. Air, unlike liquids, is compressible so the effect, as applied to a braking system, is similar to that produced when a spring is placed between the driver's foot and the brake pedal.

Figure 8.10.14 shows the layout of a simple braking system. Force applied by the piston in the master cylinder is transmitted through the brake lines to the wheel cylinders. Pressure is the same thoughout the system so the brakes will start to apply on each wheel at about the same time, even if the movement of one wheel cylinder is greater than the others.

Leakage due to fracture of a pipe will prevent the build-up of pressure and this will result in failure of all brakes unless special provision is made.

The action of a brake system may be considered by referring to Figure 8.10.15.

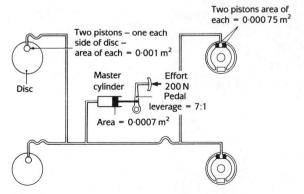

**Fig. 8.10.15** Layout of hydraulic brake system

### Example

When friction is neglected:

Pedal effort = 200 N

Force applied to master cylinder

$$= 200 \times \text{leverage}$$
$$= 200 \times 7$$
$$= 1400 \text{ N}$$

Area of master cylinder plunger:

$$= 700 \text{ mm}^2$$
$$= 0.000\,7 \text{ m}^2$$

(since there are $1000 \times 1000 \text{ mm}^2 = 1 \text{ m}^2$). Pressure in system:

$$= \frac{\text{force (N)}}{\text{area (m}^2)}$$
$$= \frac{1400}{0.0007} = \frac{14\,000\,000}{7} \text{ N/m}^2$$
$$= 2\,000\,000 \text{ N/m}^2$$

or 20 bar (since 1 bar = $100\,000 \text{ N/m}^2$ OR $10^5 \text{ N/m}^2$).

This pressure is transmitted throughout the system. The thrust on each wheel cylinder piston is given by:

$$\text{thrust} = \text{pressure} \times \text{area}$$

Each front brake piston has an area of $0.001 \text{ m}^2$. Therefore:

$$\text{thrust} = 2\,000\,000 \times 0.001$$
$$= 2000 \text{ N}$$

$$\text{Total 'load' at front brakes} = 4 \times 2000$$
$$= 8000 \text{ N}$$

Each rear brake piston has an area of $0.000\,75\,\text{m}^2$. Therefore:

$$\text{thrust} = 2\,000\,000 \times 0.000\,75$$
$$= 1500 \text{ N}$$

$$\text{Total 'load' at rear brakes} = 4 \times 750$$
$$= 6000 \text{ N}$$

This example shows how an effort of 200 N can produce a 'load' of 14 000 N. By making the front wheel cylinders larger than the rear, a greater braking action can be obtained from the front wheels.

## 8.11 Velocity, acceleration and braking efficiency

### Velocity

The velocity of a body is the rate in m/s at which it moves in a given direction

$$Velocity = \frac{distance\ covered\ (metres)}{time\ (seconds)}$$

or

$$v = \frac{s}{t}$$

The expression 'distance covered/time' is also used for determining the *speed* of a body; the difference between the terms speed and velocity is that speed does not consider the direction of motion.

### Acceleration

Acceleration is the rate of increase in velocity and is expressed in metres per second per second (m/s$^2$). The velocity/time graph shown in Figure 8.11.1 represents a vehicle accelerating from rest at a constant rate of 2 m/s$^2$. It shows that after each second of time the velocity increases by the amount $a$ which in this case is 2 m/s. ·

Over a period of 3 seconds the increase in velocity is 6 m/s, or:

$$\begin{aligned}
acceleration &= 6\ m/s\ per\ 3\ s \\
&= 6\ m/s/3\ s \\
&= 2\ m/s/s = 2\ m/s^2
\end{aligned}$$

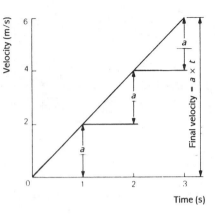

**Fig. 8.11.1** Velocity/time graph

From the graph it will be seen that:

$$final\ velocity = acceleration \times time$$
$$v = a\,t$$

where  $v$ is in m/s
  $a$ is in m/s$^2$
  $t$ is in s

The force of gravity causes an object to accelerate at a constant rate which has a value that varies slightly in different parts of the world. It has been agreed internationally that the average value should be 9.806 65 m/s$^2$.

Braking force and efficiency are measured by using a roller-type tester recessed in the workshop floor. Resisting torque given by the vehicle brakes opposes the rotation of the power-driven rollers. An in-cab control and display unit allows the complete test to be conducted from the driver's seat.

*Crypton*

For general work this is approximated to either 9.81 m/s$^2$ or 10 m/s$^2$ – the value used depends on the accuracy required.

When a motor vehicle is slowed down, the velocity decreases. This negative acceleration is called *deceleration*: the instrument used to measure this rate of retardation is called a *decelerometer*.

## Braking efficiency

Gravitational acceleration of $g$ can be used as the standard for brake efficiency. If a vehicle on a level road was decelerated by the brakes at the rate of 9.81 m/s$^2$, the braking efficiency is said to be 100%.

> ***100% brake efficiency = deceleration at the rate of*** g

To produce an efficiency of 100%, the brakes must give, at the road surface, a retarding force equal to the total weight of the vehicle; this would require a coefficient of friction between the tyre and road of 1.0 (Figure 8.11.2). This friction value is far above the average; an efficiency higher than 90% is seldom achieved.

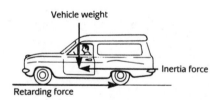

**Fig. 8.11.2** Brake efficiency is 100% when retarding force = total vehicle weight

> ***100% brake efficiency is obtained when the brakes apply a retarding force equal to the total weight of the vehicle including its load***

Statutory regulations specify the minimum efficiency for each type of vehicle, e.g. a four-wheeled car: foot brake 50%, hand brake 25%.

Figure 8.11.3 shows that a deceleration of the vehicle causes an inertia force which is equal to the retarding force. The combined effect of these forces causes a weight transference from the rear to the front and for this reason the front brakes have a larger braking capacity.

The force of impact during a collision (Figure 8.11.4) can cause a deceleration in excess of 30$g$. Subjecting a driver to high decelerations of this order produces a force

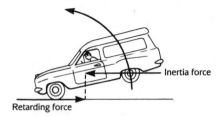

**Fig. 8.11.3** Couple produced by the two forces gives an overturning action

**Fig. 8.11.4** Force of impact can cause a deceleration in excess of 30$g$

on his body greater than thirty times his weight. Special chassis constructions, which are designed to give a concertina effect on impact, are intended to decrease the deceleration felt by the vehicle's occupants and so reduce the risk of injury.

## Kinetic energy

A braking system converts kinetic energy (the energy of motion) to heat energy. The rate at which this energy is converted governs the distance required to bring the vehicle to rest. Kinetic energy can be calculated from:

$$KE = \tfrac{1}{2} mv^2$$

where    $KE$ = energy (J)
   $m$ = mass (kg)
   $v$ = velocity (m/s)

When a vehicle is moving at a given velocity then:

kinetic energy = work stored

= retarding force

× stopping distance

$$\therefore \text{ stopping distance} = \frac{\text{kinetic energy}}{\text{retarding force}} = \frac{\tfrac{1}{2} mv^2}{F}$$

This expression enables the following conclusions to be formed:

1) The stopping distance is governed by the ratio of the retarding force to the vehicle mass (Figure 8.11.5).
2) The stopping distance varies as the square of the velocity, e.g. the distance required to stop a vehicle travelling at 90 km/h is nine times as great as that required for a speed of 30 km/h (Figure 8.11.6).

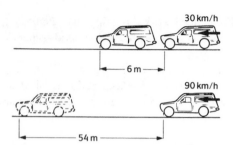

**Fig. 8.11.6** Stopping distance varies as the square of the velocity

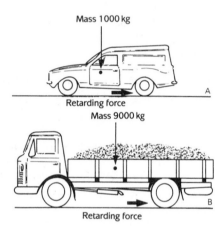

**Fig. 8.11.5** Stopping distance of vehicle B is similar to that of vehicle A because retarding force is proportional to mass

## REMEMBER

**Velocity is**

- distance covered in a given time
- expressed in *metres per second*

**Acceleration is**

- rate of change of velocity
- expressed in *metres/second/second*
- at rate of about 10 m/s$^2$ when a body falls freely due to gravity

**Brake efficiency is**

- 100% when retarding force is equal to the total weight of the vehicle
- 100% when the vehicle retardation is at the rate of '*g*' i.e. 10 m/s$^2$

# PROGRESS CHECK 8

1. The definition: 'that which changes a body's state of rest or of uniform motion in a straight line' applies to:
(a) force
(b) work
(c) energy
(d) power.

2. Which one of the following is a unit of force:
(a) newton
(b) kilogram
(c) joule
(d) newton metre.

3. The quantity of matter in a body is expressed in:
(a) newtons
(b) kilograms
(c) joules
(d) newton metres.

4. The rate of increase in velocity is called:
(a) speed
(b) acceleration
(c) movement
(d) mass.

5. What force is required to accelerate a mass of one kilogram at the rate of 1 metre per second per second?
(a) 1 kg
(b) 9.81 kg
(c) 1 N
(d) 9.81 N.

6. The force of the earth's gravity on a body is called its:
(a) mass
(b) acceleration
(c) weight
(d) energy.

7. Due to the earth's gravity, a body falling freely in a vacuum will accelerate at a rate of about:
(a) 1 m/s$^2$
(b) 9.8 m/s$^2$
(c) 32 m/s$^2$
(d) 32.2 m/s$^2$.

8. A jack supports a mass of 0.5 tonne. The force given by the jack is about:
(a) 500 kg
(b) 1000 kg
(c) 51 N
(d) 4.9 kN.

9. An object placed on a bench exerts a force of 98.1 N due to gravity. The mass of the object is:
(a) 10 N
(b) 94 N
(c) 10 kg
(d) 98.1 kg.

10. What is torque?
(a) force times distance moved
(b) acceleration due to gravity
(c) work applied to a body
(d) a turning moment.

11. A force of 100 N acts as a radius of 0.5 m. The torque is:
(a) 0.005 Nm
(b) 0.05 Nm
(c) 50 Nm
(d) 500 Nm.

12. A nut has to be tightened to a torque of 80 Nm. What force must be applied at a right angle to a spanner of length 0.25 m?
(a) 20 N
(b) 32 N
(c) 200 N
(d) 320 N.

13. The theoretical point at which the total mass of a body is considered to act is called the:
(a) weight
(b) action point
(c) gravity point
(d) centre of gravity.

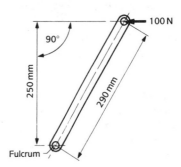

**Fig. PC 8.1**

14. Figure PC 8.1 shows a force being applied to a lever. The turning moment about the fulcrum is:
(a) 25 Nm
(b) 29 Nm
(c) 100 Nm
(d) 290 Nm.

15. A couple is formed by two forces of 25 N each which act at a distance of 120 mm. The magnitude of this couple is:
(a) 3 Nm
(b) 6 Nm
(c) 25 Nm
(d) 50 Nm.

16. The height of the centre of gravity affects the:
(a) angle of roll when cornering
(b) load on the front and rear wheels
(c) load on the front wheels when the vehicle is stationary
(d) extra load imposed on the rear wheels when braking.

17. Rearranging the load on a vehicle causes the centre of gravity to shift towards the rear axle. This alteration in position causes:
(a) the load on the rear axle to decrease
(b) the load on the front axle to increase
(c) an increase in the braking torque needed to lock the rear wheels
(d) a decrease in the braking torque needed to lock the rear wheels.

18. A rotating shaft is in a state of balance when the centre of gravity is situated on the:
(a) circumference
(b) axis of rotation
(c) heaviest side
(d) lightest side.

19. A wheel and tyre is stated to be 'out-of-balance'. This is normally corrected by:
(a) reducing the mass on the heavy side
(b) moving the centre of gravity towards the heavy side
(c) fitting a counterbalance mass diametrically opposite the heaviest point
(d) attaching a weight to the rim diametrically opposite the lightest point.

20. What is 'energy'?
(a) the capacity for doing work
(b) force times perpendicular distance
(c) the rate of doing work
(d) force times distance moved.

21. The SI unit of energy is the:
(a) newton
(b) joule
(c) watt
(d) ft lbf.

22. What is the technical meaning of the term 'work'?
(a) force times distance moved
(b) distance moved in a given time
(c) force times radius
(d) force obtained from energy.

23. The SI unit of work is the:
(a) joule
(b) watt
(c) kilogram
(d) ft lbf.

24. An engine converts energy. In which order does the energy change to complete the process between the time that fuel is supplied, and power is produced?
(a) heat energy, mechanical energy, chemical energy
(b) heat energy, chemical energy, mechanical energy
(c) chemical energy, mechanical energy, heat energy
(d) chemical energy, heat energy, mechanical energy.

25. How much work is done when a force of 200 N is required to lift an object a distance of 5 m?
(a) 1 kJ
(b) 40 Nm
(c) 40 J
(d) 1000 mN.

26. What is meant by the term 'power'?
(a) the rate of doing work
(b) the capacity for doing work
(c) force times perpendicular distance
(d) force times distance moved.

27. The SI unit of power is the:
(a) watt
(b) joule
(c) newton
(d) horsepower.

28. A force of 200 N acts over a distance of 5 m for a time of 4 s. This represents a power of:
(a) 10 W
(b) 250 W
(c) 1000 W
(d) 4000 W.

29. What is friction?
(a) a form of heat energy
(b) work stored in a body
(c) a force which opposes motion
(d) the change of state of a substance.

30. In which one of the following applications is friction regarded as a disadvantage?
(a) piston
(b) clutch
(c) brake
(d) fanbelt.

31. Assuming that the operating conditions are normal, which one of the following factors does **not** affect the frictional resistance?
(a) nature of the surfaces
(b) area of surfaces
(c) condition of surfaces
(d) force pressing surfaces together.

32. Which words are required to make the following statement correct: high friction is obtained when the surface is .... and ....?
(a) smooth .... dry
(b) smooth .... wet
(c) rough .... dry
(d) rough .... wet.

33. Why does friction cause wear? Because the:
(a) heat causes the surfaces to harden
(b) heat expels the air from the surfaces
(c) surfaces cannot obtain a supply of air
(d) surfaces interlock, heat, weld and tear.

34. How does a normal lubricant reduce friction? The lubricant:
(a) allows air to pass between the surfaces
(b) keeps the surfaces apart
(c) smooths the surface of the metal
(d) prevents the generation of heat.

35. During the lubrication process the oil particles move over each other. The resistance of one particle to leave adjacent particles of the lubricant is called:
(a) oiliness
(b) additive
(c) flow
(d) viscosity.

36. The expression 'static friction' means the:
(a) resistance to motion
(b) resistance to separate two surfaces
(c) force which resists motion when one surface is sliding over another at a constant speed
(d) force which opposes the initial movement of one surface relative to another.

37. If $F$ is the force needed to overcome friction and $W$ is the force pressing the surfaces together, then coefficient of friction is:
(a) $W - F$
(b) $W + F$
(c) $F \times W$
(d) $F/W$.

38. Coefficient of friction is normally represented by the symbol:
(a) $\pi$
(b) $\mu$
(c) $\eta$
(d) $\theta$.

39. A typical value for the coefficient of friction of a rubber tyre on a dry road surface is:
(a) 0.2
(b) 0.6
(c) 1.0
(d) 1.4.

40. What is the effect of increasing the friction area of a disc brake pad?
(a) the friction will be increased
(b) the coefficient of friction will be increased
(c) the rate of wear will decrease
(d) the pad will operate at a higher temperature.

41. Heating a friction brake lining to a temperature greater than 300°C causes the:
(a) lining to grab
(b) material to 'fade'
(c) coefficient of friction to increase
(d) material to weld to the metal surface.

42. A friction force of 24 N is required to slide one surface over another. If the force pressing the surfaces together is 75 N the coefficient of friction is:
(a) 0.18
(b) 0.3125
(c) 0.32
(d) 0.385.

43. Two surfaces having a coefficient of friction of 0.24 are pressed together with a force of 50 N. The frictional force is:
(a) 12 N
(b) 24 N
(c) 48 N
(d) 208 N.

44. A lubricant reduces friction by:
(a) absorbing the friction energy
(b) applying pressure in the direction of motion
(c) polishing the two surfaces
(d) holding the surface apart.

45. The property of a lubricant to 'cling to a metal surface' is called:
(a) oiliness
(b) friction
(c) viscosity
(d) stiction.

46. The expression 'boundary lubrication' is used to describe a condition where an oil film is maintained by the:
(a) viscosity property of the lubricant
(b) oiliness property of the lubricant
(c) pressure supplied by an oil pump
(d) force which pushes the two metal surfaces together.

47. The viscosity of an oil is indicated by the:
(a) SAE number
(b) viscosity index
(c) temperature change
(d) temperature index.

48. An oil having a high viscosity index is one in which the viscosity:
(a) increases as the temperature increases
(b) remains constant over a large temperature range
(c) varies relatively little with change in temperature
(d) alters a large amount if the temperature is changed.

49. An oil classed as 'multigrade' or 'crossgrade' is one which:
(a) gets thicker with increase in temperature
(b) maintains a constant viscosity when heated
(c) has a low viscosity index
(d) has a high viscosity index.

50. Compared to an oil rated as SAE 40, one advantage of using the multigrade oil SAE 20W 50 in an engine is that the multigrade oil:
(a) is thicker at high temperatures
(b) is thicker at low temperatures
(c) does not alter its viscosity
(d) can be used throughout the year.

51. Grease is a substance which consists of:
(a) a lime and soap solution
(b) lime-soap, bentone and lithium
(c) a mixture of low viscosity lubricants
(d) heavy oil mixed with a retaining base.

52. The torque transmitted by a plate type clutch is given by $T = Sp\mu r$. During the life of the clutch which two factors in the expression $Sp\mu r$ decrease in value and cause 'slip':
(a) $S$ and $p$
(b) $p$ and $\mu$
(c) $\mu$ and $r$
(d) $r$ and $S$.

53. A single plate clutch of mean radius 120 mm has a total spring thrust of 500 N and coefficient of friction of 0.3. The torque transmitted is:
(a) 18 Nm
(b) 36 Nm
(c) 18 kNm
(d) 36 kNm.

54. When an object moves in a circular path a force acts towards the centre of rotation. This force is called:

(a) centrifugal
(b) centripetal
(c) inertia
(d) reactive.

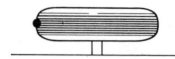

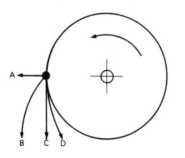

**Fig. PC 8.2**

55. A road wheel is mounted horizontally on a balancing machine and rotated at a high speed. During this operation a stone, which was embedded in the tread, is released. Reference to Figure PC8.2 shows that the path of the stone is indicated by the letter
(a) A
(b) B
(c) C
(d) D.

56. When the centrifugal force acting on one side of the axis of a road wheel is not equal to the force which acts on the other side, then the effect is:
(a) vibration
(b) slip
(c) reduced adhesion
(d) wheel cannot be moved.

57. After efficiently balancing a road wheel statically, the wheel is found to be out-of-balance when it is rotated. This is because the:

(a) static balance mass is too small
(b) static balance mass is too large
(c) centrifugal forces are forming a couple
(d) centre of gravity does not coincide with the axis of rotation.

58. What is a machine? A device for:
(a) transmitting energy
(b) generating energy
(c) increasing the work done
(d) reducing load and effort.

59. Another name for a pivot is:
(a) effort
(b) fulcrum
(c) centre of gravity
(d) turning moment.

60. Which one of the following expressions gives the force ratio?
(a) effort + load
(b) effort × load
(c) effort ÷ load
(d) load ÷ effort.

61. Which one of the following expressions gives the movement ratio?
(a) movement of effort + movement of load
(b) movement of effort × movement of load
(c) movement of effort ÷ movement of load
(d) movement of load ÷ movement of effort.

62. A straight lever of length 500 mm is pivoted at a point 50 mm from the end at which the load is applied. Neglecting friction what load will be given if an effort of 90 N is applied at a right angle to the end of the long arm of the lever?
(a) 9 N
(b) 10 N
(c) 810 N
(d) 900 N.

63. A crowbar gives a leverage of 30:1. If the efficiency is 90%, an effort of 90 N will lift a load of:
(a) 2.7 N
(b) 3.3 N
(c) 2.43 kN
(d) 3 kN.

64. A machine has a force ratio of 20 and movement ratio of 40. The efficiency is:
(a) 0.5
(b) 2.0
(c) 20
(d) 60.

65. A pinion with 25 teeth drives a gearwheel having 75 teeth. When the input speed and torque is 2100 rev/min and 60 Nm respectively, the output speed and torque are:
(a) 700 rev/min and 180 Nm
(b) 6300 rev/min and 20 Nm
(c) 700 rev/min and 180 Nm if efficiency is 100%
(d) 6300 rev/min and 20 Nm if efficiency is 100%.

66. A pinion of a pair of gears has 40 teeth and rotates at 700 rev/min. If the output shaft turns at 280 rev/min, the number of teeth on the meshing gear is:
(a) 10
(b) 16
(c) 100
(d) 160.

67. A vehicle is fitted with a simple hydraulically operated brake system. If the left-hand front hose fractures, the effect will be that the:
(a) vehicle will pull to the left
(b) vehicle will pull to the right
(c) rear brakes only will operate
(d) brakes will not operate on any wheel.

68. Although correctly tensioned, a worn vee belt, which contacts the sides and bottom of the pulley, does not transmit full power because the belt:
(a) has lost its wedging action
(b) has a reduced coefficient of friction
(c) surface has become glazed
(d) has stretched.

69. A simple epicyclic gear train gives the greater reduction when the:
(a) sun wheel is driving and the annulus is held
(b) annulus is driving and the sun wheel is held
(c) arm is driving and the annulus is held
(d) sun wheel is driving and the arm is held.

70. The velocity of a body is the:
(a) speed
(b) change in acceleration
(c) rate at which it changes its speed
(d) rate at which it moves in a given direction.

71. The acceleration of a body is the:
(a) rate at which it moves
(b) rate of change in velocity
(c) distance moved in a given time
(d) distance moved in a given direction.

72. Which one of the following represents the approximate value and correct unit for 'acceleration due to gravity'?
(a) 10 m/s
(b) 10 m/s$^2$
(c) 32 m/s
(d) 32 m/s$^2$.

73. A vehicle accelerates at a constant rate from rest to a velocity of 48 m/s in 24 seconds. Its acceleration is:
(a) 0.5 m/s
(b) 2 m/s
(c) 0.5 m/s$^2$
(d) 2 m/s$^2$.

74. A brake efficiency of 100% means that the:
(a) vehicle is stopped instantly
(b) brake mechanism has no friction
(c) brakes apply a retarding force equal to the total weight of the vehicle
(d) coefficient of friction between the brake shoe and drum has a value of 1.0.

75. The 'kinetic energy' of a body is the:
(a) energy of motion
(b) heat produced by the brakes
(c) work lost to friction
(d) retarding action given by a force.

76. How does the kinetic energy of a vehicle travelling at 100 m/s compare with that given at a speed of 50 m/s? The kinetic energy at 100 m/s is:
(a) less
(b) equal
(c) twice as great
(d) four times as great.

# *Heat*

---

## What is covered in this chapter:

→ heat and temperature
→ temperature scales
→ heat transfer
→ conversion of heat
→ change of state
→ thermal expansion and contraction
→ gas laws

The internal combustion engine is a heat engine. Fuel burnt in an engine raises the temperature of gas contained and compressed in a cylinder; this in turn increases the gas pressure and forces a piston down the cylinder to produce crank movement. From this simple description you will see that heat plays an important part in the working of an engine, so you will need to know the nature of heat and its effects to understand the full operation of an engine.

There are many other occasions where a knowledge of heat is useful; these occur when you study engine cooling systems, brake operation and other components that are subject to heat generated by either their operation or workshop activities during repair.

## 9.1 Heat and temperature

### The nature of heat

A substance is made up of tiny particles called molecules and these consist of even smaller particles called atoms. Observations of these tiny particles shows that each one is vibrating; the amount of vibration depending on the 'hotness' of the substance. So:

*Heat is internal energy and is capable of doing work*

Heat engines obtain their power by burning fuel – the chemical energy in the fuel is released by ignition to

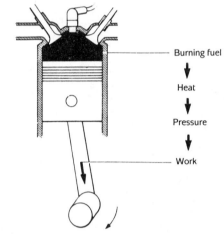

**Fig. 9.1.1** Heat changed to work

make the gas very hot. This causes a force which pushes the piston down the cylinder (Figure 9.1.1).

### *Heat flows from a hot to a cold surface*

A hot object placed beside a cold surface will cause the heat to 'flow' until the two things are the same heat. (Figure 9.1.2 & 3)

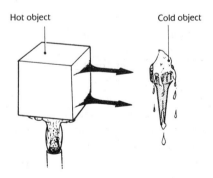

**Fig. 9.1.2** Heat flows from a hot object to a cold object

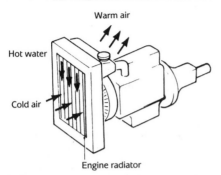

**Fig. 9.1.3** Hot water gives up heat to cold air

**Temperature**

The temperature of a body is defined as the degree of *hotness*. This is different to the heat contained in an object, e.g. more energy will be required to heat four litres of water than that used to heat one litre to a similar temperature.

Although terms like 'hot' and 'cold' give an indication of the temperature, they lack accuracy and can lead to misunderstanding, e.g. A hot day means something different to a hot engine.

### *Temperature is measured by a thermometer*

Most substances grow bigger (or expand) as they are heated and this feature is used in the common type of thermometer. This type consists of a thin, sealed glass tube having a bulb containing mercury or alcohol at one end (Figure 9.1.4). When the mercury is heated it expands and flows along the fine bore. The temperature is read by noting the position, relative to a scale, of the end of the thin column of the liquid. Mercury in glass thermometers are often used in the laboratory but are rarely used on motor vehicles because of their obvious fragility. Modern vehicles use electrical thermometers of the type shown in Figure 9.1.5.

**Fig. 9.1.4** Typical domestic thermometer

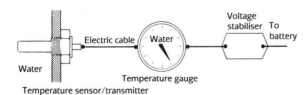

**Fig. 9.1.5** Coolant temperature indicator

## 9.2 Temperature scales

Most temperature scales are based on two fixed points given by the temperature of:

a) steam from water boiling under standard atmospheric pressure
b) pure melting ice.

*Celsius scale* Every day temperature measurement uses a scale which is similar to that introduced in 1742 by the Swedish scientist Andreas Celsius. In this case the freezing point of water is marked 0°C and the boiling point 100°C; temperatures below zero are given negative values. For many years this scale was known as Centigrade but nowadays it is recommended that the name Celsius be used.

*Fahrenheit scale* A scale commonly used in Britain in the past. The upper fixed point was marked 212°F and the lower point as 32°F; the interval between divided into 180 degrees. To convert °F to °C the formula is

$$C = (F - 32) \times \frac{5}{9}$$

*Kelvin scale* The SI unit of temperature is the 'kelvin'. This has the same size of degree or temperature interval as the Celsius scale, but has a zero about $-273°C$. To convert from Celsius to kelvin add 273, e.g.

$$16°C = 16 + 273$$
$$= 289 \text{ K}$$

The reader will note that the degree symbol is not used with the kelvin scale. Value 273 was obtained by noting the behaviour of a gas and this indicated that heat ceased

### REMEMBER

**Heat is**

• a form of energy
• passed from a HOT to a COLD surface
• transmitted by conduction, convection and radiation

**Temperature is**

• the degree of hotness
• measured by a thermometer
• converted from degrees Celsius to kelvin by adding 273

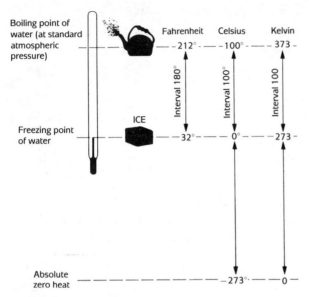

**Fig. 9.2.1** Temperature scales

to exist at that temperature. A temperature of $-273°C$ (zero K) is sometimes called the absolute zero (Figure 9.2.1).

### Example

A carbon steel having a carbon content greater than 0.8% can be hardened by heating to a temperature of 800°C (cherry red) and quenching in water or oil. Convert this temperature to kelvin.

$$800 + 273 = 1073 \text{ K}$$

### Example

After hardening a steel chisel the brittleness can be relieved by tempering. This is performed by heating to a temperature of 573 K (violet colour) and quenching in oil or water. Convert this temperature to Celsius.

$$573 - 273 = 300°C$$

## 9.3   Heat transfer

Heat is transferred or transmitted from one substance to another by one or more of the following ways:

● Conduction
● Convection
● Radiation

The actual process is complex so we only need to deal with the effects and application of each.

### Heat conduction

Heat transfer which takes place within the material is called conduction. Human beings discover at an early age that heat travels along a metal object. The heat given to the object is passed from particle to particle until the whole thing is at a near uniform temperature.

*Conductivity of metals*   Some materials such as metals are good conductors of heat whereas materials like asbestos resist the passage of heat and would be called either a bad heat conductor or a good heat insulator. If the heat of an object is to be retained it must be lagged (wrapped) with a heat insulation material (Figure 9.3.1). On the other hand, if a large heat 'flow' is required, a material having a good thermal conductivity should be used. Two examples of this are:

a) *Aluminium alloy pistons*       compared to a cast iron, aluminium alloy has a much higher thermal conductivity so this type of piston operates at a lower temperature.
b) *Copper soldering iron bit*       copper is an exceptionally good heat conductor so heat is readily transferred to the material being soldered.

Liquids such as water, petrol and oil are poor conductors of heat and gases are even poorer. Liquids and gases normally transfer their heat by convection.

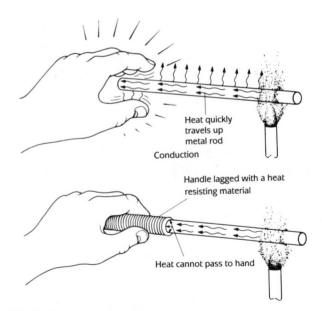

Heat quickly travels up metal rod
Conduction

Handle lagged with a heat resisting material

Heat cannot pass to hand

**Fig. 9.3.1** Example of heat insulation

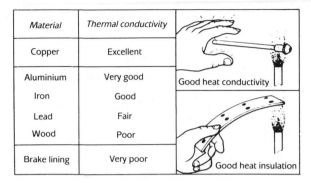

| Material | Thermal conductivity |
|----------|---------------------|
| Copper | Excellent |
| Aluminium | Very good |
| Iron | Good |
| Lead | Fair |
| Wood | Poor |
| Brake lining | Very poor |

Good heat conductivity

Good heat insulation

**Table 9.3.1** Thermal conductivity comparisons

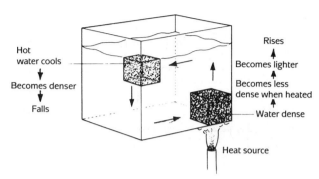

Rises
Becomes lighter
Becomes less dense when heated
Water dense

Hot water cools
Becomes denser
Falls
Heat source

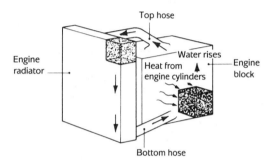

Top hose
Water rises
Engine block
Heat from engine cylinders
Engine radiator
Bottom hose

**Fig. 9.3.3** Water cooling system by convection currents

### Heat convection

Heat transfer due to the movement of a fluid or gas is called convection. Most readers will have seen cases where fluid has been heated and movement of the fluid has taken place. Experiments similar to Figure 9.3.2 shows that when water at a temperature above 4°C is heated, it expands, decreases its density and rises towards the surface.

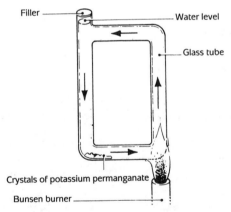

Filler
Water level
Glass tube
Crystals of potassium permanganate
Bunsen burner

**Fig. 9.3.2** Demonstration of convection using colour trace

*Water gets hotter → expands → gets lighter → rises*

Similar effects can be demonstrated by using other liquids and gases, e.g. air.

Movement of water by convection can be employed to operate a simple engine cooling system (Figure 9.3.3).

### Heat radiation

Heat transfer by infra-red rays which behave similar to light rays. One of the best examples of this form of heat transfer is the sun. Although the distance between the sun and earth is great, the sun's rays are powerful and are capable of travelling through space. In a similar way, the heat from any source can be felt when there is no interruption to the path of the rays. This radiant heat consists of invisible electromagnetic waves which behave in a manner similar to light waves: they travel in a straight line and they can be reflected as shown in Figure 9.3.4.

Rate of heat transfer by radiation depends on:

- temperature of the source
- area of its surface
- nature of its surface.

Obviously the hotter the source the greater will be the transfer. Increasing the area has the effect of 'spreading out' this hot surface and allows the heat to be given up more readily.

The nature of the surface is the finish, a dull black finish radiates heat better and also absorbs heat better than a highly polished surface.

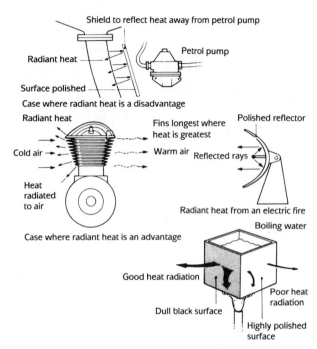

**Fig. 9.3.4** Examples of radiant heat

Motor vehicle applications of radiation include:

a) Fins around an air–cooled engine cylinder which increase the surface area exposed to the air (Figure 9.3.4)

b) Radiator of a liquid cooling system where a large area of hot water is presented to the air.

In these cases the rate of flow will depend on the difference in temperature between the hot surface and the cold air.

## 9.4  Conversion of heat

Heat is a form of energy. To raise the temperature of a substance, energy must be given to it. When we speak about heat being supplied to an object, we mean the amount of energy being delivered. Since the unit of energy is the joule, then

> *Quantity of heat is the energy in joules*

### Heat capacity

Temperature and heat are two independent terms which should not be confused. It will be remembered that temperature is the 'degree of hotness' of a body. Figure 9.4.1. shows an example in which two materials have a similar 'hotness', i.e. temperature, yet the amount of heat

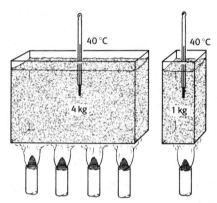

**Fig. 9.4.1** To achieve the same final temperature a mass of 4 kg requires four times the heat required by a mass of 1 kg

contained in each one is very different. The larger mass takes four times as much heat to raise its temperature a given amount, but after heating contains four times the heat energy of the smaller mass at the same temperature. In this example, the mass of 4 kg is said to have a larger heat capacity than the 1 kg mass.

> *Heat capacity of a body is the heat required to raise its temperature by 1°C*

The SI unit of heat capacity is the joule per degree C (J/°C or J/K).

### Specific heat capacity

The heat capacity varies with substances. If equal masses of oil and water are heated as shown in Figure 9.4.2, the oil temperature will rise at a faster rate. This indicates that

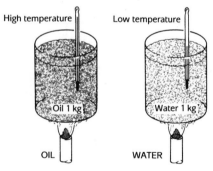

**Fig. 9.4.2** When equal quantities of oil and water are heated, the oil temperature will rise at a faster rate since the specific heat capacity of water is greater

the water requires more heat to raise its temperature a given amount, i.e. the water has a higher heat capacity.

The heat capacity of a substance can be found by consulting a table. When a mass of 1 kg is used as a standard the heating value is called the specific heat capacity.

*Specific heat capacity is the heat required to raise one kilogram of a substance through 1°C (J/kg°C or J/kg K)*

The table of specific heat capacities (Table 9.4.1) shows that water has a very high value and this property makes water very attractive to use as a cooling or quenching medium.

| Substance | Specific heat capacity (J/kg K) |
|---|---|
| Water | 4200 |
| Ice | 2100 |
| Oil | 1700 |
| Aluminium | 900 |
| Steel | 480 |
| Iron | 460 |
| Copper | 400 |
| Brass | 380 |
| Zinc | 380 |
| Lead | 130 |

**Table 9.4.1** Specific heat capacity

## Example

A cooling system contains 5 litres of water at a temperature of 16°C. How much heat is required to raise the water temperature to 96°C? (Specific heat capacity of water = 4200 J/kg k.)

$$\text{Mass of 1 litre of water} = 1 \text{ kg}$$
$$\text{Heat energy} = \text{Mass} \times \text{specific heat capacity}$$
$$\times \text{temperature change}$$
$$= 5 \times 4200 \times (96 - 16)$$
$$= 5 \times 4200 \times 80$$
$$= 1\,680\,000 \text{ J}$$
$$= 1680 \text{ kJ (OR 1.68 MJ)}$$

## Heat exchange

On motor vehicles there are many cases of heat being exchanged from one substance to another. The transfer follows the law that

*Heat lost = heat gained*

Figure 9.4.3 shows a simple example where a hot object is quenched in a cold liquid. This method could be used

## REMEMBER

**Heat capacity is**

● heat required to raise the temperature of a body by 1°C
● expressed in joules

**Specific heat capacity is**

● heat required to raise 1 kg of a substance through 1°C
● expressed in joules per kilogram kelvin (J/kg K)
● affected by the substance
● 4200 J/kg K for water

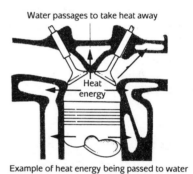

Water passages to take heat away

Heat energy

Example of heat energy being passed to water

Oil or water

Temperature of liquid increases

Heat energy given up to liquid

**Fig. 9.4.3** Heat exchange

to find the specific heat capacity of a substance. The liquid container, or calorimeter as it is often called in experimental work, should be insulated against heat loss to the atmosphere if accurate results are required.

## Energy conversion

You are aware that if you rub your hands together, heat is generated. The work done overcoming friction is converted into heat and this warms your hands.

The relationship between mechanical units of work and heat energy was first proved by James Joule. His experiments showed that energy given to water by falling masses caused the water temperature to increase. Today we take this energy conversion for granted, but in order to honour James Joule for his achievements in showing that mechanical, electrical and chemical energy could all be converted into heat, his name is used as the unit for energy.

With the Imperial system a conversion factor is necessary in order to change mechanical units of work to heat energy and vice versa. This factor is given as:

$$778 \text{ ft lbf of mechanical work} = 1 \text{ Btu}$$

(Btu stands for British thermal unit – the heat required to raise the temperature of 1 lb of water by $1°F$).

This relationship is called the mechanical equivalent of heat, or Joule's equivalent. In SI units the joule is used as the unit of heat energy as well as the unit of mechanical energy, so nowadays the term 'mechanical equivalent of heat' has no use.

There are many cases where mechanical work is converted to heat and vice versa; some of these are shown in Figure 9.4.4.

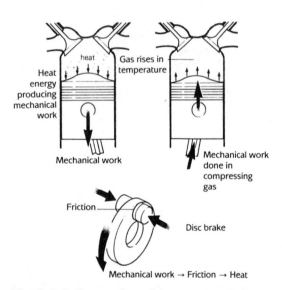

**Fig. 9.4.4** Conversion of energy

### Example

To stop a vehicle, the energy of motion has to be converted into heat by the brakes. What temperature will be reached by a brake disc if an energy of 69 kJ is converted by each brake? (Assume all of the heat is transferred to the disc and no heat is lost to the air.)

Mass of disc = 3 kg
Specific heat capacity of disc = 460 J/kg K
Initial temperature = 20°C
Mechanical energy = heat energy = 69 000 J
Heat gained by disc = mass × specific heat capacity
× temperature change

$$69\,000 = 3 \times 460 \times (t - 20)$$

where

$$t = \text{final temperature of disc in }°C$$

$$t - 20 = \frac{69\,000}{3 \times 460}$$

$$t = \frac{69\,000}{3 \times 460} + 20$$

Final temperature of disc = 50 + 20 = 70°C

In practice the temperature would be less than 70°C because the heat would also be transferred to:

1) the air by radiation;
2) the caliper assembly which in turn will heat the fluid;
3) the hub by conduction.

It is for this reason that special grease having a high melting point is used in the hubs of vehicles having disc brakes.

### Calorific value of a fuel

When a fuel is burnt, heat is generated. The quantity of heat liberated is determined by burning a given mass of fuel in a special calorimeter (Figure 9.4.5) and measuring the heat given out. The value obtained is called the calorific value.

*Calorific value of a fuel is a measure of the heat units contained in a given mass of fuel*

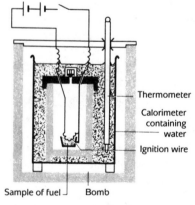

**Fig. 9.4.5** Bomb calorimeter: amount that the water is heated depends on the heat given out by the fuel

Typical values are:

Petrol  44 MJ/kg (44 megajoule per kilogram)
Diesel fuel 42 MJ/kg

The variation in calorific values between different petrols is very small, so for practical purposes the very small differences between the various grades does not justify further consideration. Calorific value of a fuel is used when the thermal efficiency of an engine is to be calculated.

## 9.5  Change of state

### States of matter

Substances exist in one of three states; solid, liquid or gas.

- A *solid* has a definite shape and volume: it resists any alteration to its shape or volume.
- A *liquid* readily changes its shape to suit the container but resists any change of its volume.
- A *gas* has no definite shape or volume and readily fills any container into which it is placed, but in doing so changes its density.

It is possible to alter the state of a substance by changing its temperature; the temperature at which the change occurs depends on the substance, e.g. ice changes to water at 0°C, whereas steel does not change to a liquid until a temperature of about 1400°C is reached.

Since water changes from solid to gas over a small temperature range this substance is normally chosen to illustrate the change of state process.

Figure 9.5.1 shows a block of ice at a temperature of −20°C being heated at a constant rate. As heat is supplied, the temperature gradually rises, and this is shown by the graph. From −20°C to 0°C the heat is causing the temperature to increase so the heat is called *sensible heat*, i.e. heat which can be detected by the senses.

When the temperature reaches 0°C, the steady rise in temperature is halted and a period of time elapses where the heat is unable to produce any increase in temperature. During this period the heat is used to create a change of state from ice to water and the heat required to produce this change is called *latent heat*, i.e. hidden heat.

Once the ice has all been melted, the temperature begins to rise again at a steady rate; the heat supplied to the water during this phase is sensible heat.

Assuming normal atmospheric conditions prevail, at 100°C the water 'starts to boil', which is the everyday expression for the physical change of state of water to steam. The time taken, or heat energy required, for this change is far greater than that needed to change ice to water, or expressing this in a more precise manner – the latent heat of vaporization is greater than the latent heat of fusion.

As soon as the water has all become steam the temperature of the steam rises and the heat is once again sensible heat.

### Melting and freezing

The process by which a solid turns into a liquid is called *fusion* or *melting*, and the reverse process by which liquid turns into a solid is called *solidification* or *freezing*.

The change from liquid to vapour is called *vaporization*: this may take place relatively slowly and from the surface of the liquid only, in which case it is called *evaporation*: or it may take place rapidly with bubbles of vapour forming within the bulk of the liquid itself and rising to the surface, in which case it is known as *ebullition* or *boiling*. The reverse process by which a vapour changes into a liquid is called *condensation*. These changes generally take place at definite temperatures in any particular material, but at different temperatures in different materials.

Pure water freezes at a temperature of 0°C (273 K) when exposed to normal atmospheric pressure, and during the process of freezing its volume increases slightly. This expansion on solidification is shared by some other materials (e.g. cast iron, in which the expansion on solidification helps in obtaining accurate castings) but not by all. Paraffin wax is an example of a material which shrinks on solidification (Figure 9.5.2) and conversely expands on melting – hence its use in one type of thermostat.

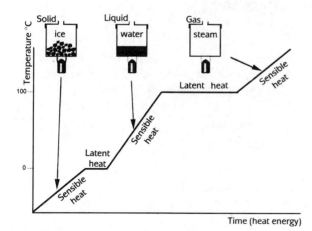

**Fig. 9.5.1**  Stages of sensible and latent heat

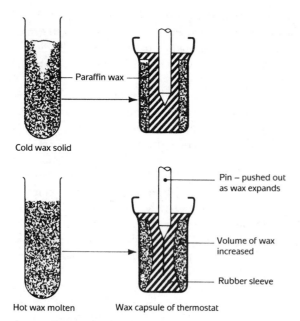

**Fig. 9.5.2** Effect of heat on wax

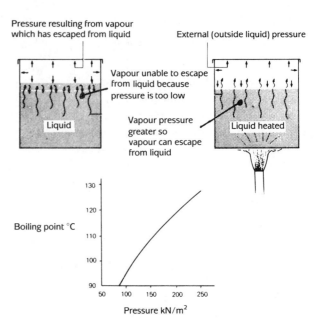

**Fig. 9.5.3** Vapour pressure and boiling point: effect of pressure on boiling point of water

### Pressure and boiling point

All liquids tend to form vapour in the space above the surface. Some vapourise more readily than others and petrol and alcohol are good examples – these are said to be *volatile*.

Consider a case where the space above a liquid is enclosed. Any vapour which escapes from the liquid will create a pressure in the air space which will prevent any more vapour from leaving the liquid (Figure 9.5.3).

If the temperature of the liquid is raised, the greater internal pressure, i.e. vapour pressure, will enable more vapour to escape from the liquid. In turn this vapour will increase the external pressure, and prevent further escape of vapour

By repeating this process a temperature is reached when the internal pressure becomes equal to the external pressure. At this point the vapour leaves the liquid in a vigorous manner and the liquid is said to boil.

### A liquid boils when the vapour pressure equals the external pressure

When the lid of the container is removed, the external pressure is that of the atmosphere so if this external pressure is increased the previous example shows that the liquid must attain a higher temperature to boil.

Similarly if the atmosphere pressure is lowered, the vapour pressure to equalise this will be reached at a lower temperature, i.e. the liquid will boil at a lower temperature. So:

### The boiling point of a liquid depends on the pressure

Motor vehicle applications of pressure and boiling point include:

a) *Cooling system*    The heat flow from the combustion chamber to the coolant depends on the temperature difference and the coolant should be kept as hot as possible for efficient running. This is difficult

## REMEMBER

### Heat is

- needed to produce a change of state
- called *latent heat* when substance is changed from either solid-to-liquid or liquid-to-gas
- called *sensible heat* when the temperature of a substance is altered

### Water

- changes to ice at 0°C and steam at 100°C when pressure is atmospheric
- boils at temperatures higher than 100°C if pressure is higher than atmospheric
- has a higher density than ice

with a cooling system which is open to the atmosphere because if it is operated in excess of about 90°C there is a risk of the coolant boiling. By pressurising the system the operating temperature can be raised and the engine becomes more efficient.

b) *Fuel lines*    The petrol in the pipe between the tank and the pump is at a pressure less than atmospheric. This low pressure will allow the petrol to give off more vapour and may result in a reduced petrol supply, or on a hot summer's day, no supply whatsoever. To prevent this trouble the pipe from the tank to the pump should be as short as possible.

### Temperature sensing and control

Physical changes which occur when substances are heated can be utilised to form temperature sensing devices, e.g. the thermostat fitted in the cooling system. Both types of thermostat, the bellows and wax capsule, operate on this principle but whereas the change of state in a bellows type is from liquid to gas, the wax capsule uses the change from solid to liquid. Figure 9.5.4 shows the action of the bellows type thermostat.

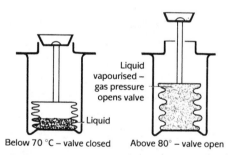

**Fig. 9.5.4** Bellows type thermostat operation

The element of this type is partly filled with a liquid such as alcohol, which has a boiling point of about 80°C under normal atmospheric pressure conditions. When the temperature reaches about 80°C the pressure given off by the vapour causes the bellows to expand.

## 9.6    Thermal expansion

The fact that most substances increase in size on heating and decrease in size on cooling has already been mentioned. The general effect is the same for all substances, but there are important differences in detail between what happens in solids, in liquids and in gases.

### Expansion of solids

Heating a solid causes it to expand in all directions but one of the most important considerations is its increase in length called *linear expansion* (Figure 9.6.1).

***Linear expansion is the expansion in length***

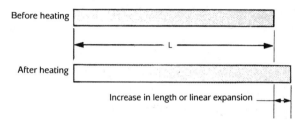

**Fig. 9.6.1** Linear expansion

This increase in length must be taken into account when the mechanic assembles a component, since failure to observe this fact may result in considerable damage to the unit. The most common way to prevent damage is to consider the amount that the item will expand and then allow a clearance for this to take place. There are a number of interesting cases in motor vehicles where linear expansion is taken into account by giving a clearance (Figure 9.6.2).

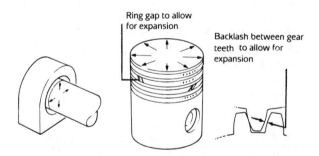

**Fig. 9.6.2** Expansion of motor vehicle components

a) *Shafts running in bearings*    When the shaft gets hot its diameter increases, so if the bearing did not expand the same amount, seizure would occur.

b) *Piston in a cylinder*    Both get hot but the piston generally expands more than the cylinder. An aluminium piston of diameter 80 mm expands about 0.5 mm when it is heated to its working temperature.

c) *Gear teeth*    On heating, the teeth get bigger, so a backlash (clearance between gears) is provided.

***All materials do not expand at the same rate***

Linear expansion varies with different materials; e.g. aluminium expands more than twice as much as cast iron and this shows why a piston made of aluminium alloy must be given a larger clearance than a similar piston of cast iron. In the case of pistons, expansion is a nuisance so in order to control it, the designer may either restrict the heat flow or incorporate in the piston a 'strut' to resist the expansion. A material for such a 'strut' is Invar. Figure 9.6.3 illustrates the expansion properties of various metals.

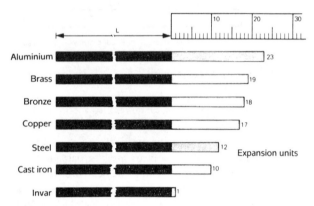

**Fig. 9.6.3** Comparison of linear expansion of material

*The bimetal strip*   We have seen that brass and steel expand at different rates so if these two materials are joined together the effect of heating will be to bend the strip (Fig. 9.6.4). This principle is often used to operate various devices fitted to motor vehicles, e.g. electrical contacts in instruments.

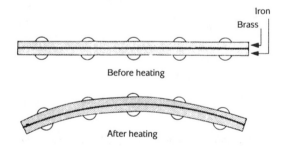

**Fig. 9.6.4** Effect of heat on bimetallic strip

*Motor vehicle applications of expansion of solids*   Linear expansion can be utilised by the mechanic to aid him when assembling or dismantling units:

a) *Flywheel starter ring gear*   A tight fit must be provided between gear and flywheel. The gear is heated until the diameter is large enough to accept the flywheel (Figure 9.6.5).

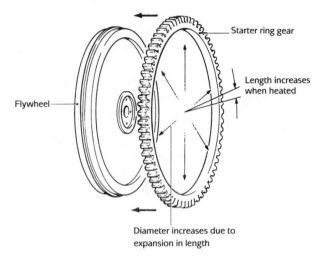

**Fig. 9.6.5** Fitting a starter ring gear to flywheel

b) *Gudgeon pin in piston*   If the pin is tight to remove, the piston can be expanded in hot oil – the pin can be easily removed because the piston expands more than the pin (Figure 9.6.6).

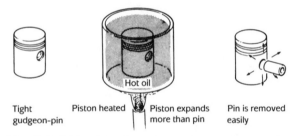

**Fig. 9.6.6** Applying heat to remove gudgeon-pin

c) *Seized pins*   There are occasions when a pin cannot be removed and heat is applied to the female part. Special consideration must be given to the effect of the heat on the material before using this method (Figure 9.6.7).

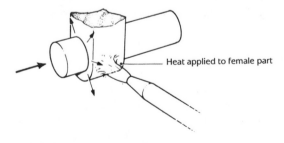

**Fig. 9.6.7** Removal of tight or seized pins

*Application of contraction*   All the above examples are based on expansion – sometimes the material is made to contract, e.g.:

*Valve guides and valve inserts*   sometimes these are fitted after they have been contracted by immersion in a very cold liquid 'gas' such as carbon dioxide (Figure 9.6.8). This gas changes to liquid at a temperature of 195 K ($-78°$C).

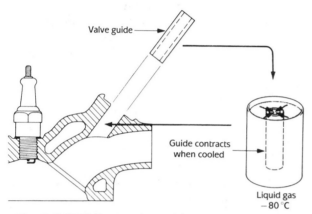

**Fig. 9.6.8** Fitting a valve guide

### Linear expansion of solids

Linear means the measurement in one dimension only, so the term linear expansion is used when the expansion in one direction only is considered, e.g. the increase in length of a material when it is heated.

The extent of the expansion of the rod shown in Figure 9.6.9 is governed by the type of material and the amount that it is heated. Experiments with different materials show that for general purposes the following expression may be used to find the linear expansion.

Expansion = original length × temperature rise × $\alpha$

In this expression the symbol $\alpha$ (pronounced alpha) is called the *coefficient of linear expansion*. The value of $\alpha$ varies with different materials as shown in Table 9.6.1.

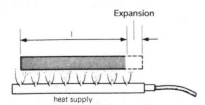

**Fig. 9.6.9** Expansion caused by heating

| Metal | Coefficient of linear expansion (per °C or per K) |
|---|---|
| Aluminium | 0.000 023 |
| Brass | 0.000 019 |
| Bronze | 0.000 018 |
| Copper | 0.000 017 |
| Steel | 0.000 012 |
| Cast iron | 0.000 010 |
| Invar steel | 0.000 001 |

**Table 9.6.1** Coefficients of linear expansion

*The coefficient of linear expansion is the fraction of its original length by which a material expands per degree rise in temperature*

### Example
Determine the expansion of a steel push rod of length 200 mm when its temperature is raised by 50°C.

Expansion = original length × temperature rise × $\alpha$
         = 200 × 50 × 0.000 012
         = 0.12 mm

### Superficial expansion
When a plate (Figure 9.6.10) is heated the area increases. Then:

Increase in area = original area × temperature rise
                   × coefficient of superficial expansion

For general purposes:

Coefficient of superficial expansion
                   = 2 × coefficient of linear expansion

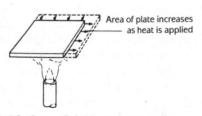

**Fig. 9.6.10** Superficial (area) expansion

### Expansion of liquids
Owing to their nature, the expansion of liquids must be treated on a volume basis. As shown by the mercury in a thermometer, most liquids increase their volume as they are heated, but the real amount they expand is difficult to demonstrate since it must take into account the expansion of the container. If the container did not alter its size then the diagram (Figure 9.6.11) would indicate the *real volumetric expansion* of various liquids. When the

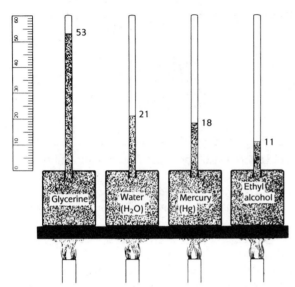

**Fig. 9.6.11** Relative expansion of a liquid for a given temperature rise: containers are assumed to maintain constant volume, which is impossible in practice

container expansion is not considered the term is *apparent volumetric expansion.*

It has been stated that most liquids expand on heating – this means that there are exceptions and water is one of these special cases. Above 4°C (277 K) water expands on heating but if the temperature is lowered below 4°C the water also expands. This means that at 4°C the water is at its greatest density. When the temperature is lowered to 0°C water changes to ice and this is accompanied by a considerable increase in volume.

The expansion due to the change of state from water to ice can cause considerable damage to a liquid cooled engine. Large forces, sufficient to crack a cylinder block, occur at the change, so to prevent this possibility, the risk of freezing must be reduced. This is achieved by adding to the water a liquid such as ethylene glycol. As the quantity of 'anti-freeze' in the water is increased so the temperature of freezing is decreased.

Many other liquids are used in motor vehicles and if any of these are heated, an increase in their volume will occur.

*Motor vehicle applications of expansion of liquids*   These include:

a) *Cooling system*   An overflow is provided to allow for expansion. Some systems provide a separate container to collect this discharge so as to enable it to be returned when the system has cooled.

b) *Braking system*   An air vent and expansion space is provided in the reservoir. If the reservoir was completely filled with brake fluid when the system was cold, then the system would overflow after the brakes had been used.

c) *Lubricating oil in steering box, gearbox, final drive etc.*   Unless a breather is provided, expansion of the oil would build up a pressure which could force the oil past the oil sealing arrangements.

### Volumetric expansion of liquids

For calculation purposes, liquids can be treated in a similar manner to the previous examples, except that the expansion is now considered on a volume or cubical basis. So

expansion of liquid = original volume
$\qquad\qquad\qquad\times$ temperature rise
$\qquad\qquad\qquad\times$ coefficient of cubical expansion

With liquids the value for the coefficient varies with the temperature and also depends on the container which is used. If it was possible to use a container which did not expand on heating, then the increase in volume of the liquid would appear to be greater than in the case where the container increases in size. In motor vehicle situations the container also expands, so in this event the coefficient is called the *coefficient of apparent expansion of a liquid.*

### Example

A cooling system containing 9 litres of water at 16°C discharges 0.324 litre of water by the overflow as the temperature is raised to 96°C. If this discharge represents the expansion, what is the mean coefficient of cubic expansion?

Expansion = capacity (volume) × temperature rise
$\qquad\qquad\qquad\times$ coefficient

$$\text{Coefficient} = \frac{\text{Expansion}}{\text{Capacity} \times \text{temperature rise}}$$

$$= \frac{0.324}{9 \times 80} = 0.000\,45 \text{ per }°C$$

Coefficient of cubical expansion for this temperature range = 0.000 45/°C.

This example gives some indication of the amount that liquids expand on heating. When this is applied to such things as hydraulic brakes, it will be realised that special provision must be made to allow for the increase in volume of the liquid.

### Expansion of gases

Solids and liquids are almost incompressible and there is very little difficulty in determining their rate of expansion. Gases, however, can easily be compressed, so in order to determine the expansion due to heating great care must be taken to ensure that the pressure of the gas is not altered.

Consider a given volume of gas contained in the cylinder shown in Figure 9.6.12 which is fitted with gas-tight piston and loaded with a mass to maintain a constant gas pressure. During heating the gas will expand and this will cause the piston to move. So:

**The volume of a gas increases as the temperature increases, if the pressure is kept constant**

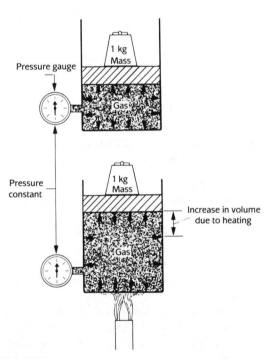

**Fig. 9.6.12** Demonstration of increase in volume with temperature at constant gas pressure

By conducting a similar experiment with the piston locked to form a closed cylinder (Figure 9.6.13) the effect of a constant volume can be examined. In this case the gas is prevented from expanding, therefore it exerts a pressure which gets higher and higher as the temperature increases. So:

**The pressure of a gas increases as the temperature increases if the volume is kept constant**

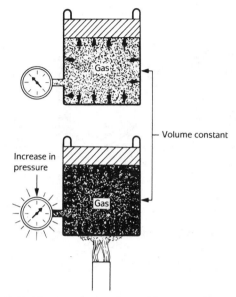

**Fig. 9.6.13** Demonstration of increase in pressure with temperature at constant volume

*Motor Vehicle applications of expansion of a gas* These include

a) *Gas in an engine cylinder* ignition of the fuel causes a rapid rise in temperature while the piston is positioned about top dead centre, so there is practically no change in volume of the gas during this burning process. As a result of this temperature increase, a considerable rise in pressure occurs and it is this pressure which provides the force on the piston to drive the engine.

b) *Air in a tyre* the rotation of a wheel causes heat to be generated which raises the temperature of the tyre. The volume remains about the same, so the pressure will increase. To allow for this, the manufacturers normally state that tyres should be checked when 'cold'.

Besides the effect of altering the temperature of a gas we must also see what happens to the pressure when only the volume is altered. This can be visualised when a gas is trapped in a cylinder (Figure 9.6.14) and the volume is reduced. The graph shows that if the volume is halved the pressure is doubled. So:

**The pressure increases as the volume decreases, if the temperature is kept constant**

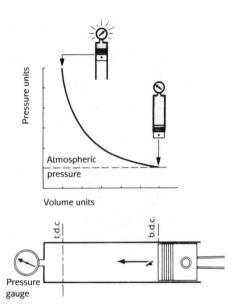

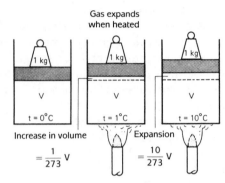

**Fig. 9.7.1** Expansion of gas (Charles' law)

**Fig. 9.6.14** Graphical representation of increase in pressure as volume decreases at constant temperature

---

## REMEMBER

**Thermal expansion is**

- linear, when length is changed
- superficial, when area is changed
- volumetric, when volume is changed
- indicated by a coefficient of expansion
- calculated from:

*length × temp. rise × coeff. of expansion*

**Gas pressure increases:**

- when temperature is increased
- when volume is decreased

---

## 9.7 Gas laws

**Charles' Law**

If a gas in a cylinder is heated it will expand just like most other substances. The ease in which a gas changes its pressure and density is a feature which must be controlled if the expansion is to be demonstrated.

Figure 9.7.1 shows an example of a gas being maintained at a constant pressure by allowing the piston to slide in the cylinder; the pressure of the gas is governed by the 'weight' acting on the piston.

Consider the effect when heat is applied: an increase of temperature will cause the gas to expand and this will be shown by an increase in the volume, i.e. the piston moves upwards a small amount. By starting this experiment at 0°C, the increase in volume for a 1°C rise in temperature will be 1/273 of the volume that it occupied at 0°C. This result is generally known as Charles' Law which states that:

*The volume of a fixed mass of gas at constant pressure expands by 1/273 of its volume at 0°C per °C rise in temperature*

Figure 9.7.2 shows the expansion due to heating the gas and contraction due to cooling the gas. In the latter case the volume decreases by 1/273 for every 1°C fall in temperature, so if this situation continued to a temperature of −273°C, the gas would cease to exist. This 'gas disappearance' does not apply in practice, because the gas changes to a liquid before the temperature of −273°C is reached.

A temperature of −273°C is considered to be the temperature at which heat ceases to exist and is called *absolute zero*. This was proved by Lord Kelvin, and for his work in this field his name was chosen as the SI unit for temperature. Zero on kelvin scale is −273°C, so to

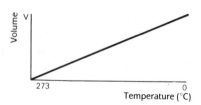

**Fig. 9.7.2** Graph showing that if the temperature is lowered the volume will decrease

convert degrees Celsius to kelvin add 273 to the Celsius value. Temperatures based on the kelvin scale do not use the degree symbol, e.g.

$$16°C = 16 + 273 = 289 \text{ K}$$

Having introduced the meaning of absolute zero, it is now possible to express Charles' Law in symbol form.

Assuming the pressure is kept constant:

$$\frac{V_1}{t_1} = \frac{V_2}{t_2}$$

where
$V_1$ = initial volume
$V_2$ = final volume
$t_1$ = initial temperature
$t_2$ = final temperature

The temperature scale for $t_1$ and $t_2$ must be based on absolute zero – so the kelvin scale is used.

## REMEMBER

**Absolute zero of temperature is**

- $-273°C$
- where heat ceases to exist
- expressed in degrees kelvin
- calculated by adding 273 to the Celsius temperature e.g:

$$20°C = 20 + 273 = 293 \text{ K}$$

- used for gas law calculations

### Example

Gas in the cylinder shown in Figure 9.7.3 has a volume of 60 cm³ at 27°C. What is the volume of the gas at 77°C?

Let $V_2$ = final volume (cm³)

$$\frac{V_1}{t_1} = \frac{V_2}{t_2}$$

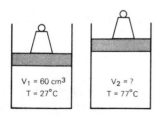

$V_1 = 60 \text{ cm}^3$
$T = 27°C$

$V_2 = ?$
$T = 77°C$

**Fig. 9.7.3** Example of gas law

where
$V_1$ = initial volume cm³ = 60
$V_2$ = final volume cm³ = ?
$t_1$ = initial temperature K = 27 + 273
$t_2$ = final temperature K = 77 + 273

$$V_2 = \frac{V_1 t_2}{t_1}$$

$$V_2 = \frac{60 \times 350}{300} = 70 \text{ cm}^3$$

### Boyle's Law

Earlier studies showed that the pressure of a gas increases when the volume is decreased, assuming the temperature is kept constant. The relationship between pressure and volume is summarised by Boyle's Law which states that:

*The volume of a fixed mass of gas is inversely proportional to the pressure, provided the temperature remains constant*

This statement can be simplified by considering Figure 9.7.4. Assuming the temperature is kept constant, the effect of decreasing the volume is to raise the pressure. Compressing the gas into half its original volume doubles the pressure, and if this was continued to a point where the volume is $\frac{1}{8}$ of its original volume, i.e. a compression ratio of 8 : 1, then the final pressure would be eight times as great as the original pressure. This pressure/volume relationship is shown in Figure 9.7.5.

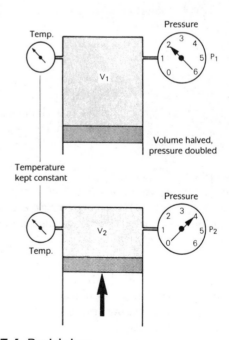

**Fig. 9.7.4** Boyle's law

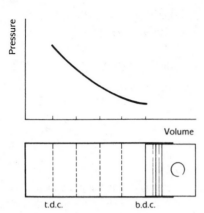

**Fig. 9.7.5** Graph showing that decrease in volume causes an increase in pressure

The pressure of the gas must be expressed as an absolute pressure. Zero on the absolute pressure scale is the point where no pressure exists, i.e. a 'perfect' vacuum. Using this scale:

**Standard atmospheric pressure is 101.4 kN/m$^2$ or 760 mm of mercury**

For practical purposes this can be approximated to:

**Atmospheric pressure = 100 kN/m$^2$ or 100 kPa or 1 bar**

The pascal, Pa, is the SI unit of pressure: $1\ Pa = 1\ N/m^2$. Boyle's Law can also be expressed as

$$pV = \text{constant}$$
or
$$p_1 V_1 = p_2 V_2$$

where $p_1$ and $p_2$ = initial and final absolute pressures
$V_1$ and $V_2$ = initial and final volumes

**Example**

An engine cylinder contains 480 cm$^3$ of air at an absolute pressure of 1 bar (100 kN/m$^2$). Assuming the temperature is kept constant, what will be the absolute pressure when the volume is reduced to 60 cm$^3$?

$$p_1 V_1 = p_2 V_2$$

where $p_1$ = initial absolute pressure = 1 bar
$p_2$ = final absolute pressure = ?
$V_1$ = initial volume = 480 cm$^3$
$V_2$ = final volume = 60 cm$^3$

$$p_2 = p_1 \frac{V_1}{V_2}$$
$$p_2 = \frac{1 \times 480}{60}$$
$$= 8 \text{ bar or } 800 \text{ kN/m}^2 \text{ or } 800 \text{ kPa}$$

**Working pressure** The expression $V_1/V_2$ or initial volume/final volume is also the compression ratio of an engine. Applying this to the example above (assuming the temperature remains constant) indicates that the

final pressure = initial pressure × compression ratio

During a compression test, this subject shows that a warm engine in good condition should give a minimum compression pressure of about $p_1$ × compression ratio.

If the throttle does not restrict the entry of air, i.e. the throttle is fully open, then the initial pressure should be about 1 bar or 100 kPa.

Since heat is generated by the compression of the gas, then the increase in pressure caused by this heat will raise the final pressure even higher.

**Example**

A compression test is conducted on an engine having a compression ratio of 9.2 : 1. Estimate the compression pressure.

Estimated initial pressure = 1 bar

Excluding effect of 'compression heat' during the test, estimated compression pressure
$$= 1 \times 9.2$$
$$= 9.2 \text{ bar or } 920 \text{ kN/m}^2 \text{ or } 920 \text{ kPa}$$

**Combination of laws**

Previous examples show that in most applications of gas laws there is an alteration to the pressure, volume and temperature of the gas. These situations can be met by combining the two gas laws to give

$$\frac{p_1 V_1}{t_1} = \frac{p_2 V_2}{t_2}$$

**Example**

Under normal operating conditions the compression stroke of a C.I. engine causes air in a cylinder of volume 1200 cm$^3$ to be compressed into a chamber of volume

75 cm³. During this stroke the pressure increases from 100 kPa (1 bar) to 4000 kPa (40 bar). If the initial temperature is 87°C, what is the final temperature?

$$\frac{p_1 V_1}{t_1} = \frac{p_2 V_2}{t_2}$$

$$p_1 V_1 t_2 = p_2 V_2 t_1$$

$$t_2 = \frac{p_2 V_2 t_1}{p_1 V_1}$$

where  $p_1$ = pressure   = 1 bar
       $p_2$ = pressure   = 40 bar
       $V_1$ = volume     = 1200 cm³
       $V_2$ = volume     = 75 cm³
       $t_1$ = temperature = 87 + 273 = 360 K

Substituting values gives

$$t_2 = \frac{40 \times 75 \times 360}{1 \times 1200} = 900 \text{ K}$$

$$= 900 - 273 = 627°C$$

This example shows that if fuel oil having a self-ignition temperature of about 400°C is injected into this heated air, then combustion of the fuel will occur.

## REMEMBER

**Charles' Law is**

- volume of gas at constant pressure expands by 1/273 of its volume at 0°C for every 1°C rise in temperature
- expressed as

$$\frac{V_1}{t_1} = \frac{V_2}{t_2}$$

**Boyle's Law is**

- volume of fixed mass of gas is inversely proportional to its pressure provided the temperature remains constant
- expressed as

$$p_1 V_1 = p_2 V_2$$

**Combination Law is**

- product of Charles' and Boyle's Laws
- expressed as

$$\frac{p_1 V_1}{t_1} = \frac{p_2 V_2}{t_2}$$

# PROGRESS CHECK 9

1. What is meant by the term 'heat'?
(a) the hotness of a body
(b) the degree of hotness
(c) internal energy capable of doing work
(d) work which is stored in a body.

2. The temperature of a body is the:
(a) heat contained in that body
(b) degree of hotness
(c) change of state
(d) rate of conduction.

3. A temperature of 6° Celsius is the same as:
(a) 6° Fahrenheit
(b) 6° Centrigrade
(c) 6 Kelvin
(d) 6 mm mercury.

4. It is considered that heat ceases to exist at a temperature of absolute zero. This occurs at:
(a) 0 K
(b) 273 K
(c) 0°C
(d) 32°C.

5. What is the SI unit of temperature? The:
(a) Centigrade
(b) Fahrenheit
(c) Celsius
(d) Kelvin.

6. State the method of transferring the heat from the piston crown to the piston skirt:
(a) expansion
(b) conduction
(c) convection
(d) radiation.

7. State the method of transferring the heat from the cylinder block to the radiator:
(a) expansion
(b) conduction
(c) convection
(d) radiation.

8. Which one of the following materials has the highest heat conductivity?
(a) asbestos
(b) aluminium
(c) lead
(d) steel

9. Which one of the following is the best conductor of heat: steel, water, oil, air?
(a) steel
(b) water
(c) oil
(d) air.

10. What causes convection in an engine cooling system?
(a) as water is heated it expands, gets lighter and rises
(b) as water is cooled it expands, gets heavier and falls
(c) the pressure given by the pump
(d) the pressure drop at the narrow top hose.

11. What type of heat can be reflected?
(a) conducted
(b) convected
(c) radiant
(d) light.

12. What is the purpose of the fins around the cylinder of a single cylinder engine?
(a) to control expansion
(b) to strengthen the cylinder
(c) to radiate the heat
(d) to reduce the noise.

13. The quantity of heat is the:
(a) energy in joules
(b) hotness of a body
(c) temperature of a substance
(d) heat required to raise the temperature of a substance by 1°C.

14. The heat required to raise the temperature of a body by 1°C is the:
(a) quantity of heat
(b) mechanical equivalent of heat
(c) temperature
(d) heat capacity.

15. The SI unit for specific heat capacity is the:
(a) J
(b) K
(c) J/K
(d) J/kg K.

16. The heat required to raise one kilogram of a substance through 1°C is the:
(a) temperature
(b) quantity of heat
(c) heat capacity
(d) specific heat capacity.

17. The quantity of heat liberated by burning a given amount of fuel is the:
(a) heat capacity
(b) calorific value
(c) specific heat capacity
(d) thermal efficiency.

18. Which one of the following is a typical calorific value for petrol?
(a) 4.4 MJ/kg
(b) 44 MJ/kg
(c) 440 MJ/kg
(d) 4400 MJ/kg.

19. The calorific value of a fuel is needed for calculation of:
(a) thermal efficiency
(b) fuel consumption
(c) specific fuel consumption
(d) indicated power.

20. Which one of the following values represents the specific heat capacity of water?
(a) 900 J/kg K
(b) 1700 J/kg K
(c) 2100 J/kg K
(d) 4200 J/kg K.

21. The heat energy required to raise the mass of 10 kg of water from 16°C to 66°C is:
(a) 500 J
(b) 10.56 kJ
(c) 2100 kJ
(d) 37 632 kJ.

22. Given that the specific heat capacity of oil is 1700 J/kg K, the quantity of heat energy required to raise a mass of 2 kg of oil from 15°C to 65°C is:
(a) 170 kJ
(b) 1950 kJ
(c) 33 150 kJ
(d) 170 000 kJ.

23. A substance which resists any alteration to its definite shape and volume is a:
(a) gas
(b) vapour
(c) liquid
(d) solid.

24. Heat which causes a substance to increase in temperature is called:
(a) latent heat
(b) intense heat
(c) sensible heat
(d) radiant heat.

25. A bellows type thermostat OPENS when the substance changes its state from a:
(a) solid to a vapour
(b) solid to a liquid
(c) liquid to a vapour
(d) liquid to a solid.

26. A wax capsule type of thermostat OPENS when the substance changes its state from a:
(a) solid to a vapour
(b) solid to a liquid
(c) liquid to a vapour
(d) liquid to a solid.

27. What is meant by the term 'linear expansion'?
(a) the heat required to produce expansion
(b) the expansion of any straight object
(c) the increase in length due to expansion
(d) the gradual expansion of aluminium.

28. What provision is made to allow for thermal expansion of a piston ring?
(a) a gap clearance is given
(b) the ring is kept in contact with the cylinder wall
(c) the ring is pegged
(d) the ends of ring are butted together.

29. Which one of the following is a suitable method for fitting a starter ring gear onto a flywheel?
(a) the gear is cooled and forced into the flywheel
(b) the flywheel is heated and forced into the gear
(c) the gear is heated until it is larger than the flywheel
(d) the flywheel is cooled until it is smaller than the gear.

30. Which one of the following is a suitable method of removing a tight gudgeon pin from a piston?

(a) the pin is cooled by immersion in air at temperature of −78°C
(b) the pin is cooled by immersion in air at temperature of 195 K
(c) the piston is expanded by immersion in water at temperature of 110°C
(d) the piston is expanded by immersion in oil at temperature of 110°C.

31. When a brass/steel bi-metal strip is heated the effect is that the strip:
(a) lengthens equally on both sides
(b) twists in a clockwise direction
(c) bends in a direction away from the brass
(d) bends in direction towards the brass.

32. Which one of the following has the highest rate of linear expansion:
(a) aluminium
(b) brass
(c) cast iron
(d) invar steel.

33. The greatest density of water occurs at:
(a) −2°C
(b) 0°C
(c) 4°C
(d) 40°C.

34. Antifreeze is added to a cooling system to:
(a) prevent the system freezing
(b) prevent ice forming at temperatures below 0°C
(c) lower the temperature at which freezing occurs
(d) control the increase in volume when water changes to ice.

35. A cracked cylinder block has resulted from freezing of the coolant. The crack occurs when the:
(a) water changes its state
(b) ice changes its state
(c) ice changes to water
(d) water changes to steam.

36. A liquid boils when the vapour pressure equals the:
(a) external volume
(b) external temperature
(c) internal pressure
(d) external pressure.

37. When a cooling system is pressurised the effect is to:
(a) lower the boiling point
(b) raise the boiling point
(c) allow the engine to heat up quicker
(d) allow the engine to heat up slower.

38. Which two words make the following statement correct? When the petrol in the fuel line is at a pressure . . . . than atmospheric it will vapourise at a . . . . temperature
(a) lower . . . . constant
(b) higher . . . . constant
(c) lower . . . . lower
(d) higher . . . . lower.

39. The expansion of a rod is found by using the expression:
(a) final length $\times \alpha$
(b) original length $\times \alpha$
(c) original length $\times$ temperature rise $\times \alpha$
(d) final length $-$ original length $\times$ temperature rise $\times \alpha$.

40. The expansion of some pistons is restricted by casting in a plate across the gudgeon pin bosses. This plate is made of:
(a) brass
(b) copper
(c) invar
(d) bronze.

41. A connecting rod has a length of 150 mm at 15°C. If the coefficient of linear expansion is 0.000 012 per K the length of the rod at 215°C is:
(a) 150.0018 mm
(b) 150.0024 mm
(c) 150.36 mm
(d) 150.387 mm.

42. A gas at constant pressure increases its volume by a given amount for every 1°C rise in temperature. Raising the gas temperature from 0°C to 1°C causes the volume to increase by:
(a) $\frac{1}{100}$
(b) $\frac{1}{273}$
(c) 1 cm$^3$
(d) 1 mm$^3$.

43. The absolute zero of temperature is:
(a) $-460$°C
(b) $-273$°C
(c) $-100$°C
(d) 0°C.

44. A temperature of 0 kelvin is:
(a) $-460$°C
(b) $-273$°C
(c) $-100$°C
(d) 0°C.

45. A temperature of 43°C is:
(a) 503 K
(b) 316 K
(c) 143 K
(d) 43 K.

46. The gas law $V_1/t_1 = V_2/t_2$ is known as:
(a) Kelvin's law
(b) Boyle's law
(c) Joule's law
(d) Charles' law.

47. Gas in a cylinder occupies a volume of 48 cm$^3$ at 27°C. If the pressure is kept constant, the volume of the gas at 77°C is:
(a) 56 cm$^3$
(b) 137 cm$^3$
(c) 179 cm$^3$
(d) 187 cm$^3$.

48. Gas in a cylinder occupies a volume of 50 cm$^3$ at 27°C. If the pressure is kept constant, the temperature required to increase the volume to 100 cm$^3$ is:
(a) 54°C
(b) 150°C
(c) 327°C
(d) 600°C.

49. For practical purposes 'atmospheric pressure' is taken as:
(a) 0 kN/m$^2$
(b) 15 kN/m$^2$
(c) 1 bar
(d) 101 bar.

50. Given that atmospheric pressure is 100 kN/m$^2$, a gauge pressure of 150 kN/m$^2$ is an absolute pressure of:
(a) 50 kN/m$^2$
(b) 250 kN/m$^2$
(c) 423 kN/m$^2$
(d) 15 000 kN/m$^2$.

# 10 *Combustion and engine performance*

## What is covered in this chapter:

→ combustion of petrol
→ combustion faults
→ fuels for compression-ignition engines
→ engine performance

Often the cause of a particular fault on a motor vehicle is obvious; evidence such as a broken or seized part clearly indicates the necessary rectification work. In many cases however, there is no visual indication of a precise cause of a fault, so you will need to apply your diagnostic skill to establish the reason why a unit produces the given symptoms. Often in your career you will experience these cases, especially those related to engine performance, and you will see how incorrect diagnosis results in high costs and bad customer relations. Furthermore it damages your pride when you do unnecessary work or fit unneeded parts.

Even with modern equipment, accurate fault diagnosis relies on a sound knowledge of vehicle systems. This understanding, combined with the results of diagnostic tests, gives you the ability to identify technical problems and recommend suitable methods of rectification.

This chapter covers some important topics associated with engine operation that you need to know to develop your diagnostic ability.

## 10.1 Combustion of petrol

### Production of petrol

Petrol, or gasoline as it is sometimes called, is obtained by refining crude petroleum. Mined in various parts of the world, the crude oil, as pumped from the ground at the oil well, appears as a thick, black, dirty substance. At the refinery this dirty oil is 'cleaned' and, by means of a distillation process, the raw material is heated and

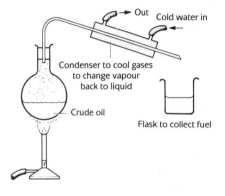

| Heat supplied to crude oil | Substance given off |
|---|---|
| Low ↓ High | Petrol (gasoline) Paraffin (kerosine) Diesel oil Lubricating oil Bitumen |

**Fig. 10.1.1** Distillation of a fuel

divided into a number of different products. Each fuel or oil separated or fractionated in this manner has a boiling point which falls within a given range; light fractions such as petrol boil at a lower temperature than heavy products of the lubricating oil family.

The principle of distillation is shown as Figure 10.1.1. As crude oil in a flask is heated, a vapour is given off from the oil which is condensed and collected by a flask. By maintaining the oil at a temperature within the range shown in the table in Figure 10.1.1 the various products are obtained.

### Combustion and air/fuel ratios

Petrol is a hydrocarbon, i.e. it contains carbon (C) and hydrogen (H), and when this is mixed with oxygen and ignited, a chemical change takes place which releases heat. The amount of heat liberated depends on the quantity of fuel burnt – the greater the quantity the greater is the heat released. However, a limit is reached in an engine when all of the oxygen in the cylinder has been consumed.

For complete combustion, 1 kg of petrol requires a mass of 15 kg of air. This value is obtained from calculations based on the chemistry of combustion and this is generally stated as:

**Chemically correct air/fuel ratio for petrol is 15:1 (by mass)**

When a larger proportion of air is supplied to a given quantity of petrol, the air/fuel ratio is increased and it is said that the 'mixture is weak'. Similarly an air/fuel ratio of 12:1 is considered to be a 'rich mixture'. If the engine uses a fuel other than petrol then the 'chemically correct' air/fuel ratio may have a value different to that stated for petrol.

**Exhaust gas composition**

When the air/fuel ratio is correct for the fuel being used, the main constituents of the exhaust gas are carbon dioxide ($CO_2$), water ($H_2O$), and nitrogen ($N_2$). See Figure 10.1.2. If petrol is considered to be CH, the engine causes the chemicals to change as shown in the table.

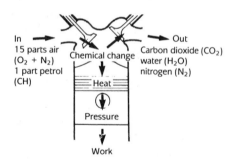

**Fig. 10.1.2** Inlet and outlet gas composition

| Entering engine | Leaving engine |
| --- | --- |
| PETROL + AIR | EXHAUST GAS |
| Petrol + (Oxygen + Nitrogen) | Carbon dioxide + Water + Nitrogen |
| CH + $O_2$ + $N_2$ | $CO_2$ + $H_2O$ + $N_2$ |

A low air/fuel ratio (rich mixture) has insufficient oxygen to complete the combustion process, so some of the fuel leaves the cylinder in a partially burnt state. In addition to the previous exhaust products, this rich

**REMEMBER**

**A chemically-correct petrol/air ratio is**

- 1 part PETROL; 15 parts AIR (by weight)
- the theoretical ideal to produce an exhaust product of $CO_2$, $H_2O$, $N_2$
- not the best for maximum power or maximum economy
- too rich, in practice, for a 'clean' exhaust

mixture produces undesirable products such as carbon monoxide (CO) together with hydrogen (H) and carbon (C). It is these carbon particles emitted from the exhaust that causes black smoke to be discharged from an engine which is running on a rich mixture.

The exhaust product from a weak mixture is 'cleaner' than that given from a rich mixture. Used in this way the word 'cleaner' indicates that health hazards and pollution problems are improved. It is for this reason that fuel systems should be set to operate on an air/fuel ratio that keeps undesirable exhaust gas products within the limits specified in the emission control regulations.

Besides carbon monoxide and free carbon there are two other exhaust gas products that are dangerous to human beings; these are nitrogen oxides ($NO_x$) and free hydrocarbon (HC) particles. The $NO_x$ is formed when the combustion temperature is designed to be exceptionally high. Although this high temperature is good for power, for health reasons the amount of $NO_x$ must be kept below the limit stated in the regulations. Emission of hydrocarbons occurs when unburnt fuel passes to the exhaust; a condition which reflects on the effectiveness of the ignition and carburation systems together with the efficiency of the combustion chamber design. In this chapter you will see the abbreviation for hydrocarbon is expressed in two ways: CH and HC; the alphabetic order shown in the former is recommended in chemistry and the latter is the way it is expressed in many statutory regulations.

Before a manufacturer can sell a new model, a vehicle of the type must be tested in a laboratory and a certificate granted by the appropriate authority to show that all emissions from the vehicle are within the statutory limits. Furthermore an emission test is now a part of the annual MOT test. To perform emission checks, the test centres must use an approved and regularly calibrated infra-red exhaust gas analyser; this measures CO, $CO_2$ HC and $O_2$. The analyser shown as Figure 10.1.3 takes a gas

**Fig. 10.1.3** Many engine tests incorporate 4-gas emission analysers. To minimize the number of control cables, the equipment can be operated remotely with an infra-red handset

*Crypton*

sample from the tail pipe and, after a response time of less than about 10 seconds, indicates the percentages of CO, $CO_2$, and $O_2$ and the quantity of HC in parts per million (ppm). A printer incorporated in the tester gives a record of the test.

### Effects of variations of air/fuel ratio

In an actual engine a chemically correct mixture neither produces maximum power nor gives maximum economy. This is shown by Figure 10.1.4 which illustrates the effect of varying the air/fuel ratio between the limits of very weak to very rich.

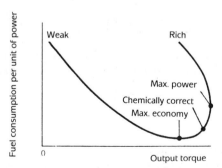

**Fig. 10.1.4** Fuel consumption and engine performance as a function of air/fuel ratio

A fuel set to give maximum economy by operating on a mixture strength which is slightly weaker than 'chemically correct' ensures that the fuel is efficiently burnt, but the slower burning rate gives lower maximum combustion temperatures and reduced power.

If the mixture is weakened beyond this point the amount of fuel required to produce one unit of power is increased and the engine may overheat due to the high heat transfer from the slow moving flame to the combustion chamber surfaces. (In the past the drop in power was clearly demonstrated when an engine was cold: pushing-in the 'choke' too early resulted in low engine power. In this case the very slow burning of the charge continued through the power and exhaust strokes, so when the new petrol/air mixture came into contact with the hot exhaust gas, the incoming charge sometimes ignited and produced 'popping-back' through the carburettor.)

Setting the mixture slightly richer than chemically correct gives a higher power output, but this is obtained at the expense of fuel consumption and exhaust cleanliness. When the mixture is enriched beyond this maximum power position, the fuel consumption rises a considerable amount, but the power only falls off a comparatively small amount. Figure 10.1.5 illustrates these factors.

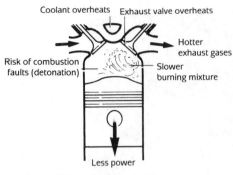

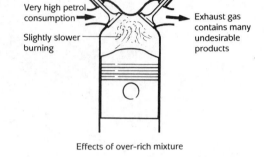

**Fig. 10.1.5** Effect of poor air/fuel ratio

## 10.2 Combustion faults

In practice the performance of an engine running on a rich mixture is often regarded as satisfactory by the driver, even although its petrol consumption has doubled, whereas a mixture which is slightly weak is soon detected. Slower burning also occurs with rich mixtures and the risk of overheating is present, but this is not so severe as that experienced with weak air/fuel ratios – the very slow burning of these weak mixtures can soon ruin an engine. For example, exhaust valves can overheat and melt ('burn'), piston seizure may occur and extensive damage can be produced by combustion faults such as pre-ignition and detonation.

**Normal combustion**

Under normal conditions the compressed petrol/air mixture is ignited by the sparking plug, and a flame, originating from the vicinity of the plug electrodes, progresses across the combustion chamber at a regular rate (Figure 10.2.1). Although the combustion process is completed in a fraction of a second, the pressure caused by the release of heat energy rises steadily to give a smooth start to the power stroke. The flame speed (or flame rate) can be varied by altering the:

1) *Compression pressure*   a high flame speed is obtained when the fuel and air particles are 'packed' close together. This is achieved by a high compression ratio or good breathing.
2) *Air/fuel ratio*   highest flame speed is obtained from a ratio which is slightly rich, whereas as the mixture is weakened the speed decreases a considerable amount.

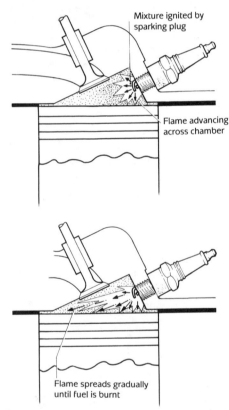

**Fig. 10.2.1** Normal combustion: regular burning gives steady heat rise which gives smooth pressure rise

3) *Degree of turbulence*   air movement in the chamber increases the flame speed.
4) *Quantity of exhaust gas present*   acts as a retarder to the flame and thereby lowers the maximum combustion temperature.

## Detonation and combustion knock

To obtain good engine power, a high flame speed is necessary, since the quicker the fuel burns, the higher will be the temperature of the gas. This requirement suggests that the factors controlling flame speed should be arranged so as to give the highest speed, but when this is attempted various combustion faults develop. To illustrate this problem, let us consider an engine which has a provision for varying the compression ratio. As the compression pressure is increased, the flame speed is also increased, but when a certain compression pressure is reached, the flame speed suddenly rises to a figure which equals the speed of sound. No longer is the fuel burnt in a progressive manner; instead the petrol/air mixture explodes to give a condition called *detonation*. The compression pressure at which detonation occurs depends on many factors; these include the grade of petrol used and the type of combustion chamber.

Examination of the combustion process prior to the onset of this severe detonation would show that a portion of the petrol/air mixture remote from the sparking plug (i.e. the end gas) would not be performing in the normal manner. Instead, this pocket of gas, which has been compressed and heated by the gas already burnt, will spontaneously ignite and cause a rapid build-up of pressure. This condition is called *combustion knock* and Figure 10.2.2 indicates the main features.

Although detonation and combustion knock are two different combustion faults, the general effects are similar. For this reason the two conditions are often grouped together. In both cases they occur *after the spark*.

Effects of detonation and knock depend on the severity of the condition, but the main results are:

- *pinking*, a sound produced by the high pressure waves; the noise described by some people as a 'metallic tapping sound' and by others as the 'sound of fat frying in a pan';
- *shock loading* of engine components;
- *local overheating* in which piston crowns can be melted;
- *reduced engine power*.

These effects show that detonation and knock should be avoided, and if this is to be achieved attention must be given to the items which promote detonation. The main factors are:

1) *Compression pressure and grade of fuel* The compression ratio is linked to the fuel used; engines having high compression ratios generally require a fuel having a high octane number.

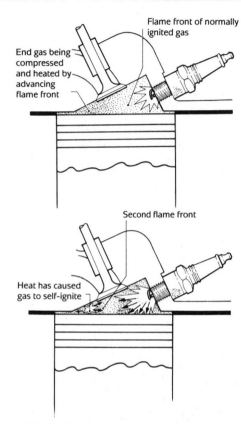

**Fig. 10.2.2** Combustion knock: mixture is burnt very rapidly; giving pinking, damage to engine and reduced power (always occurs after the spark)

2) *Air/fuel ratio* Weak mixtures are prone to detonate.

3) *Combustion chamber type* The degree of turbulence and provision for cooling of the end-gas have a great bearing on the compression ratio which is used.

4) *Ignition timing* An over advanced ignition promotes detonation.

5) *Engine temperature* Overheated components increase the risk of detonation.

### Octane rating

The octane rating of a petrol is a measure of its resistance to knock or detonate. This anti-knock quality varies with fuels, so for classification purposes the knock resistance of a fuel is compared with two reference fuels:

1) *Iso-octane* This is given the number 100 since its anti-knock quality is excellent.

2) *Heptane* This has very poor resistance so the rating given is zero.

A special single cylinder, variable compression engine, fitted with equipment for measuring the knock intensity, is used to determine the octane rating of a fuel. Raising the compression ratio a given amount makes the fuel knock, so by using a mixture of iso-octane and heptane it is possible to vary the proportions of these reference fuels until a similar anti-knock property is obtained. For example, if the fuel has a knock resistance equal to a mixture of 90 per cent iso-octane and 10 per cent heptane, by volume, then the octane number given to the fuel is 90. (It should be noted that the fuel being tested does not have to contain iso-octane.)

Recommendations which cover such things as induction temperature and ignition timing of the special engine ensure that the rating given to a fuel is standardized. Unfortunately, a number of different methods exist and this can cause confusion, e.g. a fuel having an octane rating of 95 based on the Research method has a rating of 84 when established by the Motor method.

***Anti-knock additives***   Some fuels have excellent anti-knock qualities but in general these are either expensive or in short supply. Cheaper products may be obtained by blending (mixing) these expensive fuels with other fuels which are in more plentiful supply. Alternatively, the anti-knock quality may be improved by adding a substance such as tetra-ethyl-lead (t.e.l) to the petrol. Many additives are used in a modern fuel, but substances containing lead are poisonous, so regulations are in force either to limit the quantity that is added, or, in the case of unleaded fuels, to ban its use altogether.

### Pre-ignition

This condition applies when the petrol/air charge in the cylinder is fired by a red-hot particle before it is ignited by the sparking plug. The incandescent object may be a carbon deposit or any protruding component which forms a part of the combustion chamber. Pre-ignition always occurs before the spark and is an undesirable condition which can lead to detonation, melting of the piston crown and other forms of damage. Normally pre-ignition gives a considerable reduction in the engine's power output and is often accompanied by the sound of 'pinking'.

Figure 10.2.3 shows pre-ignition of the charge, and in this case it indicates a situation whereby the rising piston is compressing a gas which is attempting to expand. This will result in a considerable increase of gas pressure and combustion chamber temperature.

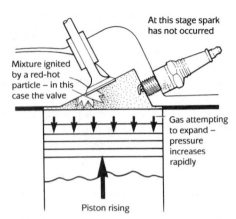

**Fig. 10.2.3** Pre-ignition (always occurs before the spark)

***Running on***   In the past an engine which continued to run after the ignition was switched off was caused by the petrol/air charge being ignited by a 'hot spot' such as a carbon deposit, defective sparking plug or valve with a sharp edge. Today the widespread use of weak mixtures makes this fault a common occurrence, so modern engines are fitted with special electrical devices to starve the engine of fuel when the ignition is switched off.

## REMEMBER

**A combustion fault is:**

- detonation (combustion knock) – ignition AFTER the spark
- pre-ignition – ignition BEFORE the spark

**Detonation is:**

- identified by a 'pinking' sound
- likely to cause structural damage to an engine
- caused by external factors such as, low octane rating of fuel, weak air/fuel ratio, over-advanced ignition, or high engine temperature

**Pre-ignition is:**

- likely to lead to detonation
- a dangerous fault that causes structural damage
- caused when mixture is ignited by some red-hot particle in the cylinder

## 10.3 Fuels for compression-ignition engines

### Ignition delay

Whereas petrol must resist being auto-ignited by the heat generated by the compression of the gas, a fuel for a C.I. engine must ignite easily. The reason for this can be seen when the process of combustion is considered.

Towards the end of the compression stroke, the fuel is injected into the cylinder. On entering, the fuel particles extract heat from the air, vaporize and eventually self-ignite. The time taken for this phase, which is called ignition delay, may be less than a second in time, but during this period the fuel is continuing to enter the cylinder. When ignition eventually takes place, the large quantity of fuel present in the chamber is also fired. This results in a sudden pressure rise that is accompanied by the noise known as *diesel knock*. Noise and vibration are problems which are associated with C.I. engines, so steps are taken to minimize these drawbacks; one way is to reduce the ignition delay period.

Ignition delay is affected by:

- atomization of the fuel
- final temperature of the compressed air
- quality of the fuel.

The fuel quality needed in this context is its ability to self-ignite, i.e. the temperature at which it will spontaneously ignite. At this stage it should be pointed out that the self-ignition temperature is NOT the flash point. The *flash point* of a fuel is the lowest temperature at which the fuel gives off a vapour that will flash when exposed to a naked flame. (Flash point for diesel fuel is about 70°C whereas the self-ignition temperature is in the region of 400°C.)

### Cetane rating

To classify fuels for C.I. engines the cetane rating is adopted. This compares the ignition quality of a fuel with two reference fuels:

- *cetane*     given the value of 100 because of its good ignition quality;
- *alpha-methyl-naphthalene*     rated as zero.

A fuel rated at 55 has a similar ability to self-ignite to a fuel consisting of 55% cetane and 45% alpha-methyl-naphthalene by volume.

The fuel used in a C.I. engine should have a cetane number just high enough to give freedom from pronounced diesel knock.

## 10.4 Engine performance

After engines have been designed and manufactured engineers need to measure the engine's output to assess the success of their work. Over the years the output power of an engine has been one of the most important considerations. This and some other performance factors are considered here.

### Power

The power output of an engine indicates the work that it can do in a set time; the SI unit of power is the *watt*. This unit is too small to use for engine output, so the term *kilowatt* is generally used. Since the introduction of the SI system, the previously used term; *horsepower* is no longer a preferred unit, but it is still in common use throughout the world. (The abbreviations *b.h.p.* and *i.h.p.* referred to *brake horse power* and *indicated horse power* respectively.)

The place on the engine at which the power is measured affects its value, so a prefix is used to denote the point of measurement. The *indicated power* is the power produced within the cylinders before any friction and pumping losses, and *brake power* is the output measured at the flywheel (Figure 10.4.1). The prefixes used are based on the methods that were used to gauge the power at each point; indicated based on the 'indicator' instrument fitted to the cylinder to show the working pressure, and brake is taken from the 'brake' type dynamometer used in the past to measure the power output of an engine.

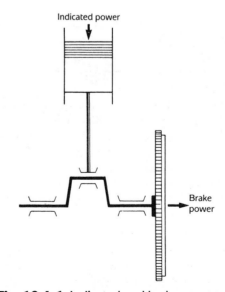

**Fig. 10.4.1** Indicated and brake power

Originally the *dynamometer* was either a rope or friction lined brake that acted against the engine flywheel. Resistance to engine motion by the brake applies a load on the engine and measurement of the torque on the brake at a set engine speed allows the power to be calculated as follows:

$$\text{power} = 2\pi nT$$

where power is in watts, $T$ = torque Nm, $n$ = speed rev/s.

## Example

The torque at a dynamometer is 35 Nm when the engine speed is 50 rev/s. Calculate the brake power.

$$\begin{aligned}\text{brake power} &= 2\pi nT \\ &= 2 \times 3.142 \times 50 \times 35 \\ &= 10\,997 \text{ W or } 10.997 \text{ kW}\end{aligned}$$

For conversion purposes: 1 hp = 746 watts (this is about 0.75 kW) so in this example the engine output is about 15 hp.

Today, torque and power output are measured by either a hydraulic or electrical type dynamometer. Normally the engine is bench-tested on a dynamometer, but special roller-type models, similar to brake testers, are available that accommodate the complete vehicle. When the floor-mounted type is used, allowance must be made for the frictional losses between the engine and the rollers of the dynamometer.

*Mechanical efficiency*   The relationship between brake power and indicated power gives an idea of the power loss between the cylinders and flywheel. It is stated as:

$$\text{mechanical efficiency} = \frac{\text{brake power}}{\text{indicated power}} \times \frac{100}{1}$$

Mechanical efficiency decreases as the engine speed is increased; a typical figure for a spark-ignition engine is 80%. In this case 20% of the indicated power is used to overcome the friction and other losses associated with the pumping of gases during the induction and exhaust strokes. Engine features, such as the use of low viscosity oils and pistons skirts designed to give a low oil drag, improve the mechanical efficiency and result in a higher brake power.

*Torque*   The torque output of an engine gives an indication of the driving force (*tractive effort*) of a vehicle. An engine having a high torque has good pulling ability

and is able to overcome a greater resistance to vehicle motion without the assistance of excessive gearing. A vehicle used to tow a trailer would benefit from an engine that develops a high torque. As with most performance factors, the torque of an engine varies with the speed.

## Fuel consumption

The rate that an engine consumes fuel is very important to most potential buyers. Before a new car is sold, a statutory regulation (*Passenger Car Fuel Consumption Order 1983*) requires the manufacturer to test a car of similar specification in a laboratory and publish the results showing the fuel consumption achieved when it is driven under urban conditions and at speeds of 90 km/h (56 mile/h) and 120 km/h (75 mile/h).

Many vehicle owners think that their vehicle should produce figures that correspond with the manufacturer's test, and this can lead to a complaint that the vehicle is using too much fuel. You must be aware that the figures quoted in the manufacturer's sales literature are based on simulated tests that do not take into account actual driving conditions such as use of the vehicle in traffic for short journeys. It would be unwise to start remedial work that is unlikely to achieve any improvement in fuel consumption. Remember, somebody has to pay the repair bill!

*Specific fuel consumption*   This is a more technical way to express fuel consumption, because it also takes into account the power output. The specific fuel consumption (s.f.c) is the quantity of fuel that is required to produce one unit of power:

$$\text{s.f.c} = \frac{\text{fuel consumption (litres/h)}}{\text{brake power (kW)}}$$

In this case the specific fuel consumption is expressed in litres per kilowatt hour (litre/kW h), but under the Imperial system it was given in pints per bhp (pt/bhp h). To convert pt/bhp h to litres/kW h, multiply by 0.76; e.g.

$$0.5 \text{ pt/bhp h} = 0.38 \text{ litre/kW h}$$

## Performance curves

The curves shown in Figure 10.4.2 represent the power, torque and fuel consumption of a typical spark-ignition engine that is operating under maximum load conditions. To obtain these results the throttle is held in the full-open position and the engine speed is varied by a dynamometer load control.

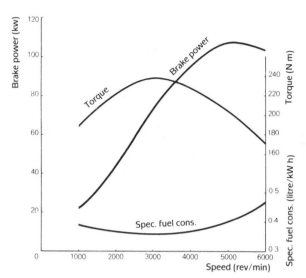

**Fig. 10.4.2** Power and consumption curves (3 litre, OHC, V8 engine)

You will see that maximum torque occurs at a comparatively low speed (3000 rev/min) and above and below that point the torque decreases due to a fall in volumetric efficiency (gas filling efficiency of a cylinder). This is caused by the failure of the fixed valve timing system used on normally aspirated engines to give good breathing over a wide speed range. The valve timing at high engine speed allows insufficient time for an adequate supply of new gas to enter the cylinder, so the torque output falls. One purpose of turbocharging is to compensate for this engine breathing deficiency.

The fall-off in torque after the speed at which it attains its maximum does not immediately affect the power. This is because the engine speed increases at a greater rate, but this only occurs up to the speed at which maximum power is achieved; at this point the two balance but beyond it the speed increase cannot compensate for the decay in torque.

**Road testing**

A vehicle is road-tested either to diagnose reported faults or to check the effectiveness of repair work that has been undertaken. To carry out this operation, you must hold the appropriate driving licence, be authorised by your company to test vehicles and be fully insured to undertake this work. During the testing sequence you must observe the highway code and be considerate to other road users.

## Good practice

### DURING A ROAD TEST, ENGINE CHECKS SHOULD BE MADE FOR:

- ease of starting, including cold-starting
- hesitation
- cutting out
- running-on
- lack of power
- poor acceleration
- black or blue smoke
- oil and coolant leaks
- fuel leaks and odours
- exhaust leaks and noises
- misfire or uneven running
- overheating or overcooling
- abnormal mechanical noises
- detonation, pinking and knocking
- fuel consumption if engine is fitted with test tank
- radio interference

Besides harnessing the various human aural and visual senses, a tester needs to develop other senses to assess, using planned functional methods, factors such as acceleration and vibration. Although the main attention of testers is directed towards the reported problems, or rectified faults, they are also required to survey the general condition of the vehicle so that any faults undetected by the driver can be reported. This is very important where vehicle safety is involved.

## REMEMBER

**Engine power is:**

- rate of doing work
- called *indicated power* when it is 'measured in the cylinders'
- called *brake power* when it is measured at the engine flywheel
- normally expressed in kW
- measured by a dynamometer
- calculated from $P = 2\pi nT$
- taken in account when calculating the s.f.c.

# PROGRESS CHECK 10

1. Petrol is obtained by:
(a) refining crude oil
(b) processing vegetable products
(c) fractionizing coal
(d) heating wooden substances.

2. The term 'light fraction' as applied to petroleum products is a fuel which:
(a) resists vaporization
(b) is used for lighting purposes
(c) boils at a low temperature
(d) boils at a high temperature.

3. Petrol consists of:
(a) oxygen and carbon
(b) carbon and hydrogen
(c) hydrogen and nitrogen
(d) nitrogen and oxygen.

4. The minimum mass of air required to give complete combustion of 1 kg of petrol is:
(a) 9 kg
(b) 12 kg
(c) 15 kg
(d) 18 kg.

5. Expressed as a ratio of masses, the chemically correct air/fuel ratio for petrol is:
(a) 9:1
(b) 12:1
(c) 15:1
(d) 18:1.

6. A 'weak mixture' is the term used to describe a:
(a) low air/fuel ratio
(b) high air/fuel ratio
(c) ratio having a number smaller than 15
(d) ratio in the region of 12:1.

7. Under ideal running conditions, the gas exhausted from a petrol engine using the chemically correct air/fuel ratio consists of:
(a) carbon monoxide and nitrogen
(b) oxygen and carbon monoxide
(c) water, carbon monoxide and carbon dioxide
(d) carbon dioxide, water and nitrogen.

8. Which one of the following chemical symbols represents carbon monoxide?
(a) CNO
(b) $NO_x$
(c) CO
(d) $CO_2$.

9. Which one of the following is an exhaust emission which is associated with high combustion temperatures?
(a) CO
(b) $CO_2$
(c) $NO_x$
(d) $H_2O$.

10. When an engine is running on a very rich mixture, the exhaust gas will consist of nitrogen, water and carbon dioxide as well as considerable amounts of:
(a) C, CO and H
(b) C, $O_2$ and H
(c) C, CO and $O_2$
(d) $O_2$, CO and H.

11. To obtain maximum power from an actual engine the air/fuel ratio should be set:
(a) slightly richer than the chemically correct value
(b) slightly weaker than the chemically correct value
(c) to the chemically correct value
(d) to give a weak mixture at low speed and rich mixture at high speed.

12. When does 'combustion knock' and 'detonation' occur?
(a) before the spark
(b) just before the spark
(c) at the time of the spark
(d) after the spark.

13. Which one of the following is associated with 'combustion knock'?
(a) Pinking
(b) Missing
(c) Popping back
(d) Explosions in the exhaust.

14. Which one of the following fuels would cause a high compression engine to knock? A fuel which has a:
(a) low octane value
(b) high octane value
(c) low calorific value
(d) high calorific value.

15. An octane rating of 80 means that the fuel:
(a) boils at a temperature of 80°C
(b) has a flash point of 80°C
(c) is made up of 80 per cent iso-octane and 20 per cent heptane
(d) has a similar anti-knock property to a reference fuel consisting of 80 per cent iso-octane by volume.

16. A typical octane rating for a petrol is:
(a) 60
(b) 74
(c) 84
(d) 97.

17. In the past t.e.l. was added to petrol to improve its resistance to knock. Modern fuels do not use this additive because it:
(a) is dangerous to health
(b) is difficult to manufacture
(c) causes damage to the valve guides
(d) makes the combustion more difficult to control.

18. When the petrol/air charge in an engine cylinder is fired by a red-hot particle the condition is called:
(a) knock
(b) detonation
(c) pre-ignition
(d) hunting.

19. The period of time between injection and initial burning of the fuel in a C.I. engine is called:
(a) flame spread
(b) ignition delay
(c) diesel knock
(d) flash time.

20. As applied to a fuel, the term 'self-ignition temperature' means the:
(a) flash point
(b) cetane rating
(c) temperature at which the fuel gives off a flammable vapour
(d) temperature at which the fuel will spontaneously ignite.

21. A typical self-ignition temperature for a fuel used in a C.I. engine is:
(a) 70°C
(b) 180°C
(c) 400°C
(d) 552°C.

22. The ignition quality of a fuel for a C.I. engine is called the:
(a) delay period
(b) knock value
(c) cetane rating
(d) octane rating.

23. The sudden pressure rise resulting from a long delay period during the combustion process in a C.I. engine causes:
(a) diesel knock
(b) rapid atomization of the fuel
(c) ignition of the fuel
(d) pre-ignition.

24. Which one of the following reduces the ignition delay in a C.I. engine?
(a) Lowering the temperature of the air charge
(b) Reducing the atomization of the fuel
(c) Using a fuel with a higher cetane value
(d) Using a fuel with a higher self-ignition temperature.

25. Which one of the following reduces 'diesel knock'?
(a) Lowering the temperature of the air charge
(b) Reducing the atomization of the fuel
(c) Using a fuel with a higher cetane value
(d) Using a fuel with a high self-ignition temperature.

26. A fuel has a cetane value of 55. This means that the fuel:
(a) contains 55% of cetane by volume
(b) contains 55% cetane by mass
(c) has a flash point similar to a fuel consisting of 55% cetane and 45% alpha-methyl-naphthalene by volume
(d) has a self-ignition temperature similar to a fuel consisting of 55% cetane and 45% alpha-methyl-naphthalene by volume.

27. A dynamometer is an instrument for measuring the:
(a) energy output of a machine
(b) energy given out by an electrical machine
(c) effort required to drive a machine
(d) water flow through an engine.

28. The power output from an engine is called the:
(a) torque
(b) dynamometer load
(c) indicated power
(d) brake power.

29. If $T$ = torque (Nm) and $n$ = speed (rev/s), which one of the following expressions represents the power in watts?
(a) $\pi n T$
(b) $2\pi T$
(c) $2nT$
(d) $2\pi nT$.

30. If the torque output of an engine is known, the brake power can be calculated by multiplying the torque in newton-metres by:
(a) $2\pi r$, where $r$ = radius in metres
(b) $2\pi n$, where $n$ = speed in revolutions per second
(c) the speed
(d) the torque arm length.

31. An engine develops a torque of 84 Nm at a speed of 3600 rev/min. Taking $\pi$ as 22/7, the brake power is:
(a) 1.9008 kW
(b) 15.84 kW
(c) 31.68 kW
(d) 302.4 kW.

32. The term 'brake' as applied to the expression 'brake power' is used to show:
    (a) the type of movement given by the engine
    (b) the point at which the power is measured
    (c) that a retarding action is applied to the flywheel
    (d) that the energy is used to act on a brake.

33. The mechanical efficiency of an engine is 82%. The 18% loss is due to:
    (a) low speed operation
    (b) a low indicated power
    (c) friction and pumping losses
    (d) the calorific value of the fuel.

34. Specific fuel consumption is:
    (a) (brake power)/(fuel consumption)
    (b) (fuel consumption)/(brake power)
    (c) brake power × fuel consumption
    (d) fuel consumption × brake power.

35. A spark-ignition engine develops a maximum torque at 2800 rev/min. When the engine speed is increased to 3500 rev/min, the torque:
    (a) decreases due to a fall in volumetric efficiency
    (b) decreases due to an improvement in the breathing
    (c) increases due to a fall in volumetric efficiency
    (d) increases due to an improvement in the breathing.

# 11 Electrical circuits

## What is covered in this chapter:

→ basic principles
→ effects of an electrical current
→ electrical units
→ batteries
→ Ohm's law
→ voltage distribution in circuits

In early days the ignition system was the only part of a vehicle that used electricity. Today we see its use spread to a point where most mechanical units are either operated or controlled by electricity. With the introduction of electronics, even more electrical components have been fitted. This is because electronic units provide an efficient method of control that take into account the operating conditions under which the vehicle has to perform.

Some people working in the repair industry regard electricity as a mystery; most probably this is due to the fact that they cannot see anything other than the final effect. Because they do not understand the basic rules, they are likely to cause extensive damage. In the past their ignorance might have been highlighted by the flash of an unexpected spark, but nowadays it will probably lead to the replacement of an expensive electronic control unit.

In this chapter you will cover electrical principles that will enable you to grasp the operation of basic electrical systems and their electronic control units. When you can apply these principles and understand the operation of the systems, you will be able to undertake the recommended testing technique to identify faulty components and advise the less-qualified of a suitable method of repair. In this age of sophisticated diagnostic equipment you should remember that if you are doubtful about performing a certain test you must enlist the help of an experienced technician; i.e. ASK before wrecking the system!

## 11.1 Basic principles

### The electrical circuit

Let us consider wiring-up a lamp to a battery. Examination of the lamp shows that it consists of a short length of fine wire called a filament: each end of this is connected to a soldered contact formed in the brass cap. The holder for this lamp enables an electric wire to connect with each end of the filament. When the ends of the two wires from the lamp are connected to the terminals of a battery, *electric current* flows from the battery and the lamp lights. This means that you have formed an *electrical circuit* – a continuous electrical path. To trace such a path start at any point in the circuit and follow the path around the pattern of wire until you return to the point of origin.

You will discover that when a wire is disconnected in the curcuit you have formed the light is extinguished. Adding a switch has the same effect. It breaks or interrupts the circuit when the light is not required. If you remove the cover of a simple switch you will see how it operates mechanically.

Circuits can be illustrated in various ways; Figure 11.1.1(a) shows a pictorial layout. To save time and space it is usual to represent the various electrical items by symbols. Some of the common items are shown here.

Fig. 11.1.1(b) shows, in theoretical (symbolic) form, a similar circuit to the one shown in Fig. 11.1.1(a). The position of the switch indicates that the circuit is broken (interrupted) or *open*, so no electrical current can flow.

*A flow of electricity cannot take place unless the circuit is closed or complete*

### Flow of electricity

Matter is made up from tiny particles called molecules and these, in turn, are built up from even smaller particles called atoms. This subdivision does not end here, because each atom consists of a large number of extremely minute particles called *electrons*, which are

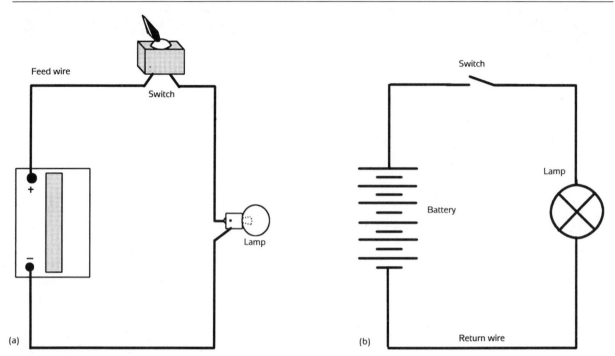

**Fig. 11.1.1** Pictorial and theoretical (symbolic) circuits

# REMEMBER

## Electrical symbols

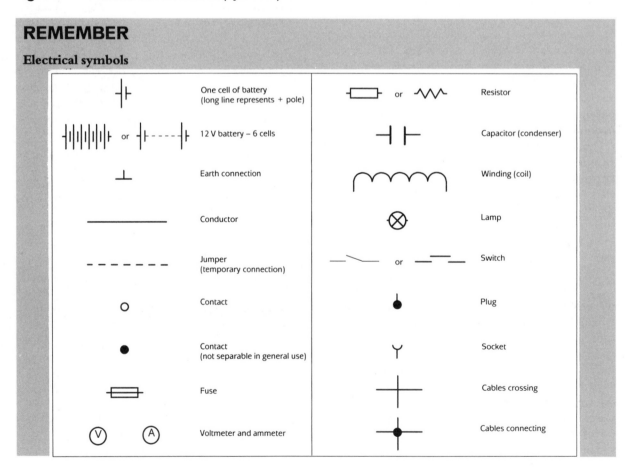

| Symbol | Description | Symbol | Description |
|---|---|---|---|
| | One cell of battery (long line represents + pole) | or | Resistor |
| or | 12 V battery – 6 cells | | Capacitor (condenser) |
| | Earth connection | | Winding (coil) |
| | Conductor | | Lamp |
| | Jumper (temporary connection) | or | Switch |
| | Contact | | Plug |
| | Contact (not separable in general use) | | Socket |
| | Fuse | | Cables crossing |
| | Voltmeter and ammeter | | Cables connecting |

| Material | | Current flow for a given electrical pressure |
|---|---|---|
| Conductors | Silver | 1 036 000 |
| | Copper | 1 000 000 |
| | Aluminium | 637 000 |
| | Nickel | 254 000 |
| | Iron | 175 000 |
| | Lead | 82 000 |
| | Carbon | 815 |
| Insulators | Glass | 0.000 000 000 2 |
| | Paper | 0.000 000 000 002 |
| | Porcelain | 0.000 000 000 000 002 |
| | Ebonite | 0.000 000 000 000 000 2 |
| | Mica | 0.000 000 000 000 000 02 |

**Table 11.1.1** Electrical conductivity of materials

orbiting, at high speed, around a fixed central particle called the nucleus.

If a battery is connected to the ends of a piece of copper wire, electrons from one atom are passed to the next atom, which in turn passes on some of its electrons. From this it is seen that the closing of the circuit allows the electrons to flow around the whole circuit, including within the battery, while the atoms remain stationary.

In some ways electricity can be likened to water – electron flow in a wire is similar to water flow in a pipe. To produce the movement of the water, some form of pump or 'forcing' device is required. This gives the necessary pressure to urge the water through the system. A battery in an electrical circuit does a similar job – the electrical 'pressure' between the two poles of the battery urges the electrons around the circuit.

The higher the 'pressure' of the battery, the greater will be the flow of electrons. The flow of electrons is called an *electric current* and the direction of the current in a circuit is governed by the *polarity* of the supply. This means that when the battery connections are reversed, the direction of flow of the current is also reversed.

Each battery terminal (or pole) is given a name, positive or negative (represented by the symbols + and −). These names were selected many years ago, since it was assumed that the flow of the current, in the circuit external to the battery, took place in the direction of positive to negative. More recent discoveries show that movement of electrons is actually from negative to positive.

## Conductors and insulators

It has already been shown that when a battery is connected to the ends of a piece of copper wire an electric current flows. This would not be the case if the copper wire were replaced by a length of rubber. A material which freely allows the passage of an electric current is called a *conductor*, whereas a material which resists the flow of current would be called a bad conductor or *insulator*. Copper is a good conductor, whereas rubber is a good insulator.

There is no definite dividing line between a conductor and an insulator, however, since most materials will act as an electrical conductor if sufficient electrical pressure is applied. In other words, a perfect insulator does not exist, and neither does a perfect conductor.

The values of current flow given in Table 11.1.1 are approximate and are only intended as a guide.

Most metals are conductors of electricity, but few can compare with copper. When this feature is linked with the fact that copper is very easily drawn into wire, it will be appreciated why the material is extensively used for electric cables on motor vehicles.

## Insulated and earth return systems

The electrical circuits shown so far in this chapter have used two cables to connect the lamp to the battery. This arrangement is known as an *insulated-return* (i.r.) system, and one lead would be called the *feed cable* and the other the *return*. Since a motor vehicle incorporates a number of separate circuits, the i.r. arrangement would give a bulky, costly assembly.

Today the majority of vehicles use the frame to act as the return lead; this arrangement is called *earth return* (e.r.). In Figure 11.1.2 the steel frame of the vehicle is called *earth* and in this case is *negative earth*, because the negative battery terminal is connected to the frame.

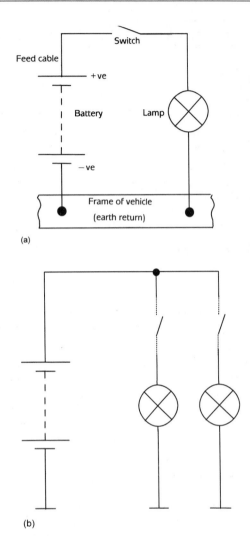

(a)

(b)

**Fig. 11.1.2** Earth return representation

The earth return system demands extra attention to insulation. If, for example, the cable linking the battery with the switch had a defective insulation covering which allowed the bare conductor to touch the metal frame, then an excessively high current would flow through this *short circuit* from the wire to the frame. The heating of the cable due to the high current could easily cause a fire. Since many sharp edges exist on the frame and vibration is always present when the vehicle is moving, the need for care in insulating, positioning and securing the cables is obvious.

On special vehicles such as fuel tankers, extra precautions are necessary. This type of vehicle generally uses the two-wire insulated return system for safety reasons.

### Series and parallel circuits

Let us consider the wiring-up of a circuit comprising two lamps, a switch and a battery. Two basic arrangements could be used and these are known as series and parallel.

*Series circuits*  Figure 11.1.3(a) shows the lamps connected in series, as can be seen from the fact that the lamps are connected end to end. This layout means that any one electron must pass through one lamp before it reaches the other lamp. Breaking a lamp filament would interrupt the flow of current from the battery and would give a similar effect to opening the switch.

Whenever the current is passed through a material which resists its passage, the electrical pressure or potential is reduced. This point can be shown clearly by means of an actual series circuit. A circuit having only one lamp may give a bright light, but when a similar lamp is connected in series with the first, it is found that the lower electrical pressure acting on each lamp causes them both to emit only a dull light. As more lamps are inserted in the circuit, the intensity of light gradually falls until a point is reached when the lamp filament does not even glow red.

*Parallel circuits*  Connecting two lamps in parallel means that the lamps are connected side-by-side as shown in Figures 11.1.2(b) and 11.1.3(b). It must be appreciated that the expression 'side-by-side' only applies to the circuit diagram. In practice the lamps may be far removed from each other within the motor vehicle.

Lamps in parallel with each other receive the maximum electrical pressure from the battery. This means that each gives its maximum useful illumination, irrespective of the number of lamps used, assuming the

Current would still flow in a circuit if the battery terminals were reversed to give *positive earth*. In this arrangement the flow of current would be in the opposite direction, but the system is still called earth return. The earth potential must be known before fitting a battery, because some electrical components are damaged if the wrong battery terminal is earthed.

Up to about 1960 most British manufacturers favoured positive earth return, but at that time a change was made to the negative earth system to align with other countries, as in Figures 11.1.1 and 11.1.2.

Diagrams can be simplified by using the symbols shown in Figure 11.1.2(b). The diagram shows two lamps controlled by separate switches. Electric current flow can be controlled by the switches to produce a flow through one lamp or two.

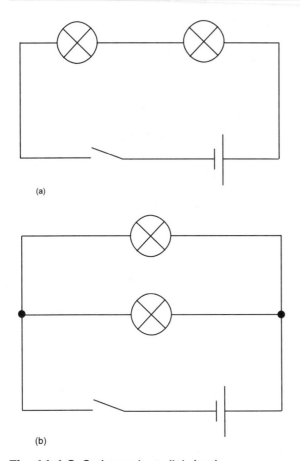

(a)

(b)

**Fig. 11.1.3** Series and parallel circuits

battery is capable of supplying the necessary current and no other items are in the circuit. Failure of any one lamp has no effect on the others because the parallel connection means that each lamp is independently connected to the battery supply.

Parallel circuits are extensively used on motor vehicles and Figure 11.1.4 shows a typical lighting

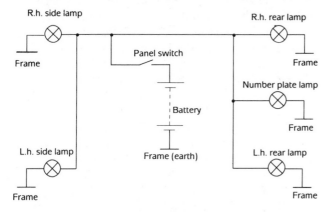

**Fig. 11.1.4** Simple lighting circuit

circuit. When the switch is moved to supply current to the side and tail lamps, it will be seen that the five lamps light to full brilliance.

## 11.2 Effects of an electrical current

An electric current can produce lighting, heating, magnetic and chemical effects and the motor vehicle utilises one or more of these to operate various electrical components.

### Heating effect

We have already seen examples of this effect when a lamp is inserted in a circuit to produce light. During an experiment it will be seen that the wire filament of the lamp is very thin, and that when an electrical current passes, the heating effect causes the filament to become white hot. Raising the electrical pressure applied to the lamp drives a greater current through it and this would, if taken far enough, raise the temperature to a point where the filament would melt.

### Magnetic effect

At some time in your life, most probably you have experimented with permanent magnets. You will remember that certain steels have the ability of retaining magnetism. The action of a magnet can be shown by placing pieces of ferrous materials (i.e. iron and steel) close to the magnet and noting the attraction between them, or by suspending a bar magnet by a length of cotton and observing the fact that it always wants to point in one direction – Magnetic North. (This is why one pole of the magnet is called North).

You will have also seen the pattern produced after iron fillings have been scattered on a sheet of paper held over a magnet. This experiment shows the presence of a magnetic field. These investigations generally lead up to the law that:

> *Like magnetic poles repel and unlike poles attract*

This law indicates that when two north poles are brought together a force is created which tends to push the magnets apart, whereas a north pole of one magnet placed near a south pole of another causes the magnets to be drawn together.

A magnet can also be produced electrically. This is demonstrated by the apparatus shown in Figure 11.2.1. A coil of wire is wound around a soft iron core and is connected to a battery. Current flow in the coil creates a magnetic field which causes the iron to become a

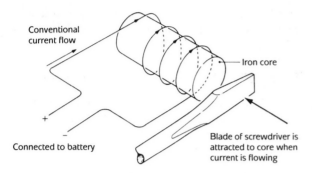

**Fig. 11.2.1** Demonstration of magnetism produced by electric coil

magnet, but on disconnecting the battery the core quickly loses most of its magnetism. If a steel core were used instead of soft iron, it would retain a large amount of magnetism. Residual magnetism of this order is generally undesirable because the unit operated by this magnet should only function when the circuit is energised.

Motor vehicles utilise the magnetic effect in the following ways to actuate switches (the application of each is shown in brackets). They are known as *actuators*:

a) *Armature*    An L-shaped frame on to which is hinged an inverted L-shaped piece of soft iron is called an armature. When current flows through the adjacent coil of wire, the core becomes energised (i.e. becomes a magnet) and the armature is attracted to the core. In this way a small current in the coil can operate on and off the electrical contacts of a much larger switch, as shown in Figure 11.2.2(a). (Cut-out, regulator, horn relays).

b) *Solenoid*    The application shown in Fig. 11.2.2(b) uses a tubular soft iron core into which is inserted a sliding, soft iron plunger. As current flows around the coil, the core becomes a magnet and the plunger is

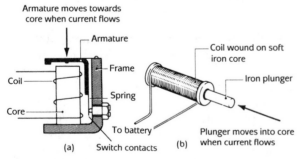

**Fig. 11.2.2** Mechanical movement created by magnetic forces

attracted to it. This arrangement is called a solenoid. In this way the plunger pushes or pulls open or closed adjacent switch contacts. (Electric petrol pumps and starter switches.)

Magnetic effects also form the basis for the operation of an alternator and starter.

### Chemical effect

This effect is demonstrated by the apparatus shown in Figure 11.2.3. An electric current is supplied to two strips of lead immersed in a jar containing a solution of sulphuric acid ($H_2SO_4$) and distilled water ($H_2O$).

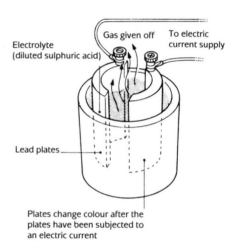

**Fig. 11.2.3** Chemical effect created by electric current

It is found that the acid solution acts as an electrical conductor and allows current to flow around the circuit. As the experiment proceeds, the lead plates change colour which indicates that a chemical change is taking place in the material of the plates. The acid solution also undergoes a change, but this cannot be seen until the current has been flowing for a considerable time. After this period it will be observed that gas bubbles are given off. If this gas is collected some of it will be found to be hydrogen, which is highly inflammable.

The chemical symbols for the acid shows that the substance consists of hydrogen, sulphur and oxygen. Passage of the electric current has caused the solution to decompose (separate). A compound which can be decomposed in this manner is called an *electrolyte*.

The chemical action just described is similar to that which takes place in a battery when it is being 'charged'.

## 11.3   Electrical units

*Ampere (A)*   The ampere, sometimes shortened to amp, is the unit used to express the rate of *current flow*. An *ammeter* is the instrument employed to measure current flow and this should be connected *in series* with the circuit in which the current is to be measured (Fig. 11.3.1a).

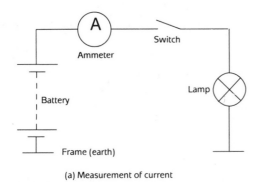

(a) Measurement of current

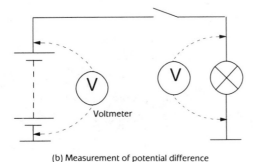

(b) Measurement of potential difference

**Fig. 11.3.1** Meter connections

*Volt (V)*   The volt is the unit of *electrical pressure* or potential (pressure) difference (p.d.). (Sometimes the term *voltage* is used instead of p.d.). A *voltmeter* is the instrument used to measure the p.d. at any part of the circuit. Figure 11.3.1(b) shows the method of connecting the meter when either the p.d. of the battery, or p.d. at the lamp, is required. The diagram shows that the meter is connected *in parallel* with the part of the circuit for which the p.d. is to be measured. Mounting the meter in this manner is termed *shunting*, since the instrument's internal circuit is forming a shunt, or parallel path for the current. Connecting an ammeter in a circuit in the manner shown for a voltmeter would destroy the instrument.

*Watt (W)*   The watt is the unit of *electric power*. One unit of power is produced when a p.d. of one volt causes a current flow of one ampere. In other words,

$$\begin{aligned} \text{power} &= \text{p.d.} \times \text{current} \\ \text{watts} &= \text{volts} \times \text{amperes} \\ W &= V \times A \end{aligned}$$

Electrical power can be related to mechanical power.

### Example
A p.d. of 12 V produces a current flow of 3 A through a certain circuit. Find the power consumed.

$$\begin{aligned} \text{Power} &= \text{voltage} \times \text{current} \\ &= 12 \times 3 \\ &= 36 \text{ W} \end{aligned}$$

### Example
A lamp is rated 12 V, 36 W. Find the current which would flow through this lamp when it is connected to a 12 V supply (i.e. a supply providing a total p.d. of 12 V).

$$\text{Power} = \text{voltage} \times \text{current}$$
$$\text{Current} = \frac{\text{power}}{\text{voltage}}$$
$$= \frac{36}{12}$$
$$= 3 \text{ A}$$

### Resistance
Opposition to the flow of electricity is termed resistance. This feature is the direct opposite to the term conductivity; i.e. a material which has a high electrical conductivity has a low resistance and vice versa.

> *The resistance of a conductor is proportional to its length and inversely proportional to its cross-sectional area*

This means that if a given p.d. produces a current flow of 4 A through a cable 100 m long, then only 2 A would flow through a cable of similar diameter and 200 m long. By doubling the cross-sectional area of this longer cable, the resistance would be halved and the current flow would be restored to 4 A.

Many circuits incorporate a special conductor to restrict the current flow to a given value. When the conductor is selected mainly for its resistance, it is called a resistor.

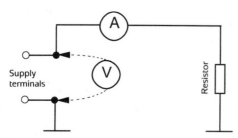

**Fig. 11.3.2** Experiment to measure resistance

Figure 11.3.2 shows the layout of an experiment whereby a resistor is connected to a supply voltage. The results of measuring the voltage and current are given in the table.

| Supply voltage (V) | Current (A) | Voltage/current (V/A) |
|---|---|---|
| 2 | 1 | 2 |
| 4 | 2 | 2 |
| 6 | 3 | 2 |
| 8 | 4 | 2 |
| 10 | 5 | 2 |

It will be noted that the ratio of voltage applied to current flow produces a constant for this circuit, and in this case gives a value of 2 units. Applying this method to a number of different circuits gives similar results. The ratio $\dfrac{\text{voltage}}{\text{current}}$ indicates the resistance of the circuit.

The unit of resistance is called the *ohm*, and the relationship between the electrical units may be stated thus:

*A p.d. of 1 V, produces a current flow of 1 A, through a circuit of resistance 1 ohm*

Applying this standard to the experiment shown in Figure 11.3.2, indicates that the resistance of the circuit is 2 ohms.

The resistance of any circuit can be *calculated* using the expression:

$$\text{Resistance} = \frac{\text{voltage}}{\text{current}}$$

or *measured* by using an instrument called an *ohmmeter*.

*Temperature effect*   Resistance of a material is affected by temperature. In most metals a rise in temperature causes the resistance to increase, but the change is not very great unless the temperature variation is large.

## REMEMBER

**Electrical units**

| | | |
|---|---|---|
| ampere | A | unit of current flow |
| volt | V | unit of potential difference or electrical pressure |
| watt | W | unit of power |
| ohm | Ω | unit of resistance |

**Prefixes**

kilo   meaning 1000

milli   meaning $\dfrac{1}{1000}$   OR   .001

micro meaning $\dfrac{1}{1\,000\,000}$   OR   0.000 001

**Examples**

3 kW = 3 kilowatt   = 3000 W

9 kW = 9 kilovolt   = 9000 V

4 mV = 4 millivolt   $= \dfrac{4}{1000}$ V   OR   0.04 V

7μV = 7 microvolt $= \dfrac{7}{1\,000\,000}$ V

OR 0.000 007 V

## 11.4   Batteries

**Electromotive force**

We have seen that some device is necessary to cause a difference in potential (pressure/voltage) in order for electrical current to flow in a conductor. The chemical cell or battery is probably the most common method which comes to mind. In this case the difference in potential between two dissimilar metal plates produces a pressure called *electromotive force* (generally shortened to e.m.f. and expressed in volts). This 'drives' the current around the circuit, and exists even when the cell is disconnected. In many ways the cell is similar to an inflated tyre – the pressure wants to escape so that it may equalise with the surrounding air, whereas the cell wants to equalise the potential in each part of a circuit.

*Potential* Let us examine the meaning of the term 'potential' more closely. The word suggests 'energy stored', and in the case of the tyre, the energy is apparent. When the electrical charges contained in two dissimilar metal plates of a battery cell are compared, it is found that the electrical charge in one plate is greater than in the other plate. If the two plates are immersed in an electrolyte and externally connected to form a circuit, then the difference in the 'charge levels' will produce a current flow through the liquid. This has the effect of lowering the potential in one plate and raising it in the other.

*Current flow* In an attempt to identify the electrical charges, one is termed positive and the other negative. In the early days it was assumed that the flow was in the direction of high potential (positive) to low potential (negative), but recent theories show that the electron flow is from negative to positive. **However to apply the basic rules of electricity, which were introduced in the nineteenth century, it is necessary to consider that the flow takes place from positive to negative.**

### Primary cells (batteries)

Chemical cells have been used for many years. In fact it was in the late eighteenth century that Volta immersed two dissimilar metals in an electrolyte and produced an electric current flow.

There are many combinations of metals and electrolytes used to produce a simple cell. One type employs a copper (+) and a zinc (−) plate immersed in a solution of sulphuric acid and water. The cell initially gives an e.m.f. of about 1.0 V, but after a short time it is seen that the zinc plate starts to dissolve and bubbles of gas form on each plate. This quickly leads to a fall-off in the output of the cell, so in this form the cell is not very efficient.

When this type of cell is exhausted – in other words, when the zinc has dissolved – it has to be replaced with new material. Since it is impossible to restore the cell by electrical means, it is called a primary or irreversible cell. (Dry-type primary cells are used in many torches and portable radios.)

### Secondary cells

Its limited life and the irreversibility of its action make the primary cell unsuitable for motor vehicles. Secondary-type cells are used, because they allow the potential to be restored by supplying the cell with an external charge current, which flows in a direction opposite to the flow given out by the cell – hence reversible.

Theoretically this type of cell should last indefinitely, but owing to mainly mechanical problems in construction, its average life seldom exceeds two or three years.

### Lead-acid batteries

A battery is a number of cells connected together: 'lead-acid' refers to the materials frequently used in the cell. This is the most common type of battery employed on motor vehicles.

Each cell consists of two sets of lead plates immersed in a solution of sulphuric acid ($H_2SO_4$) and distilled water: the solution is termed the *electrolyte*. A nominal potential difference of 2 V is obtained from each cell and by connecting cells in series the battery p.d. = 2 V × number of cells (Figure 11.4.1). Note that mounting the cells in parallel with each other has no effect on the p.d. of the battery: it remains at 2 V irrespective of the number of cells linked together but it does alter the capacity (the period of time that the battery will supply a given current).

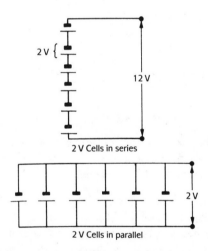

**Fig. 11.4.1** Lead-acid battery cell connections

*Charging and discharging*

When the battery is ready for use (fully charged), the positive plate is composed of lead peroxide and the negative plate is a spongy lead. Connecting the battery to an external circuit, causes a discharge current to flow. This has the effect of lowering the potential of the battery. While this flow is taking place, a chemical action called *electrolysis* is occurring within the battery. Sulphur atoms, contained in the sulphuric acid, combine with some of the lead oxide and change the plate composition to lead sulphate. As this process continues some of the acid changes to water.

Applying a charge current (a flow in the opposite direction to the discharge current) has the effect of reversing the chemical process – the plates return to lead peroxide and spongy lead and the electrolyte reverts to its original acid density.

The process is shown in the table.

| | Positive plate | Electrolyte | Negative plate | |
|---|---|---|---|---|
| CHARGE ↑ | Lead peroxide | ACID + water | Spongy lead | DISCHARGE |
| | Lead sulphate | acid + WATER | Lead sulphate | ↓ |

*Sulphation* The table shows that lead sulphate forms on each plate when the battery is in a discharged state. This substance resists the passage of an electric discharge current, but assuming the battery has not been discharged past the normal limit, then it is possible to 'break-down' the sulphate and restore the cell to its charged state. To obtain the maximum life of the battery, excessive sulphation should be avoided. In addition to the cause already mentioned, sulphation also results from topping up with acid instead of distilled water.

## 11.5  Ohm's law

*The current passing through a wire at constant temperature is proportional to the potential difference between its ends*

This law was discovered by Dr G. S. Ohm in 1826 and is now known as Ohm's Law. From the law the following expression can be formed. A potential difference of 1 volt is required to produce a current of 1 ampere through a conductor of resistance 1 ohm. Writing this in symbol form:

$$V = IR$$

where   $V$ = p.d. (volt)
     $I$ = current (ampere)
     $R$ = resistance (ohm)

therefore

$$I = \frac{V}{R}$$

and

$$R = \frac{V}{I}$$

**Example**
What voltage is required to produce a current of 6 A through a resistance of 1.5 Ω?

$$V = IR$$
$$V = 6 \times 1.5$$
$$V = 9 \text{ V}$$

**Example**
A current of 3 A flows through the primary winding of an ignition coil when it is connected to a battery having a p.d. of 12 V. Find the resistance of the coil winding.

$$V = IR$$
$$R = \frac{V}{I} = \frac{12}{3}$$
$$R = 4 \text{ Ω}$$

**Testing a coil using Ohm's Law**
This calculation shows a simple method of testing the windings of any component – a short circuit would give a lower resistance value, whereas a bad connection within the unit would give a high resistance. Comparing the result with the value given by the manufacturer enables the condition of the windings to be determined. Figure 11.5.1 shows the arrangement of the circuit for measuring the resistance of a coil winding.

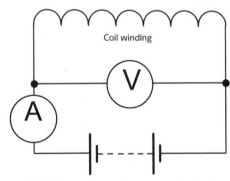
Coil winding

**Fig. 11.5.1** Measuring resistance of winding

**Example**
Determine the current flowing in a circuit of resistance 2 Ω when the supply p.d. is 12 V.

$$V = IR$$
$$I = \frac{V}{R} = \frac{12}{2}$$
$$I = 6 \text{ A}$$

## 11.6 Voltage distribution in circuits

Having seen the relationship between p.d., current flow and resistance, we can now investigate the distribution of voltage in a circuit.

To simplify the following examples, it is assumed that the cable offers no resistance to the flow of current.

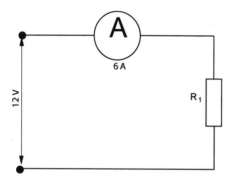

**Fig. 11.6.1** Single resistor

### Resistors in series

Consider a circuit (Figure 11.6.1) consisting of a resistor and ammeter which is connected to a 12 V supply. If the reading on the ammeter is 6 A then the value of the resistor $R_1$ would be:

$$R_1 = \frac{V}{I}$$

$$R_1 = \frac{12}{6} = 2\ \Omega$$

When a 4 $\Omega$ resistor $R_2$ is connected in series with the first resistor (Figure 11.6.2) it is found that the

current flow is now 2 A. The total resistance of this circuit is:

$$R = \frac{V}{I}$$

$$R = \frac{12}{2} = 6\ \Omega$$

or $$R = R_1 + R_2$$

This shows that:

> *The total resistance of a circuit comprising a number of resistors connected in series is obtained by adding the values of all resistors*

The p.d. at different parts of the circuit in Figure 11.6.2 may be determined by using a voltmeter connected for example across points B and C which shows a p.d. of 4 V. This reading shows that the voltage has decreased by 4 V after the current has passed through the resistor $R_1$. By connecting the meter across points C and D the reading should be 8 V. These and other results may be summarized in tabular form.

| Position of meter leads | Reading (V) |
|---|---|
| A.E. | 12 |
| B.C. | 4 |
| C.D. | 8 |

Figure 11.6.3 shows three resistors having values of 1 $\Omega$, 2 $\Omega$ and 3 $\Omega$ respectively, connected in series to a

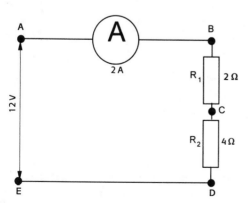

**Fig. 11.6.2** Two resistors in series

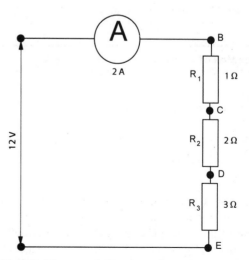

**Fig. 11.6.3** Three resistors in series

12 V supply. If the current taken from the supply is 2 A, then:

$$\text{Total resistance of circuit} = R_1 + R_2 + R_3$$
$$= 1 + 2 + 3$$
$$= 6\,\Omega$$

Connecting a voltmeter between B and C would give a p.d. of 2 V; this p.d. is often called the *voltage drop* because the resistor has the effect of lowering the potential. This drop can also be calculated from

$$V = IR$$

p.d. across resistor      = current × resistance
p.d. across 1 Ω resistor = 2 × 1 = 2 V
p.d. across 2 Ω resistor = 2 × 2 = 4 V
p.d. across 3 Ω resistor = 2 × 3 = 6 V
                Total p.d.        = 12 V

The total p.d. must equal the supply p.d.

It will be noted that the same current flows through each resistor, i.e. the current flowing through any part of a series circuit is the same.

The example shows the relationship between the total voltage applied across a number of series-connected circuit elements and the voltage across the individual elements. The ratio between the p.d. across each resistor and the supply p.d. is the same as the ratio between the individual resistance values and the total resistance of the external circuit. In other words

$$\frac{\text{p.d. across resistor}}{\text{p.d. of supply}} = \frac{\text{individual resistance value}}{\text{total resistance of external circuit}}$$

Voltmeter readings obtainable from the circuit shown in Figure 11.6.3 are given in the table.

| Position of meter leads | Reading (V) |
| --- | --- |
| B.C. | 2 |
| C.D. | 4 |
| D.E. | 6 |
| B.D. | 6 |
| C.E. | 10 |
| B.E. | 12 |

*Practical applications*   Knowledge of the behaviour of resistors mounted in series enables you to understand various practical applications. As a first example, there are occasions when a lamp of low voltage, e.g. an ignition warning lamp, is fitted to a higher voltage

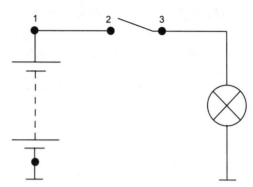

**Fig. 11.6.4** Simple lamp circuit

system. Subjecting the lamp to full battery p.d. would quickly destroy the bulb, so a resistor is connected in series with the lamp to drop the p.d. to the value required by the lamp.

As a second example, terminal corrosion, or partly broken cables, can cause an unintentional resistance in the electrical circuit of a motor vehicle. This would drop the voltage and affect the operation of the item. For example, suppose a resistance develops in the switch of the simple lamp circuit, shown in Figure 11.6.4. Replacing the switch in the diagram by a resistor (Figure 11.6.5) shows that the full battery p.d. is not applied to the lamp; the drop in p.d. depends on the value of the resistor, or the amount of corrosion.

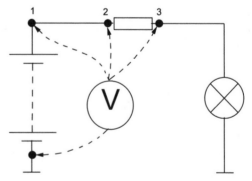

**Fig. 11.6.5** Fault finding

To locate a fault quickly, a voltmeter could be used. With the switch closed, the voltmeter should show battery p.d. at points 1 to 3, but in this case the reading at 3 will be considerably lower.

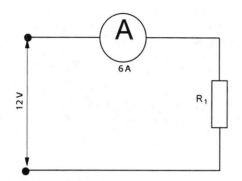

**Fig. 11.6.6** Simple circuit

### Resistors in parallel

In Figure 11.6.6 a single resistor is connected to a 12 V supply. To give a current flow of 6 A, the circuit would require a resistance value of

$$R = \frac{V}{I}$$

$$= \frac{12}{6}$$

$$= 2\ \Omega$$

If another 2 $\Omega$ resistor is fitted in parallel with $R_1$ (Figure 11.6.7), then the current that would flow through the ammeter would increase to 12 A. Study of this circuit shows that the additional resistor offers the current an alternative path, so a larger current would flow from the supply. A 2 $\Omega$ resistor will pass a current of 6 A when the p.d. is 12 V, and since this p.d. applies to both resistors, then the total current must be 6 + 6 = 12 A.

The resistance of the circuit will be

$$R = \frac{V}{I}$$

$$= \frac{12}{12}$$

$$= 1\ \Omega$$

Therefore, two resistors of 2 $\Omega$ each give an equivalent resistance of 1 $\Omega$. In other words, the two resistors are equivalent to a resistor having a value of 1 $\Omega$.

### Example

Figure 11.6.8 shows two resistors of unequal value connected in parallel and an ammeter showing a current flow of 6A. Both resistors are subject to a p.d. of 12 V, and in order to find the current flowing through each, use the expression:

$$I = \frac{V}{R}$$

Current flowing through $R_1 = \dfrac{12}{3} = 4$ A

Current flowing through $R_2 = \dfrac{12}{6} = 2$ A

Total current $\qquad = 6$ A

Obviously the greater current flows through the resistor of lower value. Thus the 3 $\Omega$ resistor carries 4/6 of the total current, and the 6 $\Omega$ resistor carried 2/6 of the total current.

Equivalent resistance of the circuit is

$$R = \frac{V}{I} = \frac{12}{6} = 2\ \Omega$$

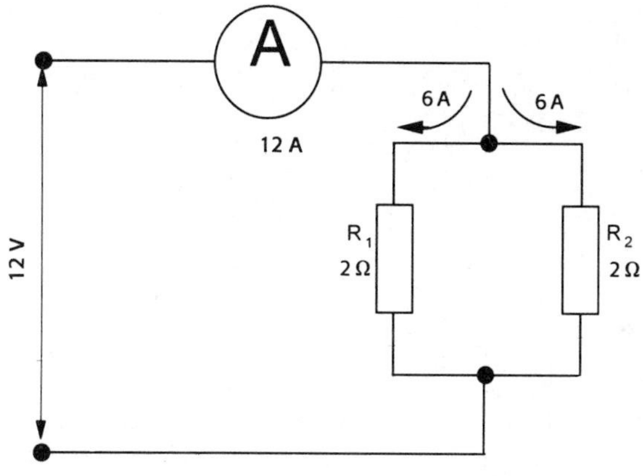

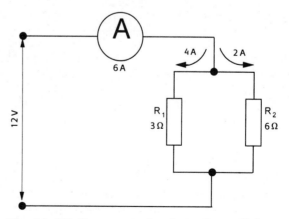

**Fig. 11.6.7** Two resistors in parallel

**Fig. 11.6.8** Two unequal resistors in parallel

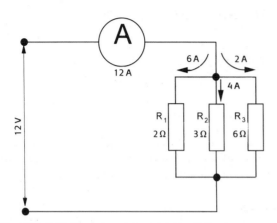

**Fig. 11.6.9** Three resistors in parallel

### Example

Let us now consider the result of connecting three resistors in parallel. Figure 11.6.9 shows a circuit consisting of three branches incorporating resistors of values 2 Ω, 3 Ω and 6 Ω. When the circuit is connected to a 12 V supply the current flowing through:

$$R_1 \text{ is } \frac{V}{R_1} = \frac{12}{2} = 6 \text{ A}$$

$$R_2 \text{ is } \frac{V}{R_2} = \frac{12}{3} = 4 \text{ A}$$

$$R_3 \text{ is } \frac{V}{R_3} = \frac{12}{6} = 2 \text{ A}$$

Total current flowing in circuit = 12 A

Equivalent resistance of circuit $= \dfrac{V}{I} = \dfrac{12}{12} = 1 \ \Omega$

### Fall of potential

All materials resist the flow of electrical current. Even a good copper cable causes a fall in potential as the current

**REMEMBER**

**Ohm's Law is**

$$V = IR$$

where    $V$ = p.d.      (volts)
          $I$ = current     (amperes)
         $R$ = resistance   (ohms)

passes along the cable. This is illustrated by considering a starter cable having a resistance of 0.0006 Ω per metre. When a typical starter current of 200 A is supplied by the cable, the drop in potential (volt drop) per metre length of cable is:

$$V = IR$$
$$= 200 \times 0.0006$$
$$= 0.12 \text{ V}$$

This does not seem much, but if the battery is positioned at a point which required 5 metres of cable, then the drop in potential amounts to 0.6 V. A cable drop of this extent added to the numerous other 'volt-drops' occurring at the various terminals, adds up to a value which can seriously affect the performance of a starter motor.

In this example, cable length has been considered, but cross-sectional area must also be taken into account; reducing the number of strands of wire increases the resistance proportionally. If the area of the starter cable in the previous example was reduced by half, then the voltage drop would then be 1.2 V. Heat generated by the current would also cause the cable to overheat and this would result in a further increase in the resistance and voltage drop.

## PROGRESS CHECK 11

1. The symbol for a battery cell is ⊣⊦
What polarity is represented
by the longer line and what symbol
is used to show this?
(a) Positive which is shown as +
(b) Positive which is shown as −
(c) Negative which is shown as +
(d) Negative which is shown as −

2. The symbol ⊗ represents a:
(a) coil
(b) lamp
(c) capacitor
(d) switch.

3. The symbol ⊥ represents a:
(a) coil
(b) lamp
(c) capacitor
(d) switch.

4. The symbol —⌣— represents a:
(a) coil
(b) lamp
(c) capacitor
(d) switch.

5. The symbol —▭—
represents:
(a) a resistor
(b) an earth connection
(c) a coil
(d) a switch.

6. A material which freely allows
the passage of an electric current is
called:
(a) an insulator
(b) an isolator
(c) a capacitor
(d) a conductor.

7. Which one of the following
materials is the best electrical
insulator?
(a) Copper
(b) Lead
(c) Carbon
(d) Porcelain.

8. As applied to electrical circuits
the abbreviation 'e.r.' is commonly
used to represent:
(a) electrical resistance
(b) extra reach
(c) earth return
(d) each resistor.

9. An 'open' circuit means that:
(a) one part of the circuit is earthed
(b) a fuse is fitted in the circuit
(c) the circuit is incomplete
(d) part of the circuit is exposed.

10. The frame of a vehicle cuts
through the covering of a cable and
causes a large current to flow to
'earth'. This fault is normally called:
(a) a frame circuit
(b) a fused circuit
(c) an open circuit
(d) a short circuit.

11. The purpose of a switch in a
lighting system is to:
(a) open the circuit when the lights
     are required
(b) open the circuit when the lights
     are not required
(c) short the circuit when the lights
     are required
(d) short the circuit when the lights
     are not required.

12. A battery in a circuit causes tiny
particles to move from one atom to
the next. These particles are called:
(a) molecules
(b) electrons
(c) volts
(d) amps.

13. The term 'negative earth' means
that the negative battery terminal is:
(a) not used
(b) insulated from the frame
(c) connected to the road
(d) connected to the frame.

14. Two lamps are connected to a
battery in an arrangement which
causes the total current supplied by
the battery to pass through each
lamp. This circuit is called:
(a) series
(b) parallel
(c) earth return
(d) insulated return.

15. Two 12 V 6 W lamps are
connected to a battery in an
arrangement which causes each
lamp to pass half of the total current
supplied by the battery. This circuit
is called:
(a) series
(b) parallel
(c) earth return
(d) insulated return.

16. Two lamps are connected in
series with each other. What is the
effect if one lamp filament breaks?
The 'good' lamp will:
(a) become brighter
(b) become dimmer
(c) operate normally
(d) not light.

17. Two lamps are connected in parallel with each other. What is the effect if one lamp filament breaks? The 'good' lamp will:
(a) become brighter
(b) become dimmer
(c) operate normally
(d) not light.

18. What arrangement is used to connect the various lamps in the side-and-tail lamp circuit of a motor vehicle. Lamps are connected in:
(a) series
(b) parallel
(c) line
(d) polarity.

19. Soft iron is often used as a core for an electromagnet because it:
(a) is not affected by a magnetic field
(b) does not retain a large amount of magnetism
(c) is a non-magnetic material
(d) keeps cool.

20. Which words makes the following statement correct: 'like magnetic poles . . . ., unlike poles . . . .?
(a) attract . . . . resist
(b) resist . . . . repel
(c) attract . . . . repel
(d) repel . . . . attract

21. What is an electrolyte? A solution which is:
(a) chemically changed by electric current
(b) used as a battery plate
(c) used as a battery separator
(d) electrically charged distilled water.

22. The unit of electrical current is the:
(a) ampere
(b) ohm
(c) watt
(d) volt.

23. The unit of electrical potential difference is the:
(a) ampere
(b) ohm
(c) watt
(d) volt.

24. The unit of electrical power is the:
(a) ampere
(b) ohm
(c) watt
(d) volt.

25. The unit of electrical resistance is the:
(a) ampere
(b) ohm
(c) watt
(d) volt.

26. Electrical 'pressure' in a circuit is measured by:
(a) an ammeter
(b) an ohmmeter
(c) a wattmeter
(d) a voltmeter.

27. The 'charge' supplied by a generator is normally measured by:
(a) an ammeter
(b) a hydrometer
(c) a voltmeter
(d) a wattmeter.

28. The power consumed when a p.d. of 12 V produces a current flow of 9 A is:
(a) 0.75 W
(b) 1.3 W
(c) 21 W
(d) 108 W.

29. An instrument shows a reading of 2 mV. The unit is a:
(a) megavolt
(b) millivolt
(c) microvolt
(d) metrevolt.

30. A fuse is fitted in an electric circuit to:
(a) prevent a short circuit
(b) prevent an open circuit
(c) protect the circuit
(d) protect the lamps.

31. A vehicle lighting circuit consists of two 12 V 48 W headlamps and four side and tail lamps of 12 V 6 W. When all these lamps are operating with the engine stationary the vehicle ammeter should register:
(a) 2.5 A
(b) 8.5 A
(c) 10 A
(d) 16 A.

32. One essential difference between a primary and secondary cell is that a secondary cell:
(a) cannot be charged
(b) is always larger
(c) contains an electrolyte
(d) is reversible.

33. How many cells has a 12 V lead-acid battery?
(a) 3
(b) 6
(c) 9
(d) 12.

34. Two 6 V batteries are connected positive to positive and negative to negative. The p.d. between the output terminals of this arrangement should be:
(a) 3
(b) 6
(c) 12
(d) 18.

35. Ohm's law states: The current passing through a wire at constant temperature is proportional to the:
(a) power supplied
(b) length of the circuit
(c) resistance of the circuit
(d) potential difference between its ends.

36. The potential difference that is required to cause a current of 8 A to flow through a resistance of 2 Ω is:
(a) 0.25 V
(b) 2 V
(c) 4 V
(d) 16 V.

37. A voltage of 20 V is applied to a circuit of resistance 2 Ω. The current flow is:
(a) 0.1 A
(b) 1 A
(c) 10 A
(d) 40 A.

38. What voltage is required to cause a current of 20 mA to flow through a resistance of 40 Ω?
(a) 0.5 mV
(b) 0.8 V
(c) 2 kV
(d) 80 kV.

39. Two field windings of equal resistance are connected in series with a battery of p.d. 12 V. If the current is 2 A, the resistance of EACH winding is:
(a) 3 Ω
(b) 6 Ω
(c) 12 Ω
(d) 24 Ω.

*Questions 40–45 apply to Figure PC11.1.*

40. The diagram shows an:
(a) earth return circuit consisting of two resistors in series
(b) earth return circuit consisting of two resistors in parallel
(c) insulated return circuit consisting of two resistors in series
(d) insulated return circuit consisting of two resistors in parallel.

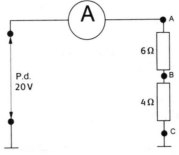

**Fig. PC11.1**

41. Assuming the resistance of the connecting wires is zero, the total resistance of the circuit is:
(a) 0.7 Ω
(b) 1.5 Ω
(c) 2.4 Ω
(d) 10 Ω.

42. The current flow in the circuit is:
(a) 2 A
(b) 8 A
(c) 13 A
(d) 15 A.

43. The current flowing through the 6 Ω resistor is:
(a) 1.7 A
(b) 2 A
(c) 4 A
(d) 10 A.

44. A voltmeter connected to points A and B will register
(a) 4 V
(b) 6 V
(c) 12 V
(d) 20 V.

45. The voltage drop across the 4 Ω resistor is:
(a) 4 V
(b) 6 V
(c) 8 V
(d) 20 V.

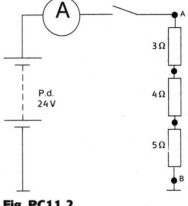

**Fig. PC11.2**

*Questions 46–50 apply to Figure PC11.2.*

46. The diagram shows a circuit with three resistors in:
(a) series and the battery negative earthed
(b) series and the battery positive earthed
(c) parallel and the battery negative earthed
(d) parallel and the battery positive earthed.

47. The resistors have a total resistance of:
(a) 1.3 Ω
(b) 2 Ω
(c) 8 Ω
(d) 12 Ω.

48. The current flow in the circuit is:
(a) 0.5 A
(b) 2 A
(c) 19 A
(d) 24 A.

49. The voltage drop across the 4 Ω resistor is:
(a) 2 V
(b) 3 V
(c) 6 V
(d) 8 V.

50. If the switch contacts develop a resistance of 4 Ω what is the p.d. between A and B?
(a) 1.5 V
(b) 6 V
(c) 16 V
(d) 18 V.

*Questions 51–54 apply to Figure PC11.3.*

51. The resistance of the circuit is:
(a) 1.5 Ω
(b) 3 Ω
(c) 8 Ω
(d) 16 Ω.

52. The current flow in the circuit is:
(a) 1.5 A
(b) 2 A
(c) 6 A
(d) 8 A.

53. The voltage drop across the 4 Ω resistor is:
(a) 6 V
(b) 20 V
(c) 24 V
(d) 32 V.

54. If the switch contacts develop a resistance of 9 Ω (i) what current will flow and (ii) what is the p.d. between A and B?
(a) (i) 1 A (ii) 3 V
(b) (i) 1 A (ii) 21 V
(c) (i) 2 A (ii) 6 V
(d) (i) 2 A (ii) 18 V.

55. What resistor must be inserted in series with a lamp of resistance 6 Ω and battery of p.d. 12 V if the p.d. required at the lamp is 6 V?
(a) 1 Ω
(b) 2 Ω
(c) 4 Ω
(d) 6 Ω.

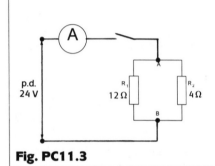

**Fig. PC11.3**

# Business Activities

# *12*                                                      *The customer*

## What is covered in this chapter:

→ motor vehicle repair industry
→ importance of the customer
→ contracts
→ customers' requirements and expectations
→ company image
→ customer relations
→ security of customers' property
→ customer complaints

When you are in business, you need to sell a product; in the motor vehicle repair industry the main product you sell is service. Sellers will have little success unless somebody, a customer, wants to buy their goods or services. Customers are the most important people in this sales chain, because no customers means failure of the business and redundant staff. It is pointless having superb premises and highly qualified staff unless customers are attracted to your product or service.

This chapter concentrates on the behaviour of customers; it will draw your attention to their needs, the way that they should be handled, and the statutory regulations and agreements that apply to the work that you undertake.

## 12.1 Motor vehicle repair industry

### The service industry

A company that services and repairs vehicles operates either to support a parent company involved in some transport undertaking such as road haulage, or to sell their service to a vehicle owner. When a firm bases its main activity on the latter, it becomes part of a service industry. This means that its main income is gained by offering some activity which a person or some other firm requires. The world of commerce can be divided into two categories: manufacturing and service. Profit in the manufacturing industry comes from the making and selling of some product, whereas a service industry engages in *support activities* such as maintenance, repair, insurance, etc.

Both manufacturing and service industries rely on selling their products at an economic price. When a company cannot sell its produce, or fails to get its minimum price, it goes out of business. Collapse of a company has many repercussions; these include the loss of jobs and money.

To survive in a modern business world, two essentials must be satisfied; the potential buyer must:

● desire the product or service
● be satisfied with the cost
● receive attention and support.

To be a successful company **all** employees must appreciate that these essentials must be tailored and tuned to suit the type of business being offered. Furthermore they must accept the fact that the success of an enterprise depends on one person – the customer and his/her (re)actions.

## 12.2 Importance of the customer

By definition a customer is '*a person to deal with*'. To sell your special service, the person to deal with must be regarded as a potential buyer. To make a sale the person should be led through the general selling process; often abbreviated to AIDA. This stands for:

**A** – *attention*: to attract the potential customer to the product or service that is being offered;

**I** – *interest*: to induce the potential customer to take a deeper look at your product or service;

**D** – *desire to own*: to create a wish to own the produce you offer, or avail themselves of the service you offer;

**A** – *action*: to finalize the sale and make the contract.

### Need for after-sales

In the past the outlined marketing objectives were often overlooked because many company executives considered that the Service Department of a repair establishment only existed in order to support the sale of a motor vehicle. Perhaps this idea was promoted by manufacturers when they insisted that their franchised (tied) dealers should provide only the minimum after-sales service for the purchasers of their vehicles. Very few manufacturers insisted that a full repair facility had to be offered.

Today the need to market all sections of the company, and make each part of the firm a profit centre, has meant that workshop areas have been upgraded and revamped so as to place more emphasise on customer needs.

### Customer service

Bearing in mind the phrase 'no customers, no work', repair shop personnel must concentrate on the requirements of customers if the company is to survive in the highly competitive world of today. The aim of all personnel is to maintain customer service to the standards set by the company. It is essential that any work undertaken must balance the customer's needs with the service that the company can provide, i.e. when the customer orders work that is beyond the scope of the company, then the limit must be clearly defined by management so that the customers are aware of this limitation before they contract for the work to be done. It is pointless making promises if they cannot be honoured. In a similar way all members of staff must not give advice beyond their capabilities – doubtful technical advice given generously by a poorly qualified person can cause many problems and costly legal battles.

Since advice is often sought from junior repair staff, a policy must exist in the company to avoid this pitfall; this plan will identify qualified persons and will give guidance on the manner in which the customer should be treated without giving offence.

## 12.3 Contracts

A contract is a legal agreement between two or more parties for the supply of goods or performance of work. Contracts can be verbal or written; they can range from the sale of a small item in a shop to an agreement to undertake extensive work involving millions of pounds. In the motor industry, verbal and written contracts fall between these two limits.

### Essentials of a contract

A contract consists of an *offer* and an *acceptance* of that offer. In English law it must be made either under seal (in a deed) or there must be consideration to support the contract, i.e. there must be some benefit to one party or some detriment to the other.

A contract is invalid (void) and unenforceable under law if it involves any one of the following:

- *illegal activity* whereby the contract would involve the infringement of the law of land, i.e. some illegal work or criminal activity;
- *incapacity* of minors (persons under 18 years of age), persons lacking mental capacity and drunkards;
- *mistake* such as legal misunderstanding, mistaken identity, or some unknown circumstance, e.g. when parties are unaware that the contract they are signing is different to that intended;
- *misrepresentation* untrue statement made by one party that induces the other to enter into the agreement;
- *duress* when undue influence is used by one party;
- *gaming* when a wager is used for any part of the contract.

### Agreements

To start a deal that is intended to lead to a *contract*, requires an agreement between two or more persons. One party will make an offer and the other will indicate their acceptance, assuming they are satisfied that the offer meets their requirements.

To make a formal contract, both parties must intend their agreement to be enforceable by law. When this is made then if either party fails to fulfil a promise undertaken by the agreement, the other party can bring a legal action, i.e. they can sue the other party for *breach of contract*.

Not all agreements are intended to be legally binding, e.g. if John agreed to loan Paul a special wrench, but later withdrew the offer, an action for damages could not be brought. In this case the agreement did not qualify as a contract, because when they entered into the agreement both parties did not intend that it should be enforceable by law.

*Offer*    Negotiation between the parties need not always lead to a contract. Offers may be invited, or inquiries made, and if an offer is made, it need not be accepted. An offer must not be confused with an *invitation to make an offer* and a *declaration of intention*. The former includes advertisements and product price tags; these are termed *an offer to treat*, so if an incorrect price is displayed on a product, the company is not obliged to sell at that price. A declaration of intention by a person proposing to do a certain thing gives no right of action by other persons who suffer loss as a result of the person not carrying out their intention.

*Acceptance*    An acceptance must be made, while the offer is still in force, before the offer has lapsed, been rejected or revoked. When the acceptance is complete, the offer becomes irrevocable, i.e. the parties must fulfil their part of the contract. The acceptance can be in writing, by word of mouth or by conduct. If an offer requires the other party to do or pay something, then that precise act must be done and nothing else.

## REMEMBER

**Essentials of a contract**

- **Offer**
  To do something

- **Acceptance**
  To agree to the offer

- **Consideration**
  To do or pay something

### Terms and conditions

Undertakings and promises in an agreement are known as the *terms of a contract*. Terms that are clearly stated in the contract are called *express terms*. When they are so obvious in the fulfilment of the contract that they are not stated they are called *implied terms*. The terms of the contract are classified in conditions and warranties.

*Condition*    is a vital part of a contract. Non-compliance with any stated condition by either party is considered as a substantial failure to perform, so the injured party can either cancel the contract and/or claim damages for breach of contract.

*Warranty*    is not a vital part of a contract. A warranty, which can be made in writing or by word of mouth, is an obligation that must be performed, but is secondary to the main substance of the contract. Any breach of a warranty does not give a party a right to terminate the contract but they can claim for damages for any loss arising from the breach.

## REMEMBER

**Contract terms**

- **Conditions**
  Vital part of contract

- **Warranty**
  Essential but not a vital part

### Service department contracts

Having covered a few of the basic legal terms, the practical aspects can now be considered.

*Reception* is the front-end of the service department, so this is the customer contact area where contracts are made. When customers enter that area they are responding to an offer made by the company to undertake some type of service or repair work. Following discussion with the staff, the two parties (customer and company) accept the offer; the company agrees to do the stated work for a given price and the customer agrees to pay this price.

Since this two-party agreement is comparatively minor, a sealed formal document is not used, so its validity as a legal contract can be judged by checking the transaction to see if there is a *consideration*. In this case the work done benefits the customer and the cash received profits the company.

The offer and the acceptance may be in the form of a written order or may be agreed verbally. The terms of the agreements are negotiated and, in the case of a written order, the conditions of the contract are clearly stated.

*Discharge of a contract* A contract may be discharged (comes to an end) by:

- *performance* when both parties have performed what they agree to do;
- *agreement* when both parties mutually agree to either end, or enter into a new contract; e.g. when circumstances arise to considerably alter the original agreement;
- *termination by notice* when the contract contains a term giving either party the power to terminate it by notice;
- *acceptance of breach* when a party fails to perform one or more of the obligations of the contract;
- *frustration* when the common object of the contract can no longer be achieved because, in the light of events, a situation arises that is different to that contemplated at the time when the parties entered into the contract.

### Supply of services

Contracts for the supply of services are subject to various Acts: these demand that the supplier must conform with the following:

1) Take reasonable care and exercise reasonable skill in the performance of the contract.
2) Do not use any clause in the contract that would restrict liability for personal injury resulting from negligence.
3) Claim in a written terms of business to be entitled to render a contractual performance substantially different from that which was reasonably expected of him.
4) Give priority over a printed clause to an oral promise made at the time of the acceptance – where printed conditions in a contract are contrary to a binding oral promise they do not give exemption.
5) Do not introduce exemption clauses into the contract after it is made – this includes notices seen by the customer after the contract has been made, e.g. the company shall not be responsible for articles stolen from your car.

Whenever the Parts and Service Departments sell any goods, the *Sale and Supply of Goods Act (1994)* demands that the goods are:

- of satisfactory quality: i.e. they are fit for the purposes for which goods of that kind are commonly bought;
- free from any defect, rendering them unsatisfactory which was not apparent on reasonable inspection of the sample.

## 12.4 Customer's requirements and expectations

Consideration of vehicle owner's needs shows that they all want a reliable vehicle that operates in an efficient manner. When the vehicle has a fault, they want it corrected cheaply and quickly. Also, most owners understand that preventative maintenance can save them a lot of money and reduce the risk of a breakdown in the future. With reluctance they accept the manufacturer's recommendation that they should have their vehicle serviced at the appropriate time.

In the past, the environment of a motor vehicle workshop was often considered hostile by car owners, especially women owners; for this reason a visit was made only when absolutely necessary. Workshop staff were often unhelpful, and sometimes rude when they had to leave their job to talk to a customer. Even the area in the workshop where the customer/mechanic meeting took place was squalid and in some cases dangerous.

Forward-looking firms identified these deficiencies and set up a *customer reception* area, staffed with trained personnel, to attend to the customer needs. Smaller firms that could not afford this facility made alternative arrangements to identify and satisfy customer requirements in this sphere.

### Customer reception

The objective of the staff in a reception area is 'to sell service'. Workshop time is the 'product' to be sold and the effectiveness of the staff can be measured by comparing the workshop hours they sell with the hours that are available. The actual product that is to be sold depends on the special services that the workshop undertakes; e.g. half the total hours may be set aside for servicing activities and the remainder for major repairs.

Clear signs should enable customers to locate the reception area without difficulty and provision must be made for easy parking. Since a reception area in fact sells produce, a normal shop environment should apply; this means that the area should be attractive and clean. Staff manning the facility must be well presented, articulate and have a helpful nature. Qualifications and experience of the staff will depend on the service that is offered by the workshop: e.g. simple booking of a periodic service may not require a highly qualified person, but all firms should make provision for customers to talk to suitably trained persons when it is necessary. Large firms are able to man reception areas with both types of staff; *receptionists* and *technical receptionists*; the latter deals with matters that require greater expertise.

Computer terminals and microfiche readers enables Aftersales Reception staff to access information from internal and external sources.

*Retail Motor Industry Federation and VAG Ltd*

The Service Reception area is the 'showroom' of the Service Department. It should be in a prominent position, be modern in appearance and be staffed by efficient, well presented personnel.

*Rover Group*

The vital role in the firm played by staff involved in customer reception duties cannot be over-stressed. Sometimes the title and status of the staff engaged in this activity are enhanced to impress the customer: titles such as Service Adviser are introduced. A successful sales-person must sell themselves before attempting to sell the produce. By gaining the customer's confidence at an early stage, the possibility of achieving a sale is more likely. The sale should not be regarded as a one-off transaction, because the trust gained from an earlier meeting can often lead to other sales.

When customers enter the reception area they should be received in a friendly manner and, following a polite greeting as laid down by the company, their requirements should be processed as fast as possible. When customers have to wait for attention without their presence being acknowledged, and then 'served' out-of-turn, annoyance must be expected. In a similar manner, a customer who has to wait while the receptionist answers the telephone, or discusses some business matter with another member of the staff, gives an unfavourable impression. Remember:

**The customer is the most important person in the firm**

### Special requirements

In addition to the basics of customer relations that apply to all sales outlets, the retail motor industry must satisfy the special requirements of customers which arise before, during and after the repair of their vehicles. These include:

- accurate estimation of time and cost of repairs
- work carried out as required by customer
- prompt reporting to the customer of difficulties and irregularities
- protection of paintwork and interior of the vehicle during repair
- vehicle available for collection at agreed time
- vehicle clean internally and externally
- repairs and parts correctly itemized and charged on invoice.

Although a friendly attitude to the customer should be encouraged, it is necessary to avoid violating company policy as regard disclosure of information. Internal issues of the company and technical defects in a given product should not be discussed unless they have a direct bearing on the work being undertaken.

### Agency

An *agent* is a person authorised to act as the representative of another. Legally an employee of a company is an agent of that company; this means that any contracts or decisions made by an authorised agent are binding on the company.

Many employees are authorised by their employer to represent the company, so it is advisable they are aware of their responsibilities as regards the *Law of Agency*. Sometimes confusion arises because the term 'agent' is often used in the commercial world as a general title to describe some activity performed by an individual or organization. For example, a garage proprietor who calls himself a motor agent is not an agent of a motor manufacturer; he may have a franchise agreement that allows him to sell a particular motor car but it does not give him the legal right to represent the manufacturer.

A receptionist is a good example of an agent; the receptionist (agent) makes a contract with a customer (third party) for the agent's employer (the principal). Since this contract is between the principal and the third party, the principal is liable for the actions of the agent, provided that the agent is acting in accordance with the actual authority granted by the principal. This authority does not have to be granted in writing.

A person professing to act as an agent, who either exceeds his authority, or has no authority to act from his principal, can be held responsible by third parties if

the agent implies that he has authority to make the original contract. However, if the third party was aware that the contract exceeded the agent's authority, then the agent would not be liable for his action. This is called a *breach of authority* and is more easily understood by an example. Suppose a receptionist makes a contract between his principal and a customer for some mechanical repair. In this case the agent is not liable for the contracted work but if he indicates to the customer that he will undertake additional work beyond his normal authority, then he is personally liable for this work.

The agent's action is binding on the principal so if an authorised agent promises to do certain work for a given price in an agreed time, the principal is obliged to undertake the work or face damages for breach of contract.

### Public liability

Any area that is open to the public must be maintained in a safe condition. This means that the premises must be structurally sound and must be free from any obstacle that may cause injury or death. Workshops are dangerous areas which should be made out-of-bounds to the general public and notices prominently displayed should inform the public that they must not pass beyond a given point. Some customers display an interest in the work activity and in order to satisfy these people a viewing window to the workshop is sometimes provided in the Reception area.

The company is liable for any negligence which can cause injury to a member of the public, so the management and staff must ensure that the premises are safe. Public liability insurance is taken out to meet any legal claim made against the company.

### Trade Descriptions Act

The object of this Act is to prevent the use of false or misleading trade descriptions. A criminal offence is committed if any person who, in the course of a trade or business, applies a false trade description to goods, or supplies or orders to supply any goods to which a false trade description is applied.

This Act has a bearing on workshop activities because it covers all parts which are either supplied or reconditioned by the company. To avoid criminal proceedings it is essential that customers are given an accurate description of products and work processes.

## 12.5    Company image

To trade successfully a company must project a good impression to its customers. This image has to be generated by all employees especially those who have face-to-face contact with the customers.

The effort needed to foster a good image often depends on the amount of rival competition, because under critical trading conditions it is vital to create an impression of quality that persuades the potential customer to seek the product or service that the company offers.

Lack of competition often spawns a 'take it or leave it' attitude; this causes many of the firm's customers to be dissatisfied with the service they receive, both from the price of the product and the way in which they are treated.

### Trading aim

A company is in business to make a profit; this profit is returned in the form of a dividend to a shareholder. Unless the dividend is in keeping with the investment risk being taken by the shareholder, the money will either be withdrawn or not be made available to the company in the first place. Employees are not always aware of this situation. If the firm employs a hard core who feel that their rewards should come before company profit, then it is highly likely that the firm will soon face financial collapse; this will result in all employees being

laid-off. Conversely a well motivated workforce who appreciate business fundamentals, will strive to make the company profitable; this will give them regular work and, in many cases, a share in the financial rewards.

*Mission statement*    Periodically the company should review its trading policy in relation to its primary business objectives. Over a period of years the development of a company results in a broadening of its activities. This diversification may be beneficial to the company as a whole, but in some cases it is necessary to prune away some of these activities to allow management to concentrate on its main line of business. A study of the company should identify the main profit source and once this has been established a mission statement is drawn up. This is a short, simple statement that lays down the principal objectives of the company; after it has been defined the mission statement will indicate to all employees the main trading purpose of the company.

### Customer's impression

Customers judge a company by the quality of service they receive. This means that the company is only as good as its employees.

The service and repair of motor vehicles is a very competitive business, so all employees must recognize the need to give customers a good service. If this is understood and practised by all, then customers will

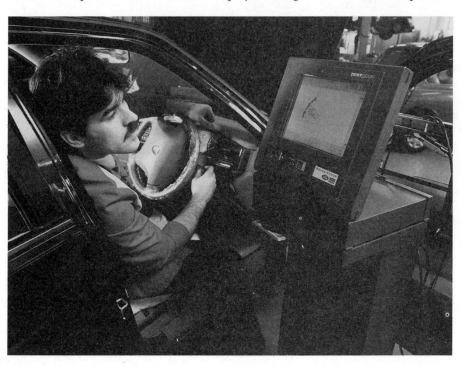

Image is enhanced by publicising the use of modern diagnostic equipment in a company's workshop. This also gives an opportunity to show prospective customers the attention given by the staff to keep the interior of a vehicle in a clean condition.

*Rover Group*

return again. In addition they will recommend the company to their friends.

A good image of a company can be easily shattered if the customer experiences either poor service or unhelpful staff on their first visit. Not only do customers need to be received in a friendly manner, they also expect their vehicle to be serviced or repaired efficiently and economically. In general they want firms to do what they say they will do and do it right first time.

Some companies spend a fortune promoting their corporate image. They advertise extensively, display their logos prominently and sometimes use the services of a specialist customer relations firm. Although all these help to get the message across to the public, the most important way is to ensure that all employees of the company do their best to promote good customer relations. Many customers may not have seen the advertisements and public messages but they all come face-to-face with the staff. It is better to keep the customer you have than spend a fortune trying to get new ones.

*Image projection* A great obstacle is overcome when new customers are persuaded to visit the company and order work to be done. This large step in the sales process must not be wasted by projecting a poor image due to shoddy premises that are staffed by untidy, inarticulate, bad mannered personnel. Poor assessment of the image at this second stage will destroy the foundation that has been set; it is most unlikely that the customer will return. To create the desired image and effective work pattern the management should provide for each employee, details of the various procedures that must be followed together with the rules and regulations that must be adopted; these details should also state clearly the presentation (e.g. dress etc.) expected of the person.

---

## Good practice

**Good company image is projected by:**

- clean, attractive premises
- well-presented staff
- knowledgeable staff
- courteous staff
- efficient work
- speedy work
- competitive prices

---

### Legal requirements

Employees who sell goods or services to customers must be aware of the various legal requirements that affect them and their companies. Ignorance of the law cannot be given as an excuse for an infringement, so it is the responsibility of both the individual and the company to be aware of the legal requirements associated with each type of transaction that is undertaken. Also, a good working knowledge of the law should act as a guide to foster a good working practice; this should minimize the number of disputes with the customer and project an image of efficiency.

### Customer care

The initial contact with the company might be made by telephone, so it is important that a suitable technique, as defined by the management, is used to promote the company image. Attention must be given to avoid the well-known pitfalls that cause customer annoyance.

Some customers like to be 'pampered' so recognition of these persons will dictate the manner in which they are treated. If a company policy can be developed to make these customers feel special, the results will be beneficial. By adopting a *customer care policy* which uses a system to give a record of the details of all work carried out, the customer can be periodically contacted by post or telephone to advise them when their vehicle needs servicing.

*Performance monitoring* It is management's responsibility to periodically monitor and assess customer reaction to the company's image. Monitoring methods include the interviewing of customers and the supply of report forms which are either included with the invoice or made available at the reception counter. In addition to these methods, a valuable indication of performance is gauged by the volume of work and profit; if these are poor then all staff should take urgent steps to rectify the situation and this should include asking the question, "What is wrong with the image of the company?"

## 12.6 Customer relations

The business term 'customer relations' relates to the communication link between company and customer. It covers the ways by which contact and communications are established between the two parties so that they can enter into some business arrangement or agreement. Good customer service is a necessity, not a luxury.

The importance of good customer relations cannot be over-stated because the image produced by fostering

The customer–dealer relationship established when the car was sold should carry through to Aftersales activities offered by the company.

*Ford Motor Co Ltd*

this relationship builds trust to mould a sound business partnership. Profit depends on keeping the customers happy, so if all employees can be persuaded to give customer satisfaction, market success should be achieved. Measurement of customer dissatisfaction will highlight the problem areas, so by using this negative yardstick, the customers will innocently convey to the company the items they consider are important in the service operation. Once this information is obtained it is the duty of management to take steps to improve the relationship.

## REMEMBER

### A customer is

- someone we are here to serve
- not dependent on us – we are dependent on them
- not an interruption
- doing us a great service by visiting us and giving us the opportunity to serve them

### Understanding customer needs

A customer that enters a company and orders repair work has a number of basic needs. Future repeat service business will depend on the way in which the firm handles its customers' needs; these embrace:

- telephone communications and booking-in procedures
- access to Reception and available parking space nearby
- customer handling and attitude of reception staff
- estimation of cost and time that is required for the work
- quality of work
- time of collection of vehicle
- cleanliness of vehicle at time of collection
- accurate costing of work carried out
- competitive cost of work done in keeping with the quality.

Some companies give their customers a questionnaire at the time they collect their cars; this allows them to express their opinions on the firm's performance. This is one way in which a company can assess the degree of satisfaction.

Research shows that customers consider the quality of workmanship to be the most important factor, so this element should receive close attention by the management to ensure that the workshop activities give customer satisfaction. It is pointless having a near-perfect reception team if the main product that they are selling is defective. Most customers are prepared to pay a little more for good quality work, but they will not return if they consider that the cost of the repair is not in keeping with the quality.

Owners do not like to be parted from their vehicles for any length of time. Bearing this in mind the repair should be started as soon as possible after the customer has left the vehicle, work executed as quick as possible and the vehicle handed back at the agreed time.

Customers judge the performance of a company by comparing the latest work with a previous repair. Often three factors come up; they are:

- was cost more or less than expected
- was vehicle ready on time
- was vehicle repaired satisfactorily the first time.

### Customer relations techniques

The techniques used in a repair facility must be governed by the customers requirements. They should follow similar rules to those used in other selling activities.

In general customers can be divided into different types. When you are approached by a customer, the initial conversation and pleasantries will allow you to assess the general category; this will suggest the technique that you should use to suit the individual. The need for flexibility in the way in which the client is served is made clear by considering the following types of customer:

- *doubtful*: needs much help to decide on a course of action
- *decisive*: mind is already made up and wants action as quick as possible
- *talkative*: time waster who makes it difficult to complete the transaction and serve other customers
- *silent*: needs much sales talk to establish requirement
- *dictatorial*: projects strong opinions, often incorrect, which should not be challenged
- *disagreeable*: objects to everything; should be given the chance to fully express themselves; unreasonable remarks should not be taken personally
- *distrustful*: soured by some previous experience; fear should be allayed and confidence restored

The technique that is used to please the fore-mentioned customers should establish a sense of partnership and trust; this will not be achieved overnight.

The attitude of many customers needs considerable patience and these should be treated carefully without being too bossy. The aim is to generate a friendly two-way communication to allow you to produce an accurate record of the customer's requirements.

---

## Good practice

**The golden rules for good customer relations:**

- keep the service promise
- do what you are supposed to do, when you are supposed to do it
- do it for a fair price

---

Although experience and training are needed to develop the various techniques, the basic method is to use common-sense, show good manners and be patient. Service Advisers are often guided by the following recommendations:

- understand your customers' need
- carefully listen to customers and comprehend essential information
- make eye contact
- learn customer's name as soon as possible
- use their name in conversation
- focus attention on customer
- give quick service
- deal with any complaints promptly.

Do not oversell a particular product or service. Although this may be impressive at the time, the customers often feel that they have been talked into something they don't want – they show their displeasure by not returning.

Many companies create a good impression when they give a little bit extra that is not charged. The good impression normally results in additional work in the future – at that time the cost of the 'extra' can be a hidden charge.

## 12.7 Security of customer's property

Vehicles left for repair often contain customer's personal property including valuable items such as cameras and radios; it is the responsibility of the company to guard these possessions against loss by theft. Also vehicles contain many expensive 'fixed' items such as in-car entertainment systems. These items are very attractive to a thief, so basic precautions must be taken to ensure that they are secure during the time the vehicle is in the care of the company.

### Care of property

It is not always appreciated that the company is legally bound to take reasonable care of the vehicle and its contents. Notices stating that the company is not responsible for vehicles and contents are not enforceable by law, so management must ensure that the security of customers property is good. Technicians working on vehicles, as well as other employees, come into contact with the customer's valuables, so it is essential that all employees are honest and trustworthy.

*Valuables* Customers should be advised by reception staff to remove all valuables before they leave the vehicle. There are two reasons for this:

1) The technician working on the vehicle cannot be expected to guard it the whole time. Workshops are open places and at a time when the vehicle is unattended the goods can 'disappear'.
2) An unscrupulous customer can allege that valuables were stolen from a car whereas the truth is that the valuables were not in the car in the first place. In such cases it is the word of one person against another. These situations waste time and always end up unsatisfactorily, especially when a member of staff is falsely accused of stealing.

Valuable items found in the car after a customer has left the premises should be taken into custody and kept in a safe place until the customer returns and takes possession of the goods. All complaints about missing items should be fully investigated and the details of the incident reported to the management.

### Care of vehicle

It is expected that care of the vehicle will be exercised whilst it is being repaired, so special precautions must be taken to protect the bodywork and interior. Chipping or denting of the bodywork and/or soiling of the interior harms customer relations; it also wastes time when staff have to deal with complaints and rectification work.

*Vehicle damage and security* One problem area is when a vehicle is manoeuvred before and after the repair, so only authorised drivers should perform this task. Parking space is always a problem: when a person has to access a vehicle in a confined parking space it is easy to cause body panel damage. Vehicles stored in a parking area awaiting collection are very tempting to a thief. The time has long gone when the vehicle could be left unlocked with the keys in place. Today a secure compound is needed to protect both the vehicle and its contents. Also some system must be devised and used to ensure that only the customer takes the vehicle; not a well-informed thief.

### Bailment

Certain legal responsibilities are placed on a company and a customer when a vehicle is entrusted to the company for any reason. Employees must be aware of these responsibilities to ensure that their dealings with customers are conducted in a legal manner and are in the best interests of all parties.

In law when a customer (*the bailor*) leaves goods (*bailment*) with a company (*the bailee*), a contract of bailment is made which requires the bailee to re-deliver the same goods to the bailor. This legal jargon means that a vehicle must be returned to the owner after it was left with a company for any reason. A contract of bailment is usually combined with the repair contract.

The bailee (company) is under a duty to take reasonable care of the bailor's property and in the event of loss or damage the burden is on the bailee to show either that there was no negligence or that the company was not liable by virtue of an exemption clause agreed at the time the goods were deposited. Exemption clauses must be reasonable and legal, i.e. they are not contrary to the provisions of the *Unfair Contract Terms Act*.

In cases where the loss or damage is caused by an event for which a third party is responsible, the company can recover damages from the third party, but has to hold the amount recovered for the customer. This situation arises when an insurance company makes a payment to the company to cover loss of, or damage to, a vehicle.

Cases associated with bailment arise when either a vehicle is retained by a repairer or is not collected by the bailor; the former arises when the repairer is not paid for his work and is called a *lien*, the latter related to the disposal of uncollected goods.

*Lien* A *possessory lien* is a right to retain a vehicle, which is in the possession of the repairer claiming the lien, until the claim is satisfied. The lien is enforced by a 'right of retention'; this means that the owner of the vehicle cannot recover his property until the repair charges have been paid. In this situation the charges cannot include storage or other expenses that arise during the period of the lien. A possessory lien is lost when:

- the repairer losses possession of the goods
- payment is made of the amount claimed
- the goods are abandoned.

A lien does not arise unless the contracted work has been completed and the vehicle has been improved by the work or expenditure. This means that the repairer has no lien when service or general maintenance work is undertaken; this is because no improvement work has been carried out.

***Uncollected goods***   Occasions arise when customers fail, for unknown reasons, to collect their vehicles after work has been carried out on them. The bailee still has to take reasonable care of the goods and is faced with two problems; the vehicle occupies valuable space and the repair account is unpaid. In situations where the vehicle remains uncollected, and the bill unpaid, after the customer has been repeatedly notified by letter, the procedure specified in *Torts (Interference with Goods) Act* can be used. This Act lays down a course of action that can be adopted; this enables the vehicle to be sold after a given time and from the proceeds of the sale, the repairer is able to deduct his full charges before handing over the balance to the owner.

### Repair work and the Law
Customer/company disputes involving bailment, lien or collection problems, are sometimes caused by workshop events which are covered by some legal regulation; to avoid these problems the workshop staff should be made aware of the main elements of consumer law that affect them.

***Implied warrantee of skill***   Under the *Supply of Goods and Services Act* there are implied terms that the supplier will carry out the service with reasonable care and skill, in a reasonable time for a reasonable charge. In the event of a dispute a court will decide the limits of the term 'reasonable'. The Act requires all repair work, including subcontracted work, undertaken by a trader on a vehicle or component to satisfy the specified conditions. Exclusion clauses to limit liability must conform to the *Unfair Contract Terms Act*; this Act excludes the use of any clause relating to death or personal injury, and clauses covering other losses due to negligence can be restricted only if they satisfy the requirement of reasonableness.

### Estimated repair work
The cost of work based on an *estimate* must be within reasonable limits of the estimate, whereas a contract based on a *quotation* is costed as stated in the quotation. In practice this means that any work undertaken in excess of reasonableness in the case of an estimate, or the actual amount given in a quotation, cannot be legally recovered. To avoid these problems customers should be consulted, and a new contract made, before undertaking work beyond the agreed limits.

A customer's order that gives precise instructions must be followed and charged accordingly, whereas vague instructions give the repairer the authority to carry-out a wide range of repairs. For example, when a customer states that his engine is lacking power and orders "the plugs to be cleaned", means that any work carried out other than plug cleaning cannot be legally charged. However, a customer who orders, "the engine should be tuned to restore its performance" is giving the repairer full authority to carry out any work that is required. Even in this case the repairer may have difficulty recovering his money because the law expects the repairer to act 'reasonably'; in a Court of Law the case will be based on the word 'reasonable'.

The situations outlined above can be avoided by making the staff aware of the legal problems. Steps should be taken to consult the customer to ensure that all work undertaken is correctly contracted; it may not secure payment for the work but it will ensure that any legal proceedings have a good chance of success.

### Ownership of spare parts
By Law all component parts removed from customers' vehicles are their property. This means that any part that might be the subject of a future dispute should be kept in a secure place for a reasonable time unless the customer gives approval for their disposal.

In a similar way any parts fitted on a vehicle are owned by the repairer until payment is received from the customer; knowledge of this fact is important when a lien is enforced for repair work.

***Authority to fit spare parts***   During a repair operation, the repairer has the implied right to fit spare parts of type and quantity as are reasonable, provided that the spare part is vital to the actual repair being undertaken. When the need to fit an expensive part is discovered after making the original contract for the work, it is the repairer's responsibility to inform the customer to obtain authority to fit the part. Sometimes a company includes a condition in the repair contract that gives them the authority to fit the necessary spare parts, but even in these cases it is advisable to contact the customer before proceeding with the job.

### Repairs on vehicles subject to hire purchase
Contracts for repair work are made with individuals, i.e. between two parties, the repairer and the customer. This agreement is independent of any hire purchase agreement, so a repairer can institute legal proceedings against a customer for breach of contract if the bill is not paid.

Any vehicle that is the subject of a hire purchase agreement are owned by the finance house, so a lien can only be enforced if the vehicle hire agreement has not been terminated before the repair contract was made.

## 12.8 Customer complaints

Customers don't complain! Surveys show that about 96% of dissatisfied customers who buy general products do not complain; about 80% of this group change their supplier after a bad experience rather than complain.

Many complaints come from customers who are dissatisfied with auto repair work. This high level is not all due to a poor standard of service given by this industry; instead it reflects the ease in which a customer can involve the various motoring organisations and consumer groups.

*Reluctance to complain* Numerous disgruntled customers feel that complaining will do not good. Many of these find it difficult to complain effectively due to both their lack of technical knowledge and frustration with the complaints procedure. Consequently, many rely on revenge by relating their bad experience to other potential customers at every opportunity. The negative advertising effect of this is very damaging, so steps should be taken to avoid this problem by identifying the possible causes. When weak trading areas have been identified, two steps should be taken – the problem must be corrected and a simple channel must be set up to monitor customers' views on the performance of the company. It is claimed that 95% of customers remain loyal to a company; results show that about 60% of customers who do complain can be satisfied if the problem can be solved quickly and amicably.

### Customer handling

Normally company employees appear to be unaware of the benefits of handling a complaint in a satisfactory manner. They do not appreciate that the complaint is an opportunity for them to turn a bad customer experience into a long-term friendship.

Earlier in this book it was stated that 'the customer is always right'. This is true up to a point; you must decide where the point is. When negotiating a settlement of a dispute it is often beneficial to tilt the settlement towards the customer; the firm will gain in the long run. Also bear in mind that if you argue with a customer you may win the argument, but most likely you will lose the customer. Normally about 99% of customers who complain have a genuine problem, so the other 1% must not cloud your judgement.

Things go wrong even in well-run companies, so ensure the problems are rectified before they develop into full-blown disputes. At an early stage apologise, and if the problem is serious follow this up with a letter; customers like this. In the case of faulty goods these should either be replaced or the money refunded. Normally, defective repairs are corrected by the person who carried out the original work, but this should only be after the actual cause of the problem has been diagnosed by a supervisor. In many cases incomplete instructions and/or incorrect diagnosis are reasons why repairs are unsatisfactory.

Remember, customers are not interested in the number of successful repairs that a firm has completed – they are only concerned with their problem.

### Front line attack

Customers consider that Reception with its *front line staff* represents the company, so this is where the bulk of service complaints are registered. When they return to complain they are giving the company the opportunity to put things right.

On the brighter side, any compliments received should be noted and passed on to the appropriate people.

Each company should have a policy for the handling of customer complaints and all personnel in the command chain should know the limit ($£x$) that they can award to a customer in goods and services without referring the matter to a more senior manager. All staff should keep a record of each complaint received together with the action taken; this will allow senior management to monitor the company's performance.

Reception staff must understand that their attitude towards the customer often dictates the way in which a dispute develops, so to maintain customer confidence the persons employed for this work must be able to strike a balance between their personal skills and technical ability.

### Customer types

At an early stage in the complaints procedure it is usual to assess the complainant to ascertain the general type. Having done this the appropriate course of action can be taken. The three basic groups are those that:

1) *Rarely complain*: these 'good' regular customers must have a genuine problem so urgent action should be taken to maintain the good will of the company.

2) *Always complain*: these complain without justification and cause much waste of time and staff bitterness; sometimes they are advised to transfer their custom elsewhere.

3) *Walk away*: these 'walk' away and transfer their business to another firm instead of making a complaint and giving the firm a chance to rectify the problem. A regular follow-up system should target this type at an early stage to detect any problem.

### Service and repair complaints

A study of the common complaints connected with service and repair transactions show up the main areas that need careful control to maximize customer satisfaction. A manager needs to monitor the following:

- booking-in and appointment procedure
- attitude of reception staff
- correct communication of customer's instructions to workshop
- accurate diagnosis of stated faults
- identification of acceptable warranty work
- no work done without authority
- accurate recording of spare parts that were used
- fair, speedy invoicing with no suggestion of overcharging
- clean condition of vehicle at time of collection
- collection of vehicle at agreed time.

Assessment of a complaint against the company's standard for items such as those stated above, should enable a judgement to be made on the validity of a customer's claim. Some complaints may be directed at the company that are outside its scope; e.g. the company's position relating to manufacturer's products should be explained to the customer.

Study of the various complaints show they can be separated into three general groups; availability, quality and information.

*Availability*   Customers do not like it when their vehicle is either immobilized and awaiting work to be done, or faulty due to a delay in the supply of a vital part. Discovery of the initial problem will have caused them to be upset, especially as the repair might involve a considerable expense. However this upset will quickly lead to anger if the repair cannot be carried out without delay. In these cases the natural mood of the customer must be appreciated and reassurance given at an early stage to 'lower the customer's temperature'; this should be followed immediately by taking the appropriate remedial action.

*Quality*   This covers products, services, company systems, and performance of individuals. Out of these, the product is perhaps the easiest to identify and correct; the

Customer complaints are minimized when work is regularly checked. These checks should include a general inspection of the vehicle to highlight any unreported defects, especially those that affect vehicle safety.

*Ford Motor Co Ltd*

## Good practice

### Complaint processing

- identify and acknowledge the customer's idea of the problem
- gather, analyse, and arrange in order of importance, the information relevant to the customer's problem
- summarize customer's problem using ideas and information gathered from them
- respond in a manner that protects the customer from unnecessary worry and aggravation

defect can be easily pin-pointed and the action taken will probably conform with the terms of the *Sale and Supply of Goods Act*.

***Referral to management***    Complaints about services can range over a wide field, so care must be taken to establish the actual problem that the customer is complaining about. Once this has been identified the necessary action can be taken. When the severity of the problem, or the insistence of the customer, requires the matter to be referred to the manager, it is advisable that the meeting between the customer and manager is delayed until the latter has been provided with the full details and documentation. Problems relating to either an individual's performance or a company system are normally management matters; in these cases the customer should be given an appointment to enable the matter to be fully discussed.

***Information***    The main complaints in this category arise from either lack of communication or incorrect information. They can occur within the company (e.g. when either a lack of information or incorrect details are given on a job card) or external such as when information is published by a manufacturer or some other source. In some cases, problems arise due to information that is communicated to a customer by the company. This can be an error on an invoice, appointment and collection time mistakes, and misunderstandings associated with the communication of regular and irregular information. Once again the priority is to establish the actual hub of the complaint so that it can be investigated to establish a suitable course of action.

***Referral to arbitration***    In the event of deadlock following a customer complaint, companies that are members of the Retail Motor Industry Federation can advise their customers to use the Investigation and Advisory Service offered by the Federation for arbitration of the dispute.

## PROGRESS CHECK 12

1. All people working in a service industry are employed:
(a) on routine maintenance of vehicles
(b) by companies serving the manufacturers with products
(c) in support activities such as maintenance, insurance, etc.
(d) by manufacturers to provide an after-sales service.

2. Salesmen use A.I.D.A. as a guide for the selling process. The letter 'I' stands for:
(a) interest
(b) intercept
(c) information
(d) involvement.

3. The three essentials of a contract are:
(a) offer, acceptance and agreement
(b) offer, acceptance and consideration
(c) a person's capacity, age and ability to pay
(d) a person's age, acceptance of goods and consideration.

4. A party can terminate a contract if:
(a) a condition is not fulfilled
(b) a warranty is not fulfilled
(c) one party cannot complete the agreed work
(d) one party cannot pay for the agreed work.

5. Undertakings and promises in an agreement are known as:
(a) terms of a contract
(b) implied terms of a contract
(c) conditions that cannot be enforced
(d) warranties that allow a contract to be terminated.

6. The *Sale and Supply of Goods Act* demands that goods are:
(a) inspected by the purchaser on receipt
(b) free from any defect and correctly priced
(c) of satisfactory quality and safe to use
(d) of satisfactory quality and free from any defect.

7. The main objective of staff in Reception should be to:
(a) sell service
(b) secure payment
(c) console irate customers
(d) interpret customer's instructions.

8. The *Trade Descriptions Act* is intended to prevent:
(a) the use of 'offers to treat'
(b) the false use of the term 'agent'
(c) use of a false or misleading trade description
(d) incorrect pricing arising from a false trade description.

9. A contract of bailment is made between a customer and a company. This contract requires the bailee to:
(a) redeliver the same goods to the bailor
(b) ensure that the bailor takes care of the bailment
(c) accept the provisions of the *Unfair Contract Terms Act*
(d) pay the agreed account at the time the goods are delivered.

10. Contracted work has been completed but the customer refuses to pay the bill. The company has the right to:
(a) retain the vehicle until the claim is satisfied
(b) recover the vehicle which is in the possession of the owner
(c) claim a possessory lien for any improvement work carried out
(d) reclaim the vehicle from the customer after the statutory time period has elapsed.

# 13                              *Company systems*

## What is covered in this chapter:

→ company services
→ costing and estimating
→ warranty
→ documentation and recording systems

The Retail Motor Industry is a large organisation so you should understand the role of your company in this industry. You will see that the type of business transacted by your company depends on its resources, i.e. the range of skills possessed by its personnel, the available equipment and its working capital.

Customers attracted to your premises often require a clear idea of the anticipated cost before they authorise any work; the price you state in this estimate must be competitive if you are to get the order. Furthermore when the work has been completed an accurately costed invoice is expected that shows clearly the work that you carried out.

As a franchised dealer your company will be required to undertake warranty work, so customers will expect your help to process their claims. This help should be given in a fair manner, because the manufacturer will expect you to ascertain the cause of failures to avoid the submission of unreasonable claims.

The business aspects outlined above require the company to operate an efficient system of documentation, so you must understand the various parts of this system in order that you can be a sound link in the chain.

## 13.1 Company services

The Retail Motor Industry is an industrial sector of companies that rely on the business that arises after a motor vehicle has been manufactured. It is a *Service Industry* that embraces firms that make the original sale and includes the after-sales companies and individuals

that are involved in support activities associated with the operation of the vehicle during its lifetime.

### Range of activities

Companies and individuals forming the Retail Motor Industry can be broadly divided into the following:

● Main dealers – contracted (franchised) with one manufacture to sell a given number of new vehicles per year, to maintain a given stock of spare parts and offer a wide service and repair facility.
● Franchised dealers – similar to main dealers but sales, stock and facilities are smaller, or in some cases hold more than one franchise but this is not liked by manufacturers due to a possible clash of loyalty; sometimes this is overcome by having separate sites.
● Non-franchised dealer – makes an occasional sale, but main activity is centred around the servicing and general repairs of a wide range of vehicles.
● Bodywork repairers – independent companies, or departments of main dealers, that specialise in body repairs, paintwork and trim; mainly engaged in accident work contracted by insurance companies.
● Petrol retailers – sometimes part of a dealership but more often a separate firm that is either an independent company or owned by a petrol company; the latter normally leases the site to a tenant or employs a manager to run the outlet.
● Fast-fit specialists – aim to give a quick, low-cost service that concentrates on one part of the vehicle, these activities include the supplying and fitting of exhaust systems, tyres, radiators, batteries, clutches, brakes and windscreens.
● Specialised repairers – firms that concentrate on the repair of one component; e.g. electrical, air conditioning, automatic transmission, and in-car entertainment systems.
● Parts supply – offer to dealers a fast supply service of spare parts other than those parts that are closely

controlled and distributed by the vehicle manufacturers.

- Mobile repairers – mobile workshops that undertake engine tuning, servicing and light repairs on the car owners' premises.
- Recovery specialists – firms that concentrate on recovering a vehicle after it has broken-down or been involved in an accident.
- Motor cycle repairers – often franchised, these dealers sell and repair motor cycles.

### Business set-up

These days a considerable investment is needed to set up an auto repair business, but if sufficient funds and expertise are available, a feasibility study is made at an early stage to assess the prospects of starting a new business, especially the strength of local competition.

If the business intends to sell new vehicles, selected manufacturers have to be approached at an early stage to find out if they will enter with you into a franchise agreement. Normally conditions are written into this contract by the manufacturer that dictate the general resources that must be provided: these include the size and layout of buildings, minimum equipment, stocks of vehicles and spare parts, and in some cases the number of staff and their qualifications. These factors show the pattern of business that must be followed by a franchised company when it starts trading.

### Resources available

The word resource means *a stock that can be drawn on.* When a company wishes to develop its business, or move into another activity, it is necessary to look at the resources available in the firm. In this case the *stock* covers items such as available finance, accommodation, equipment, staff and most important the *know-how* of the staff to undertake a given activity. When a firm has resources far in excess of its daily needs, it should take steps to harness this surplus resource and gain the profit earned from this additional work.

The nature of employment and trading conditions alter frequently; this means that companies must be flexible to accept the changes brought about by technological developments. A long established company that was able to make a fair profit over the years by providing a good service to its customers often finds that the service is no longer required. Unless management keep an eye on current developments and make the necessary changes to adapt, the profit will disappear and the company will have to close down.

Many non-franchised dealers often experience difficult trading conditions owing to technical changes in the motor vehicle. Alteration in the frequency of periodic services and reduction in the time spent on this work seriously reduces the profit earned by this activity. Furthermore the greater reliability of modern ignition systems, combined with the reduced need for routine maintenance, has decreased the time that was sold for this work. Vital changes are needed to counter these developments and success is made more difficult when the following are considered:

a) extra competition from fast-fit companies which is not helped by the fast, low-cost service offered by these firms;
b) increased use of electronic systems which require both highly qualified staff and expensive equipment;
c) difficulty in accessing technical information from manufacturers;
d) competition from mobile service units.

Far-sighted management must take into account items such as those mentioned above and they must 'tune' their service to take advantage of any niche activity (activities that other companies do not offer). When entering this new area of work management must look at the resources available in the company and, if these are deficient, they must build-up their resources to the level required. This may involve the purchase of new equipment, appointment of new staff, or retraining the existing work force.

## 13.2 Costing and estimating

A company is in business to make a profit – *no profit, no company.* The profit from a Service Department is obtained from the sale of time, i.e. the hours worked on customers' cars. To achieve a satisfactory return for the investors in the company, it is necessary for the staff to aim at selling the maximum number of hours that are available. However, this objective alone will not give a good profit unless the charge to customers for these work-hours is sufficient to cover the firm's trading costs – profit is only made after all trading costs have been recovered.

Unless management closely monitors its trading expenses and charges during the year, the annual accounts, which are drawn up at the end of the financial year, may show a serious loss. At that time it is too late to recover the loss of profits and, unless the company has sufficient reserves, the situation may have grave consequences.

To appreciate the main principles of costing, the various elements that affect customer charges are considered here. Work on a customer's car can be charged in one of two ways:

1) standard charge
2) hourly rate.

## Standard charge

This is a charge given in a published schedule to indicate to a customer the cost of specific repair and service work such as clutch replacement, brake overhaul and periodic maintenance. Some manufacturers recommend (some insist) that their dealers publish scheduled or standard charges to show customers their competitive rates with the aim of encouraging them to remain loyal to the company.

Some customers fear main-dealer's charges so they patronize smaller firms with the hope of a smaller repair bill. This is not always achieved, because the high-tech motor car often needs special tools and test equipment that the smaller firms cannot afford. In these cases the bill can be more expensive, especially when the repair is not carried out correctly on the first visit. Before customers decide on which firm to use, they wish to know the actual cost of the job, so this is where a firm that uses schedule charges will benefit.

Adoption of standard charges, as set by the company or manufacturer, does not rule out the need for the staff to keep control of working time and trading costs. In this case a tighter control must be exercised to ensure that a fair profit is obtained from each job. Sometimes the manufacturer's charge may be much lower than that attained by the firm; this may be due to the fact that the charge was based on a different working method or on the use of special tools. Unless this is identified and investigated at an early stage, it will result in each job making a loss.

## Hourly-rate charge

This system uses a pre-determined hourly charge-rate which incorporates trading costs and profit elements. Having established the rate, the charge to the customer is based on the product of the rate and total hours worked on that particular job. This simplifies the costing process and takes into account the time taken by the technician to complete a given task.

The hourly charge-rate is made up of three elements:

1) recovery of overheads needed to run the firm (indirect costs);

2) technician's hourly wage (direct costs);
3) profit.

This charge-out rate is calculated by comparing the total overheads that the firm has to pay each year with the total number of productive hours worked by the workshop staff.

## Overheads or indirect costs

These expenses relate to all outgoings involved in, or connected with, the running of the business, the incurring of which cannot be directly attributed to the repairing or selling of any particular vehicle. Overheads can be divided into two categories; these are:

1) *General expenses* – these apply to the business as a whole, e.g. rent, rates, power, etc.
2) *Departmental expenses* – these expenses are those that are incurred by individual departments in the course of their trading activity; each department has the responsibility to recover its own expenses. For example workshop tools and equipment are charged to the Service Department, whereas new car sales literature would be an overhead for the Sales Department.

*General overheads*    These include:

- rent (or rental value) and rates
- licenses, taxes and insurances
- lighting, power, and heating
- bank interest and charges
- postage, general stationery, telephone
- depreciation and maintenance of buildings and general equipment
- salaries of administrative and cleaning staff
- holiday pay.

For departmental costing purposes, general overheads are split up either in proportion to floor area, or in a way that reflects the use that is made of that overhead by the particular department; expenditure on advertising is a typical example of the latter. An estimate for each item of general overhead is obtained by using the figures from previous years as a starting point.

*Departmental overheads*    These include:

- salaries of non-productive staff; e.g. reception staff, foreman, etc.
- sick pay
- purchase and maintenance of special tools and test equipment

- component cleaning materials and equipment
- recovery vehicle; depreciation, tax, insurance and running expenses
- technicians' non-productive time
- rectification of faulty work (free-of-charge jobs)
- consumable materials; rags, nuts, bolts, washers, etc.

## Fixed and variable costs

All of the forementioned overhead expenses can be divided into two groups; fixed and variable. A fixed cost is an expense which has to be met by the company irrespective of the amount of work that is undertaken (e.g. rent and heating), whereas a variable cost depends on the volume of work (e.g. consumable materials).

## Budgets

When all items of company expenditure has been identified and apportioned (divided), the departments will be able to decide on the way in which the expenses are passed on to the customer. When the overhead budget, or share of the expenditure to be recovered, is known, it is management's duty to ensure that each department keeps within the estimated figure; i.e. some form of *budgetary control* must be used to keep each item of departmental spending within the estimated target, especially the variable expenses.

## Financial figures of merit

***Total wages paid for productive work***   This is estimated by using the previous year's figures given on the job cards and then updating them to take into account any changes in trading conditions such as inflation, wage increases and productivity improvements.

***Establishment charge ratio***   The way in which the overhead/wage ratio (establishment charge ratio) is calculated can be shown by the following example; the figures have been simplified to show the method.

Total departmental overheads per year
$$= £300\,000$$
Total wages paid for productive work
$$= £100\,000$$
Establishment charge ratio %
$$= \text{(total overheads)}/\text{(total wages)}$$
$$= (300\,000/100\,000) \times 100$$
$$= 300\%$$

The value of this ratio is the proportion of the wage that must be added to a customer's bill to recover the cost of running the company. The 300% shown in the example means that for every £1 paid to the technician for productive work, a sum of £3 must be added to cover overheads. In this case, the £4 charged to the customer might keep the technician in work and the firm's creditors happy, but it will do little to reward the investors in the company since no profit has been allowed for the company.

***Profit***   This is the 'wage' earned by a company as a reward for exposing the capital invested in a company to possible trading dangers. The proportion added to a customer's bill to cover the profit element depends on the type of business; a typical figure recommended for the Motor Vehicle Retail Industry is 20% of turnover (wages plus overheads and profit). It is claimed that this figure is required in this industry, because capital investment turns over comparatively slowly; also the risks associated with repair work are considerable. Taking into account the three elements, the proportional charge to the customer is:

| | |
|---|---|
| Technician's wage | $= £1.00$ |
| Overheads (300%) | $= £3.00$ |
| Profit (20% of turnover) | $= £1.00$ |
| TOTAL | $= £5.00$ |

***Charge-out rate***   Having to apply the above formula to every invoice is complicated, so most companies have their own *hourly labour-rate*. This method combines the three elements stated above; by using this figure, the work can be easily costed. Using an establishment ratio of 300% and hourly wage rate of £8.00, the hourly charge-out hourly rate would be made up as follows:

| | |
|---|---|
| wage rate | $= £8.00$ |
| overheads | $= £24.00$ |
| profit | $= £8.00$ |
| TOTAL | $= £40.00$ |

A job which involved 5 hours of the technician's time would then be costed as:

| | £ |
|---|---|
| Labour (5 hours @ £40/hour) | $= 200.00$ |
| V A T (17.5%) | $= 35.00$ |
| TOTAL (excluding materials) | $= 235.00$ |

Ill-informed technicians seeing this bill often overlook the firm's need to recover overheads, so these persons conclude that either the work is overpriced or that the company's profit is exorbitant.

## REMEMBER

**Elements of an invoice**

The invoiced charge to a customer must include:

- direct labour charge
- proportion of overheads
- profit
- materials used
- value added tax

## Productivity

Company overheads previously listed are either *fixed* or *variable*; the former must be met irrespective of the amount of business carried out, whereas the latter is determined by the volume of business. Fixed overheads make up a large slice of the charge-out rate, so if a larger number of jobs could be carried out by the same work force in a year, then each job would carry a smaller share of the fixed overheads and result in a lower rate. This lower and more competitive rate would attract new customers and bring in more work. The process shows how good productivity from the staff forms the basis of a healthy company.

Conversely, if the volume of work falls, each job will have to carry more of the fixed overheads with the result that the cost of each job will rise. Most probably this high charge will deter customers from trading with the company, consequently the volume of work will fall further and the amount of idle time will increase. Unless drastic action is taken to reverse this costing problem the company will be forced out of business.

*Remedial action to reduce costs*   Rarely can management reduce fixed costs without selling property, so this means that a competitive rate can only be achieved by one or more of the following:

- improve productivity (this is the purpose of an incentive scheme)
- reduce variable costs by strict budgetary control
- decrease the number of non-productive staff
- reduce non-productive and idle-time – often achieved by cutting the productive staff

## Estimating costs

The Code of Practice for the Motor Industry recommends that customers should be given a firm *quotation* for all major repairs before work is commenced. It should be understood by both parties that the acceptance of a quotation constitutes the basis of a *contract*. An *estimate* is an alternative to a quotation and the figure given indicates the expected, or target, price of a repair. Unless the final account exceeds the estimate by an unreasonable amount, the customer is expected, as contracted, to pay the bill. It is suggested that if, during the course of a repair, the work is likely to exceed the agreed estimate by a significant amount, the customer should be contacted in order to authorise the extra work.

An estimate should show clearly any extras such as materials and VAT. Often it is recommended that a company should estimate on the 'high' side, because this built-in cushion covers the unexpected and gives a good impression if the final invoice is presented below the estimated cost. Some firms wishing to promote good customer relations have a policy of either slightly undercharging for the work or giving some extra 'free' service.

## Resources available

Used in this form, a resource is the ability of a firm to sell a service or stock to a customer. Before an estimate for a repair is given, management must assess the firm's resources to determine the range of work that can be undertaken. It is pointless for a firm to contract for work that is beyond both the skill of its workforce and range of its equipment.

In cases that need a specific skill or special equipment to perform a certain operation, it is often financially beneficial to use the services of a subcontractor. Alternatively if the company assesses that a good regular profit can be made from this specialized activity, then it may be advantageous to undertake this work. Assuming space is available, the new activity will need the appointment of new fully skilled staff, or retraining of the existing staff, and the purchase of the specialized equipment. Entry into this new activity must be carefully planned and consideration must be given to the volume of work that the facility will attract. Companies cost the operation on the basis of profit per square metre of floor area, so if this does not compare favourably with the firm's other activities, it would be wiser to subcontract the work out to an established specialist.

## Standard times

Many manufacturers provide their dealers with a schedule of 'times'. They consider that these are applicable to a wide range of service and repair operations on their vehicles when the tasks are undertaken by skilled staff using the recommended tools and equipment.

Many non-franchised dealers do not have access to this information so they use an independent schedule of times which is called the *ICME Manual*. This publication gives details of periodic maintenance tasks for the common makes of vehicle together with approved times for most repairs; these are broken down into separate operations to simplify costing and estimating.

By referring to the appropriate schedule or manual, the process of preparing an estimate is quite simple. First the proposed job is split up into its main elements (e.g. dismantling, rectification and re-assembly) and then the time for each element, and part-element, is determined. Once the total time has been calculated, the estimate is costed by multiplying the time by the labour rate.

### Conditional clauses

Disputes often arise due to a misunderstanding of the actual work that was to be done. To avoid this, the estimate should contain sufficient details to make clear the work that is to be undertaken. Terms such as 'overhaul' should be avoided because these are too vague. Whenever the repair involves the possibility of additional work due to the unknown condition of a component, the estimate should make this clear by inserting a conditional clause such as:

> This estimate is based on the information obtained from a superficial examination of the component and if the condition of the component is abnormal when it is dismantled, then a supplementary estimate will be submitted for agreement before any further work is commenced.

*Supplementary estimate*   If it is discovered that some abnormal mechanical condition indicates that the original estimate will be exceeded, then an additional estimate should be given to the customer. Agreement for the extra work must be contracted before the work is undertaken.

## 13.3 Warranty

When a person buys a new product, a warranty or undertaking is given by the manufacturer to rectify, without charge, any defect, due to faulty manufacture or materials, that develops during its early life. Used in this sense, the meaning of the term 'warranty' is different to that used in the Law of Contract (see p 159). However the two meanings overlap because a contract is made whenever goods are sold and the transaction must comply with the terms laid down in the *Sale and Supply of Goods Act* or the *Supply of Goods and Services Act*.

*Sale and Supply of Goods Act*   This Act contains several conditions and warranties; one of the most important is that the goods are of *satisfactory quality* and are as *fit for the purpose* for which goods of that kind are commonly brought. The conditions imply that the goods must be of a quality as it is reasonable to expect having regard to their description, price and any other relevant circumstances. Purchasers of new vehicles have the full protection of this Act and its use can neither be made inapplicable, nor be restricted by any exclusion clauses introduced by a seller.

*The Supply of Goods and Services Act*   This Act applies in cases where the supply of a service, such as the repair of a car, is the main substance of the contract. The Act covers service activities as well as containing the main provisions of the *Sale and Supply of Goods Act*; the extra terms include the requirement for the supplier to carry out the service with reasonable care and skill in a reasonable time and for a reasonable charge.

### Product Guarantees

Loosely called a warranty, a 'guarantee' is given by a seller to avoid possible legal action (brought under the appropriate Acts) which might arise due to a defect that was not apparent at the time of sale. Details of a guarantee are normally featured in the sales literature and their appeal often encourages a customer to buy a given product. The promise made by a manufacturer, and passed on by their franchised dealers, to rectify without charge any defects for a stated time, gives the purchaser peace of mind as regards financial commitment during the early years of ownership of the product.

A typical new-car 'warranty package' given by a manufacturer includes:

- Mechanical warranty for 12 months unlimited mileage against mechanical faults which are attributable to a manufacturing or assembly defect.
- Paintwork and surface rust warranty for 3 years.
- Anti-corrosion warranty for 6 years.

Manufacturer's conditions of the warranty vary; some extend the time to three years whereas others might only offer to supply a replacement part and do not cover any labour costs. All companies stipulate conditions that cover wear and tear, neglect, need for regular servicing as recommended, fitment of non-standard parts, vehicle

**REMEMBER**

**Typical warranty**

Ace Motor Co Ltd assure you that if any part of your vehicle becomes defective due to faulty manufacture or materials within 12 months from the time you took delivery of your vehicle the part will be repaired or replaced by any of our authorised dealers completely free of charge. The only conditions are:

*conditions are then listed*

modification, and any excluded items such as tyres; these are covered by the tyre manufacturers' own warranty. Most warranties are transferable to subsequent owners.

### Extended warranties

An optional extension to the main warranty can be purchased at the time the vehicle is bought. This warranty gives cover for most of the mechanical and electrical components and normally includes labour costs. Extended warranty agreements contain a number of conditions; one common term requires the owner to show evidence that the vehicle was serviced at the recommended times by authorised dealers.

In the past these agreements were offered by a number of 'insurance' companies but poor publicity, resulting from the failure of many companies to honour their agreements, has forced some manufacturers to administer their own schemes.

### Processing warranty work

When a customer returns a defective vehicle to the service department of a company holding a franchise for that make of vehicle, it is the responsibility of the reception staff to diagnose the cause of the fault. If documents show that the vehicle is still within its warranty period, the staff must decide if the proposed repair justifies a warranty claim. If the fault is due to a defective component, and the repair is within the limits laid down by the manufacturer, the vehicle is booked in and processed as a warranty repair. After completing the work, a warranty claim is prepared and submitted to the manufacturer; assuming they accept the claim, payment is made or credit given. Settlement of a claim depends on their acceptance of the diagnosis, repair time, labour rate (often specially agreed) and approval of the spare parts used.

The customer is required to accept responsibility for payment for the repair in cases where it is uncertain that

the manufacturer will give approval. Alternatively the repair can be delayed until the manufacturer has given approval for the work; this may involve an inspection of the vehicle by the manufacturer's representative.

All defective parts removed during a warranty repair must be returned to the parts department where they are and labelled to identify them with the claim and kept secure. In some cases the parts must be returned to the manufacturer for their inspection to enable them to make the necessary design or production changes.

## 13.4 Documentation and recording systems

In early days small garages, which used the minimum paper work, relied on the foreman to remember the customer's requirements and relay them to mechanics at the time they started the job. Also these garages needed mechanics with good memories so as to state the time taken on each particular job and the parts that were used. Often this led to work not being done and the customer not being charged for spare parts. This 'system' was cheap to operate but has obvious drawbacks; the main problems are summed up by the word 'inefficient'.

### Documentation requirements

The documentation system used in a company should be tailored to suit the size of the company; it must be simple to operate and achieve its purpose with the minimum cost. Any company that uses an excess of paper to support its productive staff may claim to be efficient by recording every scrap of information, but this is foolish if the system needs extra non-productive staff to operate it.

In this electronic age many paper documents have been replaced by a computer which transmits data and information to terminals situated in the workshop and company offices. Provided the computer does not break down, this method has many advantages; messages and instructions are transmitted quickly, it allows instant access to any available information by company staff, and it provides management with up-to-date details and statistics of the workshop's performance. One disadvantage of this system is its initial cost, but once this has been recovered, the improvements in efficiency and saving in staff time are considerable. At this time many companies still use the conventional job card system, so this is described here to enable the reader to understand both the principle of this established recording system and the job control structure on which computer programmes are based.

### Job control system

The number of separate documents required to operate a production control system depends on the size of the establishment and nature of the work undertaken. A typical system used in a medium size repair establishment is built around the following:

- customer's order (confirmation of instructions)
- job cards
- time record
- record of parts used (summarized on a materials card)
- cost sheet
- invoice.

Figure 13.4.1 shows the layout of a 3-card job control system; some of the cards shown can be combined together to simplify the system.

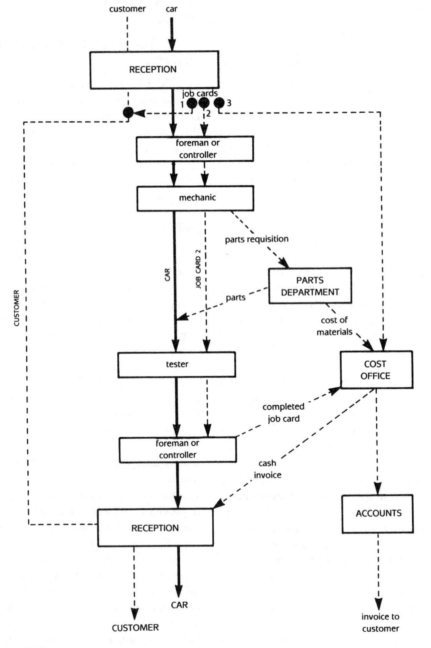

**Fig. 13.4.1** 3-card job control system

## Customer's order

This order is completed by reception staff to confirm the work required by the customer. It forms the contract and reduces the risk of any misunderstandings which might arise at a later date. The main terms and conditions of the contract are printed on the order and space is provided for the customer's signature when this formal acceptance is required by the company.

A signature does not guarantee payment because customers have successfully claimed that the order (contract) contained technical jargon that was unknown to them at the time they signed. In view of this, the receptionist must ensure that the customer is aware of the work to be done, the estimated price and the main terms of the company's contract. To minimize this problem some companies use a separate order that is worded in the 'customer's language'; others make the order the top flimsy copy of the job card set.

In all cases the wording must be precise and must avoid using vague, easily misunderstood terms such as 'overhaul'. Furthermore, the writing must be legible, especially when more than one copy is used. For routine orders many companies use a job card which lists the common tasks in a pre-printed form. This saves time and clearly indicates to the mechanics the work that is required.

## Job cards

The numbered job cards are made out by Reception after discussions with the customer have taken place to ascertain the precise work that is required. When a three-card system is used, the top copy is retained by the customer and the flimsy bottom copy is passed to the Cost Office to advise them of the work in progress. When the cards are made out, full details of the vehicle must be included, especially the mileage and the VIN (vehicle identification number); the latter is required for the company's records and for the identification of the correct spare parts.

The main copy, normally a stiff card, is handed by Reception to the foreman (or workshop controller); it is then passed on at the appropriate time to the mechanic who is selected by the foreman to undertake the repair. During the repair operation the card, which is attached to the vehicle, shows the work that has to be done and also acts as a record to co-ordinate the details of the job; these include the mechanic's name, time taken, parts used and details of any defects that should be reported to the customer. To save time these particulars are not always entered on the actual card; either they are clipped to it or inserted in the card's plastic wallet. Identification

of the job is by the number printed on the card, so when time is booked or parts requisitioned, the number is quoted.

When the work is complete and the tester has verified that the quality of the repair is to the standard set by the company, the card is passed to the foreman; this indicates that the mechanic is free to accept another job. Transfer of the card to the Cost Office, which is often a part of Reception, indicates that the job is ready for costing. The invoice is prepared by totalling the labour costs with the cost of all materials used; the latter is obtained on a Materials Card from the Parts Dept. which they prepare when they are notified that the job is finished.

The receipt by Reception of the invoice and car enables them to arrange for the customer to collect the vehicle and pay the bill. Cost sheets for credit customers, e.g. fleet operators, will be passed to the accounts section of the company; they will draw up and submit an invoice for all jobs that have been undertaken during the period.

***Reception records***   Details of all work carried out should be entered on a customer's record card. This document should contain particulars about the customer and his/her vehicle and will include warranty details and associated work. Besides containing factual information, the record will also serve as a reference for any future communications with the customer such as when follow-up letters and service reminders are sent out.

***Warranty and insurance work***   Warranty work and insurance repairs must be separated from normal work, so in these cases it is usual to have separate job cards. When the card is returned to the Cost Office, the job is costed and the claim for payment is made in the manner laid down by the respective company.

***Booking-in***   To provide the workshop with a steady flow of work, Reception must use some form of booking-in system; this can be either a booking-in diary or a workshop loading chart. By knowing the number of hours that are available for each mechanic (or section if it is a large company) the work can be planned.

***Control system***   At all times the foreman (or workshop controller) must be aware of the progress of each job and loading on the shop, so some form of progress board is used. Information shown on this board includes the job number, name of the mechanic and the time the job was started. The board display may be a simple chalk-board or it may be a computer screen. A popular design has job details entered on T-shaped cards; these are arranged in columns in a rack to indicate the progress of each job. Columns of slots in the rack are headed: work not started, work in hand, awaiting test, held up for parts, job completed, etc.

### Identification of parts

For many years a parts manual was used to identify a given part. A number of books, one for each model, was required and reference to the exploded drawings and list of components enabled the part number to be determined. A disadvantage of this system is that with constant use and repeated up-dating, the bulky manual soon became very tatty. The advent of a micro-fiche projector overcame this problem and by using the service provided by the manufacturers to regularly update the information, an accurate, speedy ordering system is obtained. This system, and later developments such as microfilm, video tapes and computers, are now in common use and since the systems are adaptable, they are installed in many workshops.

When mechanics need parts for a given model, they use the micro-fiche projector in a similar way to using a book; initially the model and major component are selected, and then the part number is identified from the drawing and list. Without leaving the job the mechanic is able to communicate this information to the Parts Department who can then pick the part and arrange for it to be supplied to the workplace. To be successful this system relies on mechanics ordering all the parts they need at one time, rather than in piecemeal fashion.

# PROGRESS CHECK 13

1. The word resource means:
(a) a count of the productive staff
(b) a stock that can be drawn on
(c) the capital available in a company
(d) the stock held by the Parts Department.

2. A non-franchised dealer is:
(a) unable to sell new vehicles
(b) not contracted with a manufacturer
(c) contracted with more than one manufacturer
(d) prevented from holding a stock of spare parts.

3. A company uses a standard charge to cost repair work. This systems requires:
(a) an estimate for each job undertaken
(b) a variable rate to cover weekly overheads
(c) the company to charge customers at an hourly rate
(d) management to keep a close check of working time and trading costs.

4. One item that is NOT included in a general overhead is:
(a) holiday pay
(b) rent and rates
(c) wages for productive staff
(d) lighting, power and heating.

5. Another name for overheads is:
(a) indirect costs
(b) general expenses
(c) departmental expenses
(d) administration expenses.

6. A technician's non-productive time is charged to a customer by:
(a) doubling the hourly rate charge
(b) allocating the cost as a charge for credit
(c) including it as a departmental overhead expense
(d) including it as a general overhead expense.

7. Free-of-charge jobs are charged to a customer by:
(a) increasing the cost of spare parts
(b) passing the cost on to the manufacturer
(c) including it as a departmental overhead expense
(d) transferring the cost to customers on their next visit.

8. The recommended profit is 20% of turnover, the overhead percentage is 400% and the technician's wage is £8 per hour. The hourly charge-out rate is:
(a) £8
(b) £40
(c) £48
(d) £50.

9. A company having a charge-out rate of £30 per hour pays its technicians £8 per hour and has overheads of £24 per hour. The use of this charge-out rate would:
(a) only cover the general overhead expenses
(b) not give the company any profit
(c) not give a competitive rate to attract customers
(d) not give sufficient funds to meet the variable costs.

10. One way of reducing the charge-out rate is:
(a) improve productivity
(b) increase variable costs
(c) charge customers for idle time
(d) increase number of non-productive staff.

11. A supplementary estimate is given when:
(a) an error is discovered in the original estimate
(b) the original estimate has to be sent to the insurance company
(c) an abnormal mechanical condition indicates that the original estimate will be exceeded
(d) a duplicate copy of the original estimate is required for submission to the insurance company.

12. An extended warranty is:
(a) an extension which can be purchased by the owner
(b) an extension given when any claim has been made on the original warranty
(c) given by a dealer to cover repairs carried-out in the first six months
(d) given by a dealer to extend the manufacturer's warranty to include all components.

13. The customer's signature on a repair order:
(a) is legally binding on the customer
(b) does not guarantee payment to a dealer
(c) must always be obtained to guarantee payment
(d) shows that the customer understands the contract.

14. The main purpose of a job card is to:
(a) record the vehicle details
(b) show the work that has to be done
(c) show the cost of the spare parts used
(d) record that the customer has authorised the work.

15. An additional, separate job card is needed when:
(a) a credit account is involved
(b) the customer wishes to retain the top copy
(c) one part of the job requires the supply of spare parts
(d) warranty work is carried-out in addition to other work.

# 14 Personnel

## What is covered in this chapter:

→ staff interdependence
→ lines of communication
→ levels and limits of authority

You often find that behind a successful company is a happy and efficient staff. This is important because you spend a large part of your life at work. To achieve a high efficiency, all members of the staff must work in harmony as a team. Management must lead and take steps to ensure that every person in the company knows their duties, the limits of their authority and the channels through which they can communicate up and down in the organisation; this channel should include means for the processing of any complaint or grievance.

This chapter highlights the need for good staff relations and effective lines of communication. Also it examines the structure of a company and shows you how your job and authority can be defined.

## 14.1 Staff interdependence

A company is a team of people in which each person performs some vital duty in the organization to allow it to achieve its stated objective. In a commercial world this objective is to make a profit for its shareholders; without these people the company would not have been set up. Furthermore, without a suitable return in the way of profit for the investors, the company would be unable to continue trading for any length of time.

### Team work

Each individual in a company may be regarded as a cog in a gear train; without the smallest cog the machine fails to operate. This is demonstrated when an individual fails to perform their given activity in a satisfactory manner; although the machine may not grind to a halt, the effect

on the smooth running of the company is soon noticed by a fall in productivity and eventually a drop in profits.

### Importance of each employee

Sometimes one hears the complaint from a person, such as a workshop cleaner, that his work is both of little importance and insignificance as regards the profitability of the company. A little thought will show that this is not the case, because with the loss of his contribution the performance and morale of the workshop staff would soon fall due to poor working conditions. Conversely, in an efficient company no one person should regard his role as being so vital that without him the company would collapse. If this is the case, then something is wrong with the organisation; either the person is not delegating his responsibilities or the management structure of the company requires modification.

One often hears the expression that 'nobody is indispensable'. A well managed company should make this statement true, so in the event of a person's absence, others can be moved around to cover the gap.

Some supervisors have an 'attitude problem' that causes them to feel that they are more important than the staff they command. This weakness should be identified by their seniors and action promptly taken to either convince them that the company is a team, or remind them that the company would be better off without them. These 'arrogant' individuals must bear in mind that the income of a Service Department is earned by the productive force, not by support staff and administrators; the administrators are there to help the people that earn the money; good support allows the company to earn more money.

*Workshop harmony* The workshop staff must work together as a team to achieve a happy working environment. If an individual finds it difficult to fit in with other workmates, the reasons should be identified by management at an early stage and action should be promptly

## REMEMBER

**Persons that a company does not need**

People who:

- have a problem for every solution
- discourage others by their actions or lack of actions
- respect punctuality at finishing time but not starting time
- find pleasure in disrupting any organised system of work
- feel that they have a right to be kept in work by the company
- set the quality of their work by the lowest standard in the workshop
- cannot respect rules and who are incapable of operating with flexibility
- find reasons for not doing work instead of finding reasons for doing work.

taken to rectify the situation. Rather than allow one person to destroy the harmony of the workshop it would be better to dispense with the individual's services.

### Exchange of information

Management must aim to foster a constructive relationship not only between staff and management but also between fellow workers. There should be a free interchange of ideas about common problems and future proposals, especially where any changes in the company are planned. Rumour can seriously destroy the morale of a company, so some communication path must be set up to ensure that the true facts of any possible changes are made known to ALL.

Various techniques can be used to exchange information and advice; these can be regular meetings, small and large, but one of the most effective is the one-to-one basis since this type of meeting can embrace both personal and company matters. The actual technique used will depend on many things such as company size, production pressures and personalities.

## 14.2 Lines of communication

A line of communication is a written or verbal link which allows individuals to maintain good working relations with colleagues at all levels in the organisation. Good communications are a vital aspect of relationships so all persons employed in a company should be aware of the various lines of communication open to them for the passage of information.

### Production and administration

Communication messages in a Service Department fall into two groups; for either *production needs* or *administrative support*. Production messages are the items of factual information that pass between the different operational sectors to ensure that both the work is carried out efficiently to the customer's instructions and the cost of the repair is correctly charged. Communications of an administrative nature cover the various activities that are needed to support the trading purpose outlined in the company's mission statement.

*Production communications* An efficient route must exist to fulfil the following functions:

1) Customer/Company information needed to agree a contract.
2) Reception/Workshop link to pass work instructions, record time taken for jobs and convey reports.
3) Parts Department/Workshop and Parts Department/Reception to obtain and charge the spare parts.
4) Reception/Accounts/Customer to prepare the invoice and secure payment.

To achieve an efficient Service Department, good communication channels must exist to allow two-way messages to be transmitted to the respective sections of the company as quickly and accurately as possible. Study of the listed routes will highlight the various problems and bottle-necks that arise if communications break down in any link of the chain. It is senseless having a good communication channel if the messages can neither be read nor understood. On numerous occasions customer complaints have arisen due to misunderstandings caused by illegible handwriting, poor spelling and the inability to comprehend written instructions. This is not always the fault of the employee because problems can stem from the way in which customers convey their instructions to Reception; this is an accepted 'hazard' that reception personnel should be trained to overcome by careful questioning.

*Administrative communications* A workshop needs administrative support to allow it to perform its given function. Overheads have to be governed, accounts have to be kept, and systems must be managed to provide the company with an even flow of work. These activities require a communication link with the workshop to transmit numerous items of support material. One important function is to pass on manufacturers' information such as software, bulletins, and manuals to the workshop staff to enable them to carry out the repairs in an efficient manner.

***Communication of sensitive material***  The passing of both sensitive and confidential information should be restricted; normally this requires a one-to-one discussion between the two parties involved. This confidentiality is destroyed if it is not transmitted directly to the person who has the authority to deal with the subject.

### Complaints and grievances

By law every company must have a procedure to handle any grievance or complaint made by employees against either the company or fellow worker. This process ensures that any personal matters such as company/employee relationships and sexual or racial harassment issues, can be communicated to the persons who are responsible for the investigation and solution of these problems.

All employees should be aware of the grievance and complaints procedure laid down by the company so that they can make use of it when they have a genuine problem that needs remedial action.

## 14.3  Levels and limits of authority

### Business classification

Often started up as a one-man concern by a working owner, many small firms gradually develop over the years from a small company employing a few people into one of the large companies that we see today. As firms

progress from small to large, the businesses would pass through the following stages:

1) *Sole proprietor.*  Firm owned and managed by one person who is solely responsible for all decisions and debts.
2) *Private limited company (Ltd Co).*  Financed and managed by private shareholders; these form a Board of Directors to control the affairs of the company under the direction of a Chairman. A managing director is appointed to deal with the day-to-day running of the company. In the event of failure of the company (i.e. when the company goes into liquidation) the financial liability of each director is limited to a given amount.
3) *Public limited company (plc).*  Listed on the Stock Exchange and financed from shares purchased on the stock market. The main stockholders elect a Chairman and Board of Directors to run the company. The liability of each shareholder is limited to the value of the stock they hold.

### Company structure

Employees in a company or organisation should be aware of its structure and should know the function of each department. A traditional motor vehicle retail establishment will have a departmental structure as shown in the Figure 14.3.1. This diagram shows the general manager is responsible for four departments.

Each department will have its own structure and Figure 14.3.2 shows a typical organisation 'tree' for a Service Department. A person's title will show where they are situated in the firm's structure and will indicate

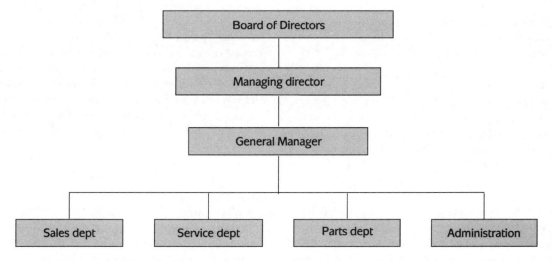

**Fig. 14.3.1** Typical organisational structure

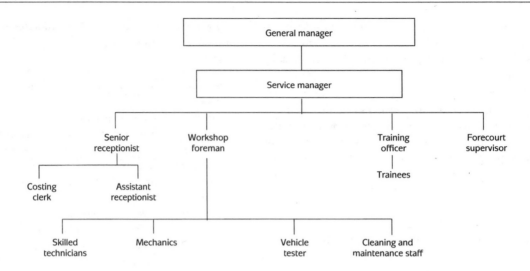

**Fig. 14.3.2** Typical departmental organisational structure

the sector of the organisation for which they are responsible, and the staff to whom they have the authority to give orders. The tree illustrates the chain of command; this is the direct path linking a given position with the General Manager. For example, the Senior Receptionist is directly responsible (reports to) the Service Manager and the chart shows that although he has authority over other reception staff he has no direct authority over the mechanics in the workshop. When describing the duties of a certain post, the terms *authority* and *responsibility* are often used. When used in this context the meaning of each term is:

- *authority* – to possess defined powers to take specific actions and make judgements; the right to enforce obedience;
- *responsibility* – being liable to be called to account for decisions; to take charge of given duties; the terms of reference.

### Limits of authority

All employees must be aware of the limit of their authority. In the course of their work they will be expected to make rational judgements, but any decision made must be within the limit of their authority. It is simple for the company to specify limits to items such as payment procedures and the maximum work for a customer that a junior manager can permit free-of-charge (FOC), but other limits are more difficult to define. Many of these are unwritten and rely on common sense, together with the individual's experience and intuition, to decide when the matter should be passed to a higher authority for a decision or opinion.

Every employee in an organisation has to accept some responsibility for decision taking. Unless this is done the firm will grind to a halt, or at best, operate inefficiently due to the supervisor or manager being overwhelmed with problems that should have been solved by a subordinate. This situation arises when a person in charge of others fails to delegate some of the routine duties to a deputy. By allocating these duties to more junior staff, managers and supervisors are able to do their most important job – namely to manage. Any duties delegated to employees does not give the employee the sole right to take decisions; it grants them limited authority which is always subject to override by the person who does the delegating.

### Job description

Problems and disputes arise when employees have no clear idea of the authority and responsibility associated with their positions. In these cases decisions are not taken and responsibility for some important task not accepted because the scope and duties are not clearly defined. This can be avoided by giving each person in the company a job description. This document names the job title, lists the main tasks that should be taken on, defines the responsibilities of the position and gives the limits of authority.

When used in conjunction with an organisation structure, the person occupying the post is able to see where the job is situated in the staff framework of the company; also it shows the line of management, upwards and, where appropriate downwards.

# JOB DESCRIPTION

*POSITION*  SENIOR TECHNICAL
RECEPTIONIST

*HOURS*  08.30–13.00 14.00–17.50
Monday to Friday inclusive
Overtime will be required on demand

*TASKS*  To receive customers, discuss, identify and progress service and repair requirements utilising diagnostic and test facilities as necessary. Promote and effect the sale of service, repairs and accessories.

*DUTIES*

1. Promote and maintain good customer relations
2. Discuss and identify service and repair requirements with customers, utilising diagnostic test facilities and specialist personnel as required
3. Formalize detailed test reports for quotations, estimates or job card development
4. Obtain authority from customer to proceed with work
5. Be aware of the workshop loading situation and the progress of work. Advise customers of delays or additional work required
6. Deal efficiently with complaints, referring to management according to company policy
7. Finalize job cards for invoicing – accept payments for work according to company policy
8. Carry out final testing and inspection – ensure vehicles are clean and correctly presented to customers on collection or delivery
9. Maintain adequate customer/workshop records
10. Promote and effect the sale of workshop repair and service facilities and appreciate facilities offered by other departments
11. Be aware of legal and safety implications affecting reception duties.

*RESPONSIBLE TO:*  Service Manager
*LIAISON WITH:*  Works foreman, Parts & Sales Dept., Accounts staff
*RESPONSIBLE FOR:*  Junior reception staff and costing clerk

## PROGRESS CHECK 14

1. The most important section of a company:
(a) is the administration department
(b) is the product sales section
(c) is the productive staff employed in the service department
(d) cannot be identified because all sections are equally important.

2. Written and verbal communications in a company should be:
(a) restricted to monthly meetings
(b) avoided to save money and time
(c) used to provide a free interchange of ideas
(d) passed to all personnel before they start work.

3. A company does NOT need a person who:
(a) has a solution for every problem
(b) finds pleasure in contributing to an organised system of work
(c) finds a reason for doing work instead of finding reasons for not doing work
(d) sets the quality of their work by the lowest standard in the workshop.

4. Communication of sensitive material should:
(a) be passed verbally down the chain of command
(b) not be necessary in a well organised company
(c) always involve the departmental manager
(d) be restricted to a one-to-one discussion between the two parties involved.

5. A company must have a complaints and grievance procedure to:
(a) comply with the law
(b) prevent sexual harassment
(c) eliminate racial harassment
(d) exclude actions against the company.

6. A private limited company (Ltd Co) is:
(a) listed on the Stock Exchange
(b) financed and managed by private shareholders
(c) financed by shares purchased on the stock market
(d) managed by a director who has to repay all debts when a company fails.

7. A person is given defined powers to take specific actions, make judgements and has the right to enforce obedience. This power is called:
(a) authority
(b) management
(c) responsibility
(d) executive rights.

8. The purpose of a job description is to:
(a) show the qualities required of a person
(b) give a list of tasks required by a customer
(c) clearly define the tasks that a person has to perform
(d) show, by means of a tree, the name of a position in a company.

# Appendices

## *A1*           *Glossary*

**AIDA**
Mnemonic used as a guide to show a sales sequence; A–attention, I–interest, D–desire to own, A–action.

**acceleration**
Rate of change of velocity measured in metres per second per second ($m/s^2$). Acceleration can be positive or negative; a negative acceleration is called deceleration.

**acetylene**
Flammable gas, lighter than air, that consists of carbon and hydrogen ($C_2H_2$). It is used with oxygen to give a very hot flame for fusion welding and general heating purposes.

**additive**
Chemical added to substances such as petroleum fuels and lubricants to improve their performance. In the past the additive tetra-ethyl-lead was added to petrol to improve the octane rating.

**agent**
Person or body who has the authority to act for another person or body. Often the word is used in a general sense to show that there is a trading link between two bodies, but when used in this way, the arrangement does not comply with the legal definition of an agent. Although motor traders state that they are agents for a manufacturer, they may not have authority to make decisions for that manufacturer.

**agreement**
Arrangement or mutual understanding between two or more parties to act in a given way. Often an agreement is embodied in a legal contract.

**alloy**
Mixture of two or more metals that are added to a base metal to improve its properties. E.g. Copper mixed with zinc form a brass alloy.

**ampere**
Unit of electrical current flow and represented by the symbol A.

**atmospheric pressure**
Force per unit area measured at sea level given by the weight of air above the ground. Atmospheric pressure varies with climatic conditions and is measured with a barometer. Under standard conditions, atmospheric pressure is 101.4 $kN/m^2$; this pressure supports a mercury column of 760 mm and gives the unit of 1 bar.

**bailment**
Contract of bailment is made when a customer (the bailor) leaves goods (bailment) with a company (the bailee). This contract requires the company to return the goods to the customer after they have been left for any reason.

**barrier cream**
Used to protect against dermatitis when the skin comes into regular contact with solvents, fuels (especially diesel fuel), hydraulic fluids, oils, greases and many other chemicals.

**battery** (or accumulator)
Electrical component used to convert electrical energy into chemical energy and vice versa. It acts as a 'storage

unit' to provide electricity for the vehicle when the engine is stationary.

### bi-metal strip
Two strips of metals, such as brass and iron, fused or riveted together to form a heat-sensing device. When the strip is heated the different thermal expansion rates cause the strip to bend. Used to open and close temperature trip switches.

### Boyle's law
Law which states the relationship between the absolute pressure and volume of a gas under constant temperature conditions. The law is stated as $pV = $ constant.

### budget
Financial estimate of revenue and expenditure.

### caliper
Instrument normally used for measuring the diameter of convex surfaces.

### calorific value
Measure of the heat units contained in a given mass of fuel. It is determined by means of a calorimeter. A typical value for petrol is 44 MJ/kg.

### catalyst
Substance which promotes a chemical change but does not undergo any change itself.

### ceramic
Non-metallic material that has excellent electrical insulation and heat resisting properties. In the past porcelain was the main ceramic used, but now aluminium oxide (corundum) is in common use.

### charge-out rate
Amount charged by a company for one hour of work. This rate takes into account the wages paid, establishment overheads and profit.

### Charles' law
Law which states the relationship between the volume and absolute temperature of a gas under constant pressure conditions. The law is stated as $V/t = $ constant.

### circuit
Continuous conducting path around which electrical current can flow. Any break in the intended path is called an *open-circuit*; this fault prevents electron flow and makes the system inoperative. Another fault is called a *short-circuit*; this allows the current to by-pass a part of the circuit with the result that components in the by-passed section fail to operate, and risks damaging those components handling the resultant *short-circuit current*.

### combustion
Rapid chemical combination that results in the generation of heat. Combustion occurs when a set quantity of volatile fuel is mixed with oxygen and ignited. The heat generated depends on the quantity of fuel and compression of the air.

### communication
Means whereby something such as information is conveyed by writing, drawings, speech or signals.

### company
Business established to offer some service for the purpose of profit. A company may be owned by a *sole proprietor*, or a group of people who form either a *private limited company (Ltd Co)* or *public limited company (plc)*.

### contract
Legal agreement between two or more parties for the supply of goods, or performance of work. It always consists of an *offer* and an *acceptance* and in English Law there must be some *consideration* (benefit to one party and detriment to the other) unless the contract is made under seal (deed).

### dermatitus
Serious and unpleasant skin disorder which starts with irritation and inflammation and leads to blistering, cracking and septic infection unless treated. The condition can be avoided if a barrier cream is applied before allowing the skin to come into contact with harmful substances such as diesel fuel oil. See *barrier cream*.

### detonation
Spontaneous combustion which quickly leads to engine damage. It occurs after the spark and is recognised by a sound called *pinking* or *combustion knock*. True detonation seldom occurs in an engine cylinder because this condition requires all of the gas in the cylinder to explode; in practice only the last portion of the burning gas (the end gas) spontaneously ignites.

### dynamometer
Instrument used to measure the torque output of an engine. When used in conjunction with a tachometer to measure the engine speed, the brake power can be calculated.

### efficiency
Relationship between the work output and the work input of a machine. The efficiency is normally expressed as a percentage and is calculated by

$$\frac{(\text{work output})}{(\text{work input})} \times \frac{100}{1}.$$

**electrolysis**
Chemical change produced by passing an electric current through a solution called an *electrolyte*. The change in composition of a battery plate is caused by the flow of electricity through the electrolyte.

**electrolyte**
Conducting solution or substance which allows the flow of electrical current. In a lead–acid battery the electrolyte is a solution of sulphuric acid ($H_2SO_4$) and distilled water ($H_2O$).

**electron**
Minute particle of an atom which orbits around a fixed nucleus. When an electron is subjected to an electric force it moves from atom to atom from a negative to a positive potential.

**estimate**
Written or verbal statement that indicates an expected financial target. An estimate for repair work gives an indication of the price of a repair and in some cases the time taken to complete a job.

**force**
That which changes a body's state of rest or of uniform motion in a straight line. The newton (N) is the SI unit of force. A force of 1 N acting on a mass of 1 kg gives an acceleration of $1 \text{ m/s}^2$.

**friction**
Force preventing one body sliding over another. It occurs in solids, liquids and gases. A measure of the friction between given materials is the coefficient of friction; this is shown by the symbol '$\mu$' and calculated from:

$$\mu = \text{(friction force)}/\text{(force pressing surfaces together)}$$

**gasket**
Sealing joint between two surfaces to prevent the entry or escape of gas. Cylinder head and exhaust manifold are two examples where gaskets are used.

**gravity**
Force of attraction between two masses, e.g. the force exerted by the Earth on an object positioned in the Earth's gravitational field. Under standard conditions the gravitational force exerted on a body of mass 1 kg is 9.806 N.

**highway code**
Official Government document that contains safety rules and recommendations to be observed by all road users, including pedestrians.

**hire purchase**
System for the payment for goods under which the buyer makes instalment payments at regular intervals for a fixed period of time. The goods are not owned by the buyer until the last payment is made.

**ignition delay**
Applies to a compression-ignition engine and is the period between the start of fuel injection and the point when the fuel ignites. It is expressed as an angle (degrees) moved by the crankshaft during the delay.

**insulator**
Thermal insulators resist or protect from the passage of heat and electrical insulators resist or protect from the flow of electricity.

**invoice**
Document or bill issued by a company to a customer that gives the final cost and details of the work done and parts supplied.

**lien**
Right to retain a vehicle, which is in the possession of the repairer claiming the lien, until the claim is satisfied.

**limits**
As applied to component manufacture, a limit is the maximum and minimum size allowable; the upper and lower limits respectively.

**lubricant**
Fluid introduced between two rubbing surfaces to reduce friction by keeping the surfaces apart.

**MOT test**
Annual inspection of a vehicle, supervised by the Department of Transport, to ensure the mechanical condition meets the statutory regulations. Introduced when the Government department was called the Ministry of Transport (MOT), the test was set up to improve vehicle safety.

**microfiche**
Small sheet of transparent film that contains graphic material that is equivalent to many pages of a paper book. A fiche of size 105 × 148 mm can contain 420 pages of text.

**microfilm**
Miniature roll of negative film used to record graphic information that would otherwise be contained in bulky paper files.

## micrometer

Precision measuring instrument based on a fine-pitched screw thread. External and internal types are made for convex surfaces and cylinder bores respectively.

## moment of a force

Moment of a force about a point is equal to the product of the magnitude of the force and the perpendicular distance between the point and the line of action of the force. This can be expressed as:

$$\text{moment} = \text{force} \times \text{perpendicular distance between point and line of action of the force}$$

## octane rating

Measure of the resistance of a petrol to knock or detonate. The rating is obtained by comparing the knock resistance of a sample of petrol measured under standard conditions with a reference fuel consisting of iso-octane and heptane.

## ohm

Unit of electrical resistance. Expressed by the symbol '$\Omega$'.

## Ohm's Law

Current passing through a wire at constant temperature is proportional to the potential difference between its ends. Expressed as $E = IR$ where $E$ is the e.m.f. (V), $I$ is the current (A), and $R$ is the resistance in ohms.

## overheads

Expenses that relate to all outgoings involved in, or connected with, the running of a business, the incurring of which cannot be directly attributed to the repairing of selling activity of any particular vehicle.

## personnel

Body of people employed in a company, establishment or organisation.

## pinking

Metallic tapping sound emitted by an engine when combustion knock (detonation) is occurring in one or more of the cylinders. A pinking sound occurs when the ignition is over-advanced.

## projection

Graphic view that shows the constructional details of a component. Various methods of projection are used such as orthographic and pictorial; the former is used to show two-dimensional full face views and the latter the three-dimensional shape of a component.

## plastics

Synthetic resinous or other substances mainly derived from petroleum that can be moulded into any shape. *Thermoplastic* plastics such as polyvinyl-chloride (p.v.c.) soften when warmed and have a high resistance to electricity. *Thermosets* such as epoxy resin and polyurethane remain rigid once set.

## polarity

Electrical potential of body as positive or negative. The identification of electrical polarity on vehicle components is necessary because damage will occur if they are wired-up incorrectly. Most batteries are connected to make the polarity of the vehicle frame negative.

## potential

Electrical charge in a body which often uses the earth's charge as a zero base. The potential difference (measured in volts) between two points makes current flow in an electric circuit. In simple terms potential is the electrical pressure that drives the current around an electrical circuit.

## power

Rate of doing work. The work done in a given time. Today the *watt* is the SI unit of power; this replaces the Imperial unit *horsepower*, which was introduced by James Watt. Work done at the rate of one joule per second gives a power of one watt.

## pre-ignition

Combustion in a spark-ignition engine initiated by means other than the spark. It is caused by some incandescent object in the combustion chamber and, if uncorrected, leads to detonation and engine damage. Pre-ignition always occurs before the spark.

## profit

Financial dividend to reward a company for the capital the directors previously invested in a business. The excess of returns over outlay.

## quotation

Definite indication of the actual charge of goods and repairs, or the actions to be undertaken in a given time. The acceptance of a quotation constitutes the basis of a contract.

## solenoid

Device that uses the magnetic effect produced by an electric winding of a coil to attract and move an iron plunger. The force on the plunger depends on the current and number of windings on the coil. The solenoid and plunger are used as an *actuator* to operate switches.

### thermometer
Instrument for the measurement of temperature to a scale of degrees. The SI system uses the Celsius scale. Under standard conditions the value 0°C represents the melting of ice to water, and 100°C as the boiling point.

### tolerance
Acceptable dimension range within which the size of a component must fall. It is the range between the upper and lower limits of size. In production a tolerance must be given because, in practice, it is impossible to make a component to an exact size.

### torque
Turning moment about a point. It is the product of the force and the perpendicular distance between the point and the line of action of the force. Torque is measured in Nm and is often expressed as: torque = force × radius.

### velocity
Rate at which a body moves in a given direction. Velocity is measured in metres per second and is expressed as: velocity = (distance covered)/(time). This expression also gives the *speed* of a body, but the difference is that speed does not take into account the direction of movement.

### vernier
Caliper measuring instrument having two scales; a main scale and a separate slidable scale. The two scales have differently spaced divisions to allow the fractional part to be read.

### viscosity
Resistance of an oil to flow and its ability to oppose a shearing action. The viscosity is measured at a set temperature with standardised test apparatus. It is expressed as an SAE number; the higher the number, the greater the viscosity. Sometimes the slang term 'thick' is used to describe a high viscosity oil.

### Viscosity index
Measure of the change of viscosity that takes place over a given temperature range. The viscosity of all oils fall when the temperature increases, but some oils fall more than others.

### volt
Unit of electrical pressure or potential difference. The symbol for a volt is V.

### warranty
As applied to new vehicles, a warranty is an undertaking given by the manufacturer to rectify without charge, any defect, due to faulty manufacture or materials that develops during a prescribed time.

### watt
The SI unit of power. A watt is work done at the rate of one joule per second. The symbol for a watt is W.

### weight
Force of gravity on a given body. At sea level a gravitational force of approximately 10 N acts on a mass of 1 kg. For general purposes the weight is given by: weight = mass × 10.

### work
Product of the force (*N*) and distance moved (*m*). It will be noted that there is no work done unless there is movement. The SI unit of work is the *joule* and is expressed as: work = force × distance moved.

# A2
# *Imperial to SI conversions*

Most of the following conversions have been approximated to give values suitable for general work. If greater accuracy is required, the internationally agreed equivalent should be used. To convert from Imperial to SI, the Imperial value is multiplied by the given conversion factor.

## Length
1 yard is exactly 0.9144 metre

| | |
|---|---|
| 1 inch (in) $\simeq$ 25.4 mm | 1 foot (ft) $\simeq$ 0.3048 m |
| 0.001 in $\simeq$ 0.025 mm | 1 mile $\simeq$ 1.6 km |

## Area
1 sq inch (in$^2$) $\simeq$ 6.45 cm$^2$     1 sq foot (ft$^2$) $\simeq$ 929 cm$^2$

## Volume
1 cubic inch (in$^3$) $\simeq$ 16.4 cm$^3$
1 cubic foot (ft$^3$) $\simeq$ 0.028 m$^3$

## Capacity
1 pint (pt) $\simeq$ 0.568 litre     1 gallon (gal) $\simeq$ 4.5 litre

## Mass
1 pound (lb) is exactly 0.453 592 37 kg
1 ounce (oz) $\simeq$ 28.35 g
1 ton $\simeq$ 1016 kg = 1.016 tonne

## Force
1 pound force (lbf) $\simeq$ 4.45 N; 1 ton $\simeq$ 10 kN

## Torque
1 pound foot (lbf ft) $\simeq$ 1.4 N m

## Pressure and stress
1 pound/sq inch (lbf/in$^2$) $\simeq$ 7 kN/m$^2$ = 7 kPa
         = 0.07 bar = 70 mbar
1 ton/sq inch (ton/in$^2$)   $\simeq$ 15 kN/m$^2$ = 15 kPa
1 atmosphere (atm)      $\simeq$ 100 kN/m$^2$
         = 100 kPa = 1 bar
1 inch mercury (in Hg)   $\simeq$ 3.4 kN/m$^2$
         = 3.4 kPa = 34 mbar

## Work and energy
1 foot pound (ft lbf) $\simeq$ 1.4 J
1 British thermal unit (Btu) $\simeq$ 1055 J = 1.055 kJ
1 Centigrade heat unit (Chu) $\simeq$ 1900 J = 1.9 kJ

## Power
1 horsepower (hp) $\simeq$ 746 W = 0.746 kW

## Velocity
1 foot/second (ft/s) $\simeq$ 0.3 m/s
1 mile/h (mile/h) $\simeq$ 1.6 km/h

## Acceleration
1 foot/second$^2$ (ft/s$^2$) $\simeq$ 0.3 m/s$^2$
$g \simeq$ 32.2 ft/s$^2$ $\simeq$ 9.81 m/s$^2$ $\simeq$ 10 m/s$^2$

## Consumption
1 mile/gal $\simeq$ 0.35 km/litre or 290 litres/100 km
30 mile/gal $\simeq$ 11 km/litre or 9.7 litre/100 km
1 pt/bhp h $\simeq$ 0.7476 litres/kW h

# A3

# Solutions to progress check questions

**Ch. 1 Page 8**

| 1 (d) | 2 (b) | 3 (c) | 4 (a) | 5 (a) | 6 (b) |
|---|---|---|---|---|---|
| 7 (b) | 8 (d) | 9 (d) | 10 (a) | | |

**Ch. 2 Page 12**

| 1 (c) | 2 (c) | 3 (b) | 4 (a) | 5 (c) | 6 (b) |
|---|---|---|---|---|---|

**Ch. 3 Page 22**

| 1 (a) | 2 (d) | 3 (a) | 4 (b) | 5 (d) | 6 (a) |
|---|---|---|---|---|---|
| 7 (a) | 8 (a) | 9 (b) | 10 (b) | 11 (b) | 12 (a) |
| 13 (c) | 14 (b) | 15 (d) | 16 (d) | 17 (a) | 18 (d) |
| 19 (a) | 20 (c) | 21 (b) | 22 (d) | 23 (c) | 24 (c) |
| 25 (c) | 26 (c) | 27 (a) | 28 (b) | 29 (d) | 30 (d) |

**Ch. 4 Page 40**

| 1 (b) | 2 (a) | 3 (a) | 4 (b) | 5 (d) | 6 (b) |
|---|---|---|---|---|---|
| 7 (d) | 8 (c) | 9 (b) | 10 (a) | 11 (b) | 12 (a) |
| 13 (d) | 14 (c) | 15 (b) | 16 (b) | 17 (d) | 18 (d) |
| 19 (a) | 20 (d) | | | | |

**Ch. 5 Page 46**

| 1 (b) | 2 (a) | 3 (c) | 4 (c) | 5 (a) | 6 (b) |
|---|---|---|---|---|---|
| 7 (b) | 8 (b) | 9 (c) | 10 (c) | 11 (a) | 12 (c) |
| 13 (d) | 14 (d) | 15 (c) | | | |

**Ch. 6. Page 56**

| 1 (a) | 2 (a) | 3 (b) | 4 (a) | 5 (c) | 6 (a) |
|---|---|---|---|---|---|
| 7 (c) | 8 (b) | 9 (c) | 10 (a) | 11 (d) | 12 (c) |
| 13 (b) | 14 (c) | 15 (c) | | | |

**Ch. 7 Page 64**

| 1 (d) | 2 (d) | 3 (a) | 4 (d) | 5 (a) | 6 (c) |
|---|---|---|---|---|---|
| 7 (b) | 8 (d) | 9 (a) | 10 (a) | 11 (a) | 12 (d) |
| 13 (b) | 14 (b) | 15 (d) | 16 (d) | 17 (d) | 18 (a) |
| 19 (c) | 20 (b) | 21 (b) | 22 (c) | 23 (a) | 24 (b) |

**Ch. 8 Page 101**

| 1 (a) | 2 (a) | 3 (b) | 4 (b) | 5 (c) | 6 (c) |
|---|---|---|---|---|---|
| 7 (b) | 8 (d) | 9 (c) | 10 (d) | 11 (c) | 12 (d) |

| 13 (d) | 14 (a) | 15 (a) | 16 (a) | 17 (c) | 18 (b) |
|---|---|---|---|---|---|
| 19 (c) | 20 (a) | 21 (b) | 22 (a) | 23 (a) | 24 (d) |
| 25 (a) | 26 (a) | 27 (a) | 28 (b) | 29 (c) | 30 (a) |
| 31 (b) | 32 (c) | 33 (d) | 34 (b) | 35 (d) | 36 (d) |
| 37 (d) | 38 (b) | 39 (b) | 40 (c) | 41 (b) | 42 (c) |
| 43 (a) | 44 (d) | 45 (a) | 46 (b) | 47 (a) | 48 (c) |
| 49 (d) | 50 (d) | 51 (d) | 52 (b) | 53 (b) | 54 (b) |
| 55 (c) | 56 (a) | 57 (c) | 58 (a) | 59 (b) | 60 (d) |
| 61 (c) | 62 (c) | 63 (c) | 64 (a) | 65 (c) | 66 (c) |
| 67 (d) | 68 (a) | 69 (a) | 70 (d) | 71 (b) | 72 (b) |
| 73 (d) | 74 (c) | 75 (a) | 76 (d) | | |

**Ch. 9 Page 124**

| 1 (c) | 2 (b) | 3 (b) | 4 (a) | 5 (d) | 6 (b) |
|---|---|---|---|---|---|
| 7 (c) | 8 (b) | 9 (a) | 10 (a) | 11 (c) | 12 (c) |
| 13 (a) | 14 (d) | 15 (d) | 16 (d) | 17 (b) | 18 (b) |
| 19 (a) | 20 (d) | 21 (c) | 22 (a) | 23 (d) | 24 (c) |
| 25 (c) | 26 (b) | 27 (c) | 28 (a) | 29 (c) | 30 (d) |
| 31 (c) | 32 (a) | 33 (c) | 34 (c) | 35 (a) | 36 (d) |
| 37 (b) | 38 (c) | 39 (c) | 40 (c) | 41 (c) | 42 (b) |
| 43 (b) | 44 (b) | 45 (b) | 46 (d) | 47 (a) | 48 (c) |
| 49 (c) | 50 (b) | | | | |

**Ch. 10 Page 136**

| 1 (a) | 2 (c) | 3 (b) | 4 (c) | 5 (c) | 6 (b) |
|---|---|---|---|---|---|
| 7 (d) | 8 (c) | 9 (c) | 10 (a) | 11 (a) | 12 (d) |
| 13 (a) | 14 (a) | 15 (d) | 16 (d) | 17 (a) | 18 (c) |
| 19 (b) | 20 (d) | 21 (c) | 22 (c) | 23 (a) | 24 (c) |
| 25 (c) | 26 (d) | 27 (a) | 28 (d) | 29 (d) | 30 (b) |
| 31 (c) | 32 (b) | 33 (c) | 34 (b) | 35 (a) | |

**Ch. 11 Page 153**

| 1 (a) | 2 (b) | 3 (c) | 4 (d) | 5 (a) | 6 (d) |
|---|---|---|---|---|---|
| 7 (d) | 8 (c) | 9 (c) | 10 (d) | 11 (b) | 12 (b) |
| 13 (d) | 14 (a) | 15 (b) | 16 (d) | 17 (c) | 18 (b) |
| 19 (b) | 20 (d) | 21 (a) | 22 (a) | 23 (d) | 24 (c) |
| 25 (b) | 26 (d) | 27 (a) | 28 (d) | 29 (b) | 30 (c) |
| 31 (c) | 32 (d) | 33 (b) | 34 (b) | 35 (d) | 36 (d) |
| 37 (c) | 38 (b) | 39 (a) | 40 (a) | 41 (d) | 42 (a) |

43 (b)  44 (c)  45 (c)  46 (a)  47 (d)  48 (b)
49 (d)  50 (d)  51 (b)  52 (d)  53 (c)  54 (c)
55 (d)

**Ch. 12 Page 172**

1 (c)  2 (a)  3 (b)  4 (a)  5 (a)  6 (d)
7 (a)  8 (c)  9 (a)  10 (a)

**Ch. 13 Page 183**

1 (b)  2 (b)  3 (d)  4 (c)  5 (a)  6 (c)
7 (c)  8 (d)  9 (b)  10 (a)  11 (c)  12 (a)
13 (b)  14 (b)  15 (d)

**Ch. 14 Page 190**

1 (d)  2 (c)  3 (d)  4 (d)  5 (a)  6 (b)
7 (a)  8 (c)

# Index